Reminiscences of a Statistician

Reminiscences of a Statistician

The Company I Kept

E.L. Lehmann

Springer

E.L. Lehmann
University of California,
Berkeley, CA 94704-2864
USA

e-ISBN-13: 978-0-387-71597-1

Library of Congress Control Number: 2007924716

Printed on acid-free paper.

9 8 7 6 5 4 3 2 1

springer.com

To our grandchildren

Joanna, Emily, Paul
Jacob and Celia
Gabe and Tavi
and great-granddaughter Audrey

Preface

It has been my good fortune to meet and get to know many remarkable people, mostly statisticians and mathematicians, and to derive much pleasure and benefit from these contacts. They were teachers, colleagues and students, and the following pages sketch their careers and our interactions. Also included are a few persons with whom I had little or no direct contact but whose ideas had a decisive influence on my work. To provide some coherence, the account is largely chronological and follows the steps of my own career.

Taken together, these sketches provide a very personal picture of the development of statistical theory from the 1930s to the 1970s. It is the period between two revolutions: that of Fisher, Neyman, and Pearson, which laid the foundations for the classical statistical theory of that period; and the second revolution, forty years later, brought about by the advent of the computer, which turned statistics in new directions.

The present account of this history is a highly selective one, which emphasizes the persons, institutions, and statistical topics that were close to my interests. One narrowing effect of this perspective stems from the fact that my career took place in the United States. As a consequence, the book focuses on American statisticians and institutions. Only the last two chapters discuss, briefly and very incompletely, developments in some other countries.

For writing these reminiscences, I did not have to rely entirely on my memory. There is much published material on many of the persons covered here, such as biographical sketches in Festschrifts and collected works, and—unfortunately—obituaries and memorial articles. Of particular value were the "Conversations," which are a regular feature of *Statistical Science,* and which provide firsthand accounts of the subjects being interviewed. An indispensable source for the Berkeley chapters was Constance Reid's book, *Neyman—from Life.*

In addition, I sent copies of their sections to all living subjects, asking them for corrections and criticism, and I am most grateful for their helpful responses. At my request, most of them also sent me pictures of themselves, which form an important part of the book. Other pictures were provided by Steve Stigler (of Raj Bahadur and Jimmie Savage), and David Brillinger (of John Tukey).

Nearly 20 pictures were put at my disposal by Ingram Olkin from the extensive collection he has assembled at Stanford; another dozen I owe to the courtesy of the archives of the Mathematische Forschungsinstitut Oberwolfach, and still others to the archives of St. Andrews University. An important source for many pictures was the Berkeley Statistics Department, and four pictures came from Reid's book, *Neyman—from Life*. To all of these I extend my thanks. For preparing the pictures for publication, the help of Julie and Tamya Shaffer was invaluable.

I also want to thank Martina Schneider for helpful correspondence concerning the section on van der Waerden; to my editor, John Kimmel, for his encouragement and support; and to Agnes Herzberg for reviewing the book for Springer, and for many corrections and suggestions. To Len Shaffer, I am grateful for his typing of the manuscript from my hard-to-read handwritten version and for correcting many errors.

To conclude these acknowledgments, I want to express my deep gratitude to Persi Diaconis and Julie Shaffer, with both of whom I discussed the project as it went along, and who gave me advice and criticism when I needed it. They also read the manuscript after its completion, corrected many errors of fact, and greatly improved the exposition. To them I owe my greatest debt.

Contents

1 Mathematical Preparation

The crucial event of my early life was the coming to power in 1933 of the Nazis in Germany. This changed my future in two fundamental ways. As an immediate consequence, we left Germany (where my family had lived for many generations), and—after five years in Switzerland and two in England—I moved to America. On January 1, 1941, I arrived in Berkeley, California, where I have lived for the last sixty-six years.

The other basic change concerned not where I was going to live but what profession I was going to follow. My love as a teenager was German literature and, had we remained in Germany, I would have expected to become a professor of literature (or perhaps a writer). Since these were not promising professions outside of Germany, instead I became a mathematician and later a statistician.

Instrumental in both these changes was my father, who had the foresight to make the difficult decision to leave Germany quite early and who persuaded me that mathematics (for which I had shown some affinity) offered much better prospects than German literature because of its international nature.

From the start, the atmosphere in Berkeley was much more encouraging than it had been in Switzerland and England, where I had felt like a foreigner who would never be fully accepted. In Berkeley, on the contrary, I immediately felt at home. In addition, the way the study of mathematics was organized was much more congenial to me than it had been in England. Within a year, it seemed as if an academic career in mathematics was a realistic possibility.

1. Edmund Landau (1877–1938)

My interest in mathematics originated not at school, where the early courses in the subject seemed boring and my performance was mediocre, but rather from my reading a book, *Der Wettlauf mit der Schildkröte* (*The Race with the Tortoise*), by Th. Wolff. It was given to me by my uncle Alfred Schuster when I was thirteen. The title chapter discusses Zeno's paradox about Achilles and the tortoise, which claims to prove that the fast runner can never catch up

with the tortoise, who has been given a start on him. I found this intriguing, but what really captured my interest was the material on prime numbers.

It presented Euclid's proof of the infinity of primes and followed it with a section titled, "The Law of Prime Numbers," in which the question is posed of whether they follow some regular pattern. It mentions that the gaps between prime numbers tend to become larger as the numbers increase, but also that nevertheless from time to time prime twins continue to appear, such as (5, 7), (17, 19), and (101, 103). What was particularly fascinating was that at that time (the book was published in 1929), as is still true today, it was not known whether there exists an infinite number of prime twins.

If the impulse for mathematics is the desire to bring order into chaos, the prime numbers provide an ideal prototype because they combine extreme simplicity with behavior that is quite chaotic despite their obviously deterministic character. Today, we know much about their properties statistically—for example, they tend to get rarer and we know at what rate—but their local behavior is still completely unpredictable. To find a pattern in the sequence of primes became a great interest for me over the next few years, and I spent much time looking, calculating, and speculating. Two years later, as a high school sophomore, I was rewarded with what seemed a surprising discovery. It appeared that for any positive integer a and any prime number p, if you raise a to the pth power and subtract a, the difference $a^p - a$ is always divisible by p.

On a vacation a few weeks later, it turned out that we were staying at the same hotel as Matthias Landau, the son of the famous number theorist Edmund Landau, whose wife had been one of my mother's closest girlhood friends. I mentioned my curious result to him, but he did not believe it, and bet me a chocolate bar that he would disprove it by the end of the day. He lost the bet but continued his efforts for another two days. He then decided to write to his father about the matter. The reply came that the result was well known as Fermat's little theorem, and that Landau would send me a proof.

In due time, his letter arrived. One would have expected it to start with an explanation—that he had heard from his son, etc., etc.—but explanations were not Landau's way. *"Sehr geehrter Herr Lehmann,"* the letter began (I was sixteen at the time), "all letters denote integers, p a prime number, x/y means x is a divisor of y," and after more notation came Theorem 1 and its proof and then Theorem 2 (Fermat), which was my result, and its proof. After this, the letter concluded: "With best regards, *unbekannterweise* [i.e., "without our having met"], E. Landau."

I did not understand one step in the proof, and in my thank-you letter I had the temerity to ask whether it did not contain a gap. By return mail came a postcard with his patient reply: "Thank you for your letter! There is no gap in the proof," followed by a slight elaboration on the point in question.

Later that year, my father asked me what I wanted to study after completing high school. The answer was obvious: My passion was German literature, my dream to become a writer, perhaps another Thomas Mann or Gottfried Keller. However, my father pointed out that Germany was barred to me (this was in 1935, two years after the Nazis had taken over Germany, and we were living in Zürich at the time), and that opportunities for German literature were extremely limited in Switzerland. He suggested that mathematics, for which I also seemed to have an affinity, was much more international in character and would provide much better career possibilities. I was used to taking directions from him and, without much inner turmoil, agreed to his suggestion. Thus, the crucial decision regarding the work in which I would spend my life came from the outside, rather than from within me. However, at this point it seemed a good idea to my father to get Landau's opinion regarding my aptitude for the subject. Because of my mother's friendship with his wife, it was not difficult for my parents to ask Landau to do this as a personal favor.

Accordingly, the next time he passed through Zürich, Landau came to our house to have a talk with me. His first words as I opened the door were: *"Machen Sie Ihre Eltern unschädlich!"* (Render your parents harmless; get them out of the way!) Next he asked me for some sheets of paper, as large as possible (the best I could produce were still not considered satisfactory but had to do). Then he withdrew with me to my room and told me about some recent results of a young Hungarian mathematician, Paul Erdös, of whom he thought very highly.

As an aside, let me mention that his assessment of Erdös, who at the time was in his early twenties, turned out to be well founded. Erdös became an outstanding, highly influential, mathematician with a phenomenal number of more than 1,500[1] wide-ranging publications, many of them written jointly with others. His collaborators eventually came to more than 450, and it became a game among mathematicians to establish their "Erdös numbers." This number was equal to 1 for anyone who had written a joint paper with Erdös; it was equal to 2 if one had written a joint paper with someone who had written a joint paper with Erdös, and so on. I have the proud distinction (which, however, I share with more than five thousand others) of my Erdös number being 2, since one of my coauthors is my friend Persi Diaconis, who once wrote a joint paper with Erdös.

But back to my session with Landau. I recall his hammering home the point, after showing how Theorem B followed from Theorem A, which he had not proved (it was too advanced), that of course I had not seen a proof of Theorem B. After he had worked with me in this way for two hours, he closeted himself with my parents and apparently recommended that math be given a try.

Many years later, I found among my mother's papers a letter from Landau's wife, Marianne. She said that she was glad that the interview went well, and that if Eddy (Landau's nickname) had given his blessings, my mother could be assured that it was okay, since she knew how many beginners he had discouraged.

The aftermath of this visit must be seen against the background of Landau's situation at the time. In the previous year, a few months after Hitler's ascent to power, he one day found the door to his lecture room in Göttingen blocked by protesting students (reinforced by some Nazi storm troopers). He asked the leader of the group, Oswald Teichmüller, to come with him to his office and explain the objections to his lecturing. At the end of the conversation, Landau requested a summarizing letter that he could use for official purposes; the next day he resigned his professorship, twenty-four years after he had first been appointed to it.

Surprisingly, a copy of Teichmüller's letter, which had long been believed to be lost, turned up a few years ago. Details are given in Schappacher and Scholtz (1992). The following is the central paragraph in the translation of Segal (2003):

> It was for me, not about making difficulties for you as a Jew, but solely about protecting German students in their second semester from being instructed by a teacher of a completely foreign race precisely in differential and integral calculus. . . . I dare as little as any other person to doubt your capability for pure international-mathematical-scientific teaching of suitable students of whatever heritage. However,

[1] These and the following figures are given in Schechter's book about Erdös, *My Brain Is Open*.

I also know that many academic lectures, especially also differential and integral calculus, at the same time have educational value and lead the student not only into a new conceptual world, but also to a different mental viewpoint *(geistige einstellung)*. Again since the mental viewpoint of an individual depends on his mentality *(geist)* which thus should be transformed; this mentality, again, according to fundamental rules, not only contemporary ones, but already long recognized, depends completely substantially on the racial composition of an individual; allowing Aryan students to be educated by a Jewish teacher, for example, ought not in general be recommended.

G.H. Hardy, in his obituary of Landau, wrote: "This enforced retirement must have been a terrible blow to him: it was quite pathetic to see his delight when he found himself again in front of a blackboard in Cambridge, and his sorrow when the opportunity came to an end" (Hardy and Heilbronn, 1938).

It is undoubtedly due to his enforced idleness that I had the privilege of his coming to our house to give me a lesson (perhaps three or four in all) whenever he passed through Zurich. On the second of these visits, he asked me what I was doing mathematically. When I told him that I was trying to learn calculus by reading Courant's book on the subject, he became very concerned. "Courant is a good friend of mine and an excellent mathematician," he said, "but he does not understand pedagogy. His book is poison for you; it will teach you sloppy thinking. If you want to learn calculus, you should do so from my book." So I dutifully bought his book, but it was written in the famous uncompromising Landau style: definition, theorem, proof; theorem, proof; . . .; without giving the reader much help by providing motivation, intuition, or geometric illustrations. Concerning the latter, Landau once explained to me that he knew geometry and had even taught it at Göttingen, but that it had no place in a calculus book since the necessary axiomatic foundation could not be given there. (It is not surprising that Landau's dry and formal way of teaching calculus had been unpopular with the students in Göttingen. Only, of course, it had nothing to do with his Jewishness. Courant was just as Jewish and his approach to calculus was the opposite of Landau's: intuitive and with much help from geometry.)

On his later visits, Landau increased the level of his mathematical discourse, and the level of my understanding decreased correspondingly. After a particularly hesitant "yes" of mine, he broke off. "Mr. Lehmann," he said, "I notice that you use three types of yes: a comprehending yes, a somewhat doubtful yes, and a noncomprehending yes. Of which kind was this last one?"

Though admired not only for his mathematical achievements but also for his honesty and integrity, Landau was considered "difficult" and was feared for his biting wit. I cannot resist giving at least one example of the latter. He had proved an important inequality that involved a universal constant—in German, *Welt Konstante* (world constant). A few years later, another mathematician was able to substantially improve Landau's result by showing that it remained valid when the constant was halved. Landau fired off a terse telegram: *"Gratuliere zur Halbweltkonstante!"* (Congratulations on the half world constant.) The joke lies in the two ways of reading this triple word. As *halb Welt-Konstante,* it means half the universal constant, but *Halbwelt* (in French *demi-monde*) indicates shadiness, ill repute. Thus: "Congratulations on your disreputable constant!"

Another example of Landau's quirky sense of humor occurs in the preface to his 1930 book on the foundations of analysis. He mentions there that the book was written partly for family use, "since—as is well known—my daughters have been at the university for several semesters, . . ." Well known? In explanation, Landau gives a reference to volume one (p. v) of his three-volume work on number theory. The dedication to this book, published in 1927, reads: "To my daughters on the day of their high school graduation."

What Landau meant to those who knew him best is indicated in a letter of condolence written to his widow by Hardy[2]:

> I suppose that his reputation stood higher in England than anywhere else in the world. It was high enough everywhere. Even his enemies could not deny that he was a great mathematician; but we owed more to him than the rest. And we admired him as a person almost as much as we did as a mathematician. We loved his directness, and his "100 percent" honesty. All his little eccentricities, his peculiar humour and his individual likes and dislikes, were entirely sympathetic to us, and made him a sort of tradition: the Landau way of writing and the Landau jokes were familiar to all sorts of people who had never met him. But for those like Littlewood and myself, who really knew him and owed so much to him, he stood, naturally, for a great deal more, and we feel that we have lost one of the best friends we ever had.

To me, in the short time I knew him, Landau was unfailingly patient, considerate, and kind, showing a gentle side which in other, more competitive, circumstances he may not always have wanted seen. The last communication I received from him, a little more than a year before his death, was a postcard:

> Dear Mr. Lehmann, since around now the conclusions of your graduation examinations are due, I should like to ask you to let me know the results. Although I have no doubt as to the success, I am curious to hear how well you did and how the report on mathematics was formulated.

Some time in 1937, my mother was in Berlin and on the occasion paid Landau a visit. He was separated from his wife (although they were on friendly terms), without a position, and depressed. He told my mother that he was having heart trouble but asked her not to tell his wife. Soon after, he suffered a fatal heart attack. At the age of sixty-one, this dynamic man, who had always been so full of vitality, died—figuratively and literally—of a broken heart.

---

[2] A portrait of this great mathematician is provided in C.P. Snow's *Variety of Men* (1967).

2. Rolf Noskwith (b. 1919)

After five years in Zurich, my parents and I came to the conclusion that Switzerland did not offer good prospects to a young German refugee and that perhaps I should continue my study of mathematics elsewhere. Thus, in the spring of 1938—as it turned out shortly before his death—we once more asked Landau for advice. He unhesitatingly recommended Cambridge, with the stars Hardy and Littlewood and an outstanding group of younger mathematicians such as Burkill, Heilbronn, and Ingham, as the best place to get a first-rate mathematical education. So in the fall of that year, I became a student of mathematics at Trinity College, Cambridge.

It was a difficult time for me: my English was rudimentary, and the organization of the mathematical curriculum at Cambridge, with its emphasis on physics and astronomy (considered applied mathematics), was not well suited to my interests and abilities. I felt lonely, but was rescued from my isolation in this new environment by a fellow student, Rolf Noskwith. A son of Polish immigrants, with a knowledge of German and similar interests to my own, Rolf soon became a friend. I saw him nearly daily in his room at Trinity, we worked together, and he helped me better to adjust to English ways.

Two years after entering Trinity, it became clear to me that I could not be successful there. In the meantime, the war had started in Europe, and the

threat of a German invasion of England seemed very real. I was not so very much worried about being hit by a bomb, but under no circumstances did I want to fall into German hands. So in the summer of 1940, I decided to leave England and continue my studies in the United States.

For a while, Rolf and I kept in touch through correspondence, but eventually this petered out. Only much later did I discover what was probably the main reason for this break. In June 1941, Rolf joined British Intelligence at Bletchley Park, where in Hut 8 he became a cryptanalyst and was part of the team that broke Naval Enigma, the code of the German Navy. This supersecret work was both very demanding and could not be written about, so correspondence became difficult.

When he left Cambridge, Rolf had already decided not to become a mathematician. "When the war ended," he writes in an account of his work at Bletchley Park,[3] "I could not tear myself away from decoding and spent a further year working on other ciphers. When I finally left to join the family business created by my father, I made sure that I could come back if a six months' trial did not work out. The option was unnecessary: I am still involved in the business."

What Rolf does not say is that over the years he greatly expanded the textile business that his father had started and made a spectacular success of it.

How do I know this, if our connection ended during the war? About fifty years later, I received a phone call asking me whether I was the E.L. Lehmann who had been a student in Cambridge in the late 1930s. It turned out to be Rolf, who was in San Francisco on business. My wife, Julie, and I had reservations at a restaurant for dinner that evening and tickets for the opera. He was an opera fan; we were able to get another ticket and he joined us.

Unlike I, who had become bald and grown a beard, Rolf had changed very little, and in the slightly stooped man of seventy I instantly recognized the student from half a century before. As a result of this renewed encounter, two years later when Julie and I were in England, we stayed for two days with him and his wife, Annette, and had a wonderful time hiking and catching up. Since then we have kept in contact.

3. Richard Courant (1888–1971)

After having lived in Germany for fifteen years, followed by five years in Switzerland and two in England, finally—in November 1940—I reached what was to be my ultimate destination, the United States. It was my intention to continue studying mathematics (which I had begun in Cambridge), but at what university? When I left Zürich, Landau had recommended Trinity

[3] For details of this work, see Noskwith (2001).

College, Cambridge, where I had studied for two years. Landau was no longer alive, but his widow had given me a letter of introduction to his Göttingen colleague, Richard Courant, who was now at New York University, where he was building up what was eventually to become the Courant Institute.[4]

Courant's name, of course, was very familiar to me, since my exposure to calculus had been through his book, against which Landau had warned me so sternly. When I told Courant my problem, he began by asking me whether I wanted to go to New York or the United States of America. I had no idea what he meant (only later did I realize that many refugees preferred New York, where they had relatives and friends and the emotional support of a large refugee community), but I said that I had no particular interest in New York. He then suggested Berkeley in California, a place and university I had never heard of. "It is an up-and-coming university," he added, "and I think you will like it."

Courant knew Berkeley. He had spent the summer of 1939 there as visiting lecturer, and he was right on both counts. Berkeley was an up-and-coming

[4] The life of Courant is recounted in Constance Reid's book, *Courant—in Göttingen and New York*"

university, in particular its mathematics department would soon become one of the leading departments in the country, and yes, I did like it—in fact, it was love at first sight.

Courant, undoubtedly as a result of Marianne Landau's letter, was very kind to me. For one of the few days remaining before I started for California, he invited me to dinner at his house in New Rochelle. The only thing I remember of that evening was that another guest was a young mathematician, Herbert Robbins, not much older than myself. At the time, he was working with Courant on their highly successful book, *What Is Mathematics?* Later he would become a statistician, and I had frequent contact with him.

I never saw Courant again after that evening, but his unorthodox recommendation of Berkeley had a determining influence on my life. Berkeley became home for the rest of my life, and was responsible for a change of profession, from mathematics to statistics. Courant over the years helped many others, but I for one owe him a great debt of gratitude.

4. Griffith C. Evans (1887–1973)

Upon arriving in Berkeley on January 2, 1941, my first task was to see about enrolling at the university as a student of mathematics. Accordingly, I went to the office of the mathematics department (then on the fourth floor of Wheeler Hall), where the staff at that time consisted of one half-time secretary, Sarah Hallam, a graduate student who was the receptionist and typed the chairman's letters. She told me that the chairman, Professor Evans, was in his office and could probably see me. Evans was welcoming and friendly when I introduced myself. The question of my status was quickly settled: although I did not have a degree, he thought that my two years at Cambridge were equivalent to an American B.A. degree, and to my amazement suggested that I start as a graduate student on probation.

What a breath of fresh air! In Cambridge I had been accepted through connections, as a favor to a high government official who was a friend of my uncle. Here I brought no letter of introduction, or even a transcript attesting to my Cambridge courses. Evans took my statements on trust. He did not ask who my parents were or whom my uncle knew. America was reported to be the land of opportunity, and now I was experiencing it firsthand. What a wonderful beginning to my American life.

I am still enormously grateful for the warmth and generosity with which Evans received me. However, I now see that there was also another reason for his unexpected behavior. Undoubtedly, at that time it was not easy to attract good graduate students. Here came this fellow Lehmann with a Swiss high school education and two years of study at Cambridge—I must have looked like a good bet.

Evans continued to keep me in mind. After I did well during the first semester, he lifted my probationary status and I became a regular graduate

student. A few weeks later, to my great surprise, he offered me a teaching assistantship. I also had a good chance of a fellowship, which would have provided the same stipend without any duties. However, without hesitation I accepted Evans' offer, since it would make me a member of the staff. It was important for me not to be an outsider but to become part of the departmental community.

The department of which I so unexpectedly had become a member was still fairly new.[5] In the early 1930s, it had fallen into disrepair. Its faculty was no longer doing research or keeping up with the rapid development of mathematics. The situation had become so damaging that other science departments were complaining to the administration, and a search committee was appointed to find a new chairman who would revitalize the department.

The committee selected Griffith C. Evans, then one of America's leading mathematicians. He had broad mathematical interests and had made fundamental contributions to potential theory and the plateau problem, as well as to the quite-unrelated area of mathematical economics.[6] In 1916, he was the colloquium lecturer of the American Mathematical Society, and he had just

[5] For a history of the Berkeley mathematics department, see Moore (2007)
[6] For a discussion of Evans' work in this area, see Weintraub (2002).

been elected to the National Academy of Sciences. Since coming to Berkeley in 1934, Evans had made many new appointments. He had added three outstanding mathematicians at the professorial level, and four promising younger men who between them covered an array of different specialties.

As a result, it was a very attractive and vigorous department that I was now joining. The atmosphere was bracing, confidence was in the air, and self-doubt not encouraged. It was assumed that you could do whatever was required; if you needed help, you could ask for it. A good example of this attitude was my first introduction to teaching, that fall.

At the time, the mathematics department employed seven teaching assistants, who—despite this title—did not assist faculty members with their courses but instead taught their own, quite independently. This included both the examinations and the assignments of grades. We shared a large office in the basement of Wheeler Hall and also a great luxury: a reader—an elderly, gruff, and taciturn man who corrected all homework papers.

When Professor Evans informed me of my appointment, he added that my assignment would be a section of analytic geometry and that the professor in charge, Professor Sciobereti, would provide me with further details. When I looked up Professor Sciobereti, he told me the title of the textbook—all sections were to use the same text—but that was the total amount of coordination. He also told me that the course would meet Monday, Wednesday, and Friday at 9:00 a.m. in Room 210 of Wheeler Hall, and then he wished me good luck. This was all the instruction I received, although I had no experience with the system. Nor was there any kind of supervision during the semester.

Toward the end of that first semester of teaching came the Japanese attack on Pearl Harbor and America's entry into the war. Soon the army asked the university to run a training program for meteorology recruits, for which I became an instructor. But the summer of 1942 brought a bigger change for me, of which Evans once more was the agent. He expressed to me his belief that I could be more useful to the war effort if I switched from pure mathematics to either physics or statistics. I greatly respected his judgment and felt that if possible, I should follow his advice. Physics had been my undoing at Cambridge and seemed out of the question, but I knew nothing about statistics, and did not even realize that there was such a subject. I agreed to give it a try.

For this purpose, Evans told me to see Professor Neyman, a member of the mathematics department whom I did not know. Neyman seemed pleased to get a new student, and our meeting resulted in the focus of my studies shifting to statistics. From then on, I had much less contact with Evans, and saw him mainly on occasions involving the whole department. One event of this kind has remained in my memory. It showed how modest Evans was despite his eminence.

When a new building was authorized to house the mathematics and statistics departments, it was decided to name it Evans Hall, and the artist Erle

Loran was commissioned to paint an official portrait of Evans. (It now hangs in the mathematics and statistics library on the ground floor of Evans Hall.) At the dinner celebrating the unveiling of the portrait, after a talk by Charles Morrey, Evans rose to reply.

His opening sentence was rather startling: "Who was Bacon?" he asked. He then proceeded to list several Bacons. "Was it Francis Bacon, who wrote the Novum Organum? No! Or the thirteenth-century philosopher and scientist Roger Bacon? No! Or perhaps the Irish painter Francis Bacon? No! But who was the Bacon after whom Bacon Hall [a campus building] is named?" And with this he sat down.

During the two years of Evans's tutelage, he became a father figure to me. His unvarying kindness and concern during a short, but for me crucial, period profoundly influenced my life, and he has served as an inspiring role model.

5. Raphael Robinson (1911–1995) and Julia Bowman Robinson (1919–1985)

In 1941, when I became a student in the Berkeley mathematics department, some of the older members from the pre-Evans era were still teaching, but I had relatively little contact with most of them. An exception was John McDonald, a sweet, rather shy man with a lovely sense of humor. When lecturing, he would arrange things so that at the end of the hour he stood close to the door. This enabled him to slip out after his last sentence without having to answer any questions. But once, in the last lecture before the final examination, he did not escape in time. "Will there by any choice questions

on the exam?" a student called out as McDonald opened the door. "They will all be choice" was his answer as he disappeared.

McDonald was my graduate adviser and in this capacity too he wasted no words. At the beginning of each term we went through the same ritual. I came into his office, having filled out my study list with the courses of my choice. He would gravely look over the list, put down his pipe in order to sign it, and wordlessly hand it back to me. I would say, "Thank you, Professor McDonald," and that would be the end of our meeting.

In addition to the holdovers from an earlier period were the men whom Evans had brought in during the six years of his chairmanship. They were a good mix of three highly regarded senior mathematicians and four recent Ph.D.'s from a variety of fields. Two of the senior appointments were Charles Morrey and Hans Lewy, both of whom had obtained results of the first rank in the area of differential equations. In addition, both were talented musicians. Morrey was an excellent pianist who sometimes played for us at parties, but I never heard Lewy play his violin. As a young man, he had long hesitated on whether to choose music or mathematics as his profession, and eventually had wound up in Göttingen as a student and collaborator of Courant.

At first, Lewy was quite unfriendly toward me, the only faculty member from whom I encountered hostility. Perhaps he was afraid that as a fellow refugee from Germany I would be an embarrassment to him. Later our relations improved, although I always found his quickness and his somewhat aggressive manner intimidating.

Evans's third senior appointment was much less conventional. Statistics at that time was essentially unknown as an academic subject, but Evans had become convinced of its importance and decided to add an outstanding person in this new field to his faculty. After a lengthy search, his choice was the Polish statistician Jerzy Neyman, then teaching in London, and in 1938 he persuaded Neyman to come to Berkeley as a professor in the mathematics department.

He followed this four years later, in 1942, with another unorthodox appointment, that of the logician Alfred Tarski. Both Neyman and Tarski were world leaders in their respective fields and over the years built up outstanding groups in statistics and mathematical foundations, respectively.

These four appointments constituted a remarkable achievement and testified both to Evans's vision of a very broadly based department and his ability to find and attract the very best people. They laid the foundation for a Berkeley mathematics department that from very inauspicious beginnings eventually rose to become one of the top departments in the country.

The four younger men whom Evans brought to Berkeley to form a second generation had all been trained in America. One of them was Dick Lehmer, a number theorist and early computer enthusiast, whose father had been a member of the department before him. At that time a nepotism rule was in force that forbade close relatives from serving in a department at the same time. So Lehmer had to wait until his father retired before he could be appointed. I took a course in number theory from him, and of all my courses in Berkeley it was the one I enjoyed the most. Number theory, which studies the properties of the integers, was the subject that had gotten me started in mathematics and with which Landau had given me a taste of mathematics on his visits to Zurich. Now for the first time I was provided with a more systematic introduction to the subject.

A second course I greatly enjoyed was group theory. It was taught by another of Evans's young men, the algebraist Alfred Foster, and it turned out to be very useful to me later. On the other hand, I never took a course from Tony Morse, a third member of this quartet. His subject was real variables, for which he had developed a system of his own, with special unconventional notation. Among the graduate students he attracted a group of enthusiastic followers, who were instantly recognizable because they adopted his very pronounced speech mannerisms. It was a kind of cult that did not appeal to me and I took this basic graduate course in the year 1941–42 from the more conventional Morrey.

The last member of this younger group was Raphael Robinson. Of the four, he had both the broadest interests and the greatest depth. When in his seventies, he gave a talk with the title, "Six Simple Theorems I Have Proved." But the theorems were simple only in the sense that Fermat's Last Theorem is simple. Each came from a different field of mathematics, and each was proved in a different decade.[7]

I took a one-year course in complex variables from him, and he opened my eyes to the beauty of this subject. This course is memorable to me also for a number of other reasons. The first concerns a technique that Robinson used in his teaching. Occasionally, he would stop his lecture to ask a question, and often the class would respond with silence. He would then sit down and make it clear that he would not continue with his lecture until we had at least tried to give an answer. What impressed me was that he stuck to his guns, no matter how long it took. Eventually, it was always one of us who broke down and made a stab at a reply.

A second reason for the strong impression the course made on me was a rather traumatic experience. During the second semester, I was very busy with my own teaching and with other courses, and I fell behind. A few days before the final examination, Robinson announced that the (in-class) examination would consist of an essay on either the gamma or the Riemann-zeta function. There was not enough time left to catch up with both, and I had to make a choice. I made the right decision (the gamma function), but I still shudder to think what might have been the consequences had I chosen incorrectly.

Lastly, the course was memorable because of two fellow students, Herb Federer (another European refugee) and Julia Bowman. All three of us

[7] Reid (1996).

eventually were elected to the National Academy of Sciences (Herb in 1975, Julia in 1976, and I in 1978), rather remarkable for a class of about ten students. Soon after taking that course, Julia married Robinson, and we kept in loose contact until her death in 1985.

She had a remarkable career, much of it devoted to a problem known as Hilbert's Tenth Problem, to the solution of which she made crucial contributions. "When it came time for me to blow out the candles on my [birthday] cake," she recalled, "I always wished, year after year, that the Tenth Problem would be solved—not that I would solve it, but just that it would be solved. I felt that I couldn't bear to die without knowing the answer."[8] Her wish was fulfilled; the missing piece was provided by a 22-year-old Russian mathematician, Yuri Matijasevich. She wrote to the author: ". . . now I know it is fine, it is beautiful, it is wonderful."

"That year when I went to blow out the candles on my cake," she recalled, "I stopped in mid-breath, suddenly realizing that the wish I had made for so many years had actually come true."

Julia was the first woman mathematician to be elected to the National Academy (in 1976) and to be nominated for the presidency of the American Mathematical Society (in 1982). Although she had some doubts about accepting the latter, in the end she "decided that as a woman and a mathematician I had no alternative but to accept. I have always tried to do everything I could to encourage talented women to become research mathematicians. I found service as the president of the society taxing but very, very satisfying."

Concerning these and other honors and the attention they attracted, she commented: "All this attention has been gratifying but also embarrassing. What I really am is a mathematician. Rather than being remembered as the first woman this or that, I would prefer to be remembered, as a mathematician should, simply for the theorems I have proved and the problems I have solved."

I used my contact with Julia in 1982 to ask her to introduce me to her sister Constance Reid, the distinguished biographer of both Hilbert and Courant, and to tell her that I thought Neyman would be a good subject for a third mathematical biography. Julia agreed to my request but added that she did not approve of the project. She felt that what mattered was the mathematical achievement and that the person behind it was irrelevant. The book eventually came into being, but that is another story (see Section 61.)

[8] Reid (1996).

2
Becoming a Statistician

In 1933, the coming to power of the Nazis had led to a radical change in my life. It caused me to leave Germany and abandon my dream of German literature, and to take up mathematics instead. Now, in 1942, world events once more changed my course. As a result of the war, I switched from pure mathematics to statistics and thus came under the influence of Jerzy Neyman.

Neyman's work in the 1930s had made statistics into a mathematical discipline within which I was able to function and to make reasonable progress. However, after two years as a graduate student in Neyman's Statistical Laboratory, World War II temporarily disrupted my studies. At Neyman's recommendation, I was asked to join an operations analysis group that was being formed to provide scientific and technical advice to some military command. As a result, I spent the year from August 1944 to August 1945 as an operations analyst on Guam, studying bombing accuracy. The work turned out to be rather routine, and did not involve much statistics. However, in a different way my year on Guam had an important effect on my future. It was the start of my joint work with Joe Hodges, who later became my principal collaborator.

After returning to Berkeley at the end of the war, I quickly completed my degree, and then had the good fortune to be appointed to the faculty Neyman was trying to build. As a result, I was able to stay in Berkeley, which had begun to feel like home.

6. Jerzy Neyman (1894–1981) and Alfred Tarski (1901–1983)

In 1942, as mentioned in Section 4, I moved to Neyman's statistics program. At the time I knew nothing about Neyman, and only much later learned his story and how he had come to Berkeley. He began his statistical career in Poland, but in the 1930s moved to England. Between 1928 and 1937 (partly in collaboration with Egon Pearson), he founded a new theoretical approach to statistics.

In 1937, he came to the attention of Griffith Evans, who was looking for someone to develop a statistics program at Berkeley. Evans, impressed by

Jerzy Neyman

Neyman's work and by reports of some lectures Neyman had recently given in the United States, decided that he was the best person for the job and offered him a position in the Berkeley mathematics department. Neyman arrived in Berkeley in August 1938, and he quickly established a core program of courses and a small organization consisting of a secretary and several teaching and research assistants. Within a few months, it officially became the Statistical Laboratory (the Stat Lab), with Neyman as its director.

In the fall of 1942, my initiation into the new subject began by my taking the first term of the introductory upper-division course. I did not find the course very interesting until Neyman introduced an element of considerable excitement for me personally. Out of the blue, he told me one day that he was leaving for three weeks and that he wanted me to take over the lectures of this, my first course of statistics in which I was a student. What made this assignment particularly scary was that the course did not use a text (in fact, no text existed at the time). Neyman outlined the material I was to cover, and then I was on my own. Somehow I muddled through, but was relieved when Neyman returned and I could revert from my role as instructor back to that of student.

After completing the first semester of the new program, I was faced with a basic decision concerning my future. I had agreed to give statistics a try, but had come to realize that I did not like it. It was lacking the element that had attracted me to mathematics as a boy: statistics did not possess the beauty that I had found in the integers and later in other parts of mathematics. Instead, ad hoc methods were used to solve problems that were messy and that were based on questionable assumptions that seemed quite arbitrary. Thus, at the end of 1942 I decided not to continue with statistics but to return

Alfred Tarski

to pure mathematics. The subject that interested me most was algebra, but I did not find the department's algebraist, Alfred Foster, very inspiring.

However, a new possibility had opened up. In the fall of 1942, the great logician Alfred Tarski had joined the mathematics department and was scheduled to give an advanced algebra course in the spring semester. I therefore asked Tarski whether I could work with him, not in logic but in algebra, and he agreed to accept me as a student.

Tarski was a Jewish refugee from Poland (though converted to Catholicism) who had come to New York in 1939 to attend a conference on the unity of science. He had left three weeks before the German invasion of Poland, and thus had escaped the fate of his parents, brother and most of his other close relatives, who were murdered by the Germans. (An exception was his wife, who was not Jewish, and his two children, who joined him in Berkeley after the war.)

Despite his reputation as one of the world's greatest logicians, Tarski[1] had difficulty finding a suitable job in America. One reason was that his field of mathematical logic was not a recognized university discipline. (In this respect, it was somewhat similar to mathematical statistics.) It was Evans, with his broad conception of mathematics combined with his aim to attract the highest caliber of faculty, who came to the rescue and created a position for Tarski in the Berkeley mathematics department. Tarski remained in Berkeley, where he continued his groundbreaking research and attracted some outstanding students.

[1] For a recent biography of Tarski, see Feferman and Feferman (2004).

Neyman and Tarski shared not only a Polish background (and a strong Polish accent), exceptional ability, and energy, but also enormous ambition. Both were empire builders.

Neyman, over the decade 1946–1956, managed to parlay the single appointment of himself as professor of mathematics into a faculty of ten tenure-track members, more than half his own students but greatly strengthened by a number of outstanding appointments from the outside. At the same time, he pushed relentlessly for ever-greater independence of his group, with the ultimate goal of an independent department of statistics. Such an expansion would not have been possible but for the growth of the discipline of statistics itself, with statistical methods becoming important in more and more fields of application and the resulting increase in the number of students requiring instruction in this new methodology.

Tarski too was eager to develop his own fiefdom. As with Neyman, the motives were a mix of personal ambition and the desire to provide an identity of its own for his subject, which hovered uneasily between mathematics and philosophy. He successfully obtained appointments for some of his students and for others working on his agenda, some in mathematics and some in the philosophy department. With such a faculty in place, he was able to deal with an obstacle faced by his students: they had to satisfy the stringent requirements of one or the other department, which were too specialized for the broad-based training involving aspects of both disciplines that Tarski considered necessary.

To overcome this problem, Tarski, with the help of a group of like-minded colleagues, proposed a new doctoral degree in logic and the methodology of science. The program was approved in 1958, but was listed in the university catalogue for the first time in 1964, with the faculty group administering it consisting of five members from the mathematics department, three from philosophy, and one each from oriental languages and statistics.

The outstanding parallel success of Neyman and Tarski was symbolized by the fact that at the 1954 International Congress of Mathematicians in Amsterdam, they were two of the five Americans (out of a total of twenty) invited to give one-hour lectures. They spoke, respectively, on "Current Problems of Mathematical Statistics" and "Mathematics and Metamathematics." It was an enormous achievement of Evans to have initiated and nurtured two such outstanding and influential programs. He came close to adding a third but that one slipped away (see Section 56).

However, these developments lay far in the future when, in December 1942, I decided to work with Tarski instead of continuing with statistics. That in the end things turned out differently is due to events that occurred in the few days after my decision and before I had been able to tell Evans and Neyman about it.

After having done all the teaching of statistics himself, with only temporary help, Neyman had finally found a young mathematician, Dorothy Bernstein, who, after having turned him down earlier, accepted a tenure-track appointment for the year 1942–43. However, after one semester, she realized—just as I had—that she did not like statistics, and she told Neyman that she did not want to renew her contract. She presumably had planned to leave at the end of the academic year, but Neyman was furious and preferred that she leave immediately.

This left Neyman shorthanded in the middle of the academic year and, not knowing that I too was planning to desert, he asked me whether I wanted to take over some of her duties: an elementary course in the spring semester that was just coming up, and the following year the upper-division course I was then taking. I was to receive a promotion to lecturer and a substantial increase in salary. There were also overtones—nothing specific, but slight hints—that this position might develop into a permanent job if things worked out.

The effect Neyman's offer had on me—that I would be willing to give up the work that attracted me for a field that I found much less appealing—may seem surprising. However, it had its cause in my situation at the time. I felt unconnected: without a country, without a language, without a community. And now Neyman was offering me the chance to become a part of a community (his laboratory), and perhaps even the possibility of Berkeley becoming a permanent home. Germany was barred to me; neither Switzerland nor England had much enthusiasm for refugees who would settle and compete for jobs; and here I was being welcomed, encouraged, and—although I was only a beginning graduate student who had not yet taken any of his exams—being offered what amounted to a junior faculty position. It was overwhelming; how could I say no?

Although I did not know it then, I was not the only student facing a choice between Neyman and Tarski. The same issue arose at about the same time for my fellow student Julia Robinson. She had taken a course from Neyman in 1939, and two years later he asked for her as a teaching assistant. Clearly he hoped she would become one of his students. However, her reaction was the same as that of Dorothy Bernstein and myself: she found statistics "very messy, not beautiful and clear and true like number theory."[2] Instead, she obtained her degree (in 1948) under Tarski, and went on to an illustrious mathematical career (see Section 5).

Julia's and my choosing between Neyman and Tarski illustrates one aspect of a rivalry that sprang up between them. They were competing for students and resources, as well as for the reputation and visibility of their programs. This competition was undoubtedly one reason why these two Polish-American colleagues in the mathematics department were not on good terms. In addition, they were so far apart on the political spectrum—Neyman being a liberal and Tarski a conservative—that they were referred to as "Poles apart." Finally, Tarski must have been aware that Neyman had strongly lobbied Evans against his appointment. He argued instead for Antoni Zygmund, another outstanding but more conventional Polish mathematician then in the U.S., without however having any effect on Evans's vision.

After deciding to continue with statistics, I had no further contact with Tarski. My new career totally absorbed me. That my life's work turned out to

[2] Reid, *Julia—A Life in Mathematics* (1996).

be in statistics still seems very surprising even today. It corresponded to no wish of mine. Three times outside forces intervened and pushed me away from what I wanted to do. My first choice was German literature, but my father said to do mathematics. Next, I tried mathematics and enjoyed it, but Evans said to do something applied. Finally, after trying statistics and finding it unappealing, I wanted to go back to pure mathematics, but Neyman offered me a job. Friends and family members who have read this account tell me that I could not have been that passive. However, this is just the way it happened. And it was not entirely due to my somewhat passive nature, but also the result of the turbulent times in which these decisions had to be made. When the whole world is shaken by cataclysmic events such as the Nazi takeover of Germany and the Second World War, individuals lose some control of their lives and have to become more adaptable.

7. Jerzy Neyman—the Teacher and Scientist

The conclusion concerning statistics that Dorothy Bernstein, Julia Robinson, and I had reached so unanimously after our first exposure to the subject turned out (fortunately) to be premature. What we did not know was that in its more advanced aspects, statistics had in the preceding decade become much more mathematical—nor did we know that Neyman was the person largely responsible for this transformation.

I found out about the much more congenial nature of this more advanced work when, in 1942–43, now a full-fledged member of Neyman's Stat Lab, I got my first real introduction to the new field to which I had committed myself. At the same time, I became acquainted with the unusual method Neyman employed in advanced teaching. He liked to call students to the board, giving preference to the women in the class ("ladies first"), and would try to get them to derive the new results under his guidance. It was something of an ordeal for the hapless victim, a fact of which Neyman seemed oblivious. In fact, once he told us that he had received a letter concerning this practice that accused him of sadism. He clearly was at a complete loss—"sadism?"—but announced that any student feeling this way would be excused from coming to the board. To the best of my knowledge, no one took him up on this offer.

For me, Neyman had reserved a special role. If the person at the board got stuck and no one else could find the next step, he would call on me: "Erich will know since he is from Vienna," he would say. I never did, perhaps because I was not from Vienna, as I told him frequently but without success.

This graduate course was largely based on Neyman's own work (together with the extensive preparation this required). The choice of material reflected the fact that in the 1930s he had developed an entirely new approach in which statistical procedures were obtained as solutions of clearly stated mathematical problems, and which he considered the only way to treat the subject. The resulting course thus had a rather narrow focus, but it had the advantage of presenting unified, logically cohesive account. The work, to my great relief, was thus much more congenial to me than what I had expected from the more elementary course of the previous year.

The new point of view that Neyman had developed in the 1930s had come to him not as a sudden inspiration at a young age but after long preparation in two different fields (mathematics and applied statistics) and as the result of a stimulating collaboration. Born to parents of Polish ancestry, Neyman had grown up in Ukraine but had moved to Poland in 1921 (at age 27) and there had become associated with the Polish school of mathematics. However, though his heart was in pure mathematics, statistics (which he had learned from S.N. Bernstein) was more marketable. After holding statistical positions in agriculture and meteorology, he obtained university appointments in Warsaw and Krakow, where he lectured on both statistics and mathematics.

In 1925, the Polish authorities, interested in his statistical work but not quite sure what to make of it, gave Neyman a fellowship to work in Karl Pearson's laboratory in London, then the center of the statistical world. But he was greatly disappointed by the low mathematical level of the work being done there and, after receiving an extension of his fellowship, he spent the second year of it in Paris, drifting back to his first love: mathematics.

He was pulled back into statistics by a letter he received in 1926 from Karl Pearson's son, Egon. This letter raised some basic questions concerning the rationale underlying current statistical methodology that captured Neyman's imagination. It resulted in joint work by Neyman and Pearson, much of which was carried out by correspondence, and reinforced by occasional visits, between Neyman in Poland and Pearson in London. The situation became easier when, on Karl Pearson's retirement, Egon became head of the Department of Applied Statistics and was able to offer Neyman a position in his department. As a result, in 1935 Neyman moved to London with the position of reader in statistics.

The joint work of the two friends dealt with the testing of hypotheses. R.A. Fisher had developed a series of tests for a number of important problems, and he had popularized this new methodology in his enormously successful book, *Statistical Methods for Research Workers* (1925). For someone with Fisher's insight, these tests had seemed to be the natural solutions to the problems in question, and he had presented them without any additional justification. The problem Pearson had raised in his letter was to find a rationale for these choices.

The key[3] to their solution of the problem was to consider not only the hypothesis to be tested but also the alternatives that might obtain if it were not true, and to measure the performance of a test in terms of the kinds of errors it could commit: rejecting the hypothesis when it is true and accepting it when it is false. The test would be required to control the probability of false rejection at a specified value α (typically 5% or 1%, as suggested by Fisher). Subject to this condition, that test was best (optimum) that minimized the probability of false acceptance. The central result of this theory, known as the Neyman-Pearson lemma, solved this problem for the case that both the hypothesis and the class of alternatives consists of a single distribution. They showed that the optimum test then rejects when the likelihood ratio, that is, the ratio of the probability density under the alternative to that under the hypothesis, is sufficiently large. They gave a full exposition of this approach, together with many applications, in their fundamental 1933 paper, "On the Problem of the Most Efficient Tests of Statistical Hypotheses."

Neyman, on his own, went on to extend this new approach of deriving statistical procedures as optimal solutions to the problem of interval estimation. The result was his theory of confidence intervals. In his basic 1937 paper on the subject, he stated his point of view very clearly:

> The theoretical aspect of the statistical problem of estimation consists primarily in putting in precise form certain vague notions mentioned in (i) [a description of the practical problem of estimation]. It will be noticed that the problem in its practical aspect is not a mathematical problem, and before attempting any mathematical solution one must substitute for (i) another problem (ii), having a mathematical sense and such that, for practical purposes, it may be considered equivalent to (i).

The implementation of this program resulted in what has been called (by some pejoratively, by others as a compliment) the mathematization of statistics. An important example was Neyman's 1934 treatment of survey sampling, which

[3] Suggested to Pearson by Gosset ("Student"). See, for example, E.S. Pearson: *"Student": A Statistical Biography of William Sealy Gosset* (1990).

for the first time put this methodology on a firm basis and profoundly affected not only its theory but also its practice.

On a related front, again as an effort of clarification, Neyman proposed a new philosophy of statistics that reinterprets the aim of statistical analysis. Instead of the traditional "inductive reasoning" as a way of learning from observation and experiment, which he considered devoid of meaning, he suggested that statistics was concerned with "inductive behavior," that is, with using the data as a guide to the most appropriate action.[4] Wald took up this idea and carried it a step further by formulating a very general abstract theory of decision-making as a framework for all of statistics. This work also contributed to making statistics a more mathematical discipline.

By developing its mathematical side, statistics attracted students who took a more theoretical view of the subject and who often were interested in pursuing mathematical issues with no immediate applications. Such work in turn again contributed to the increasing mathematization of the field.

The papers in which Neyman developed his new approach and which played such a crucial role in these changes were written between 1928 and 1937. As his work was becoming known, he began to receive invitations to lecture abroad. Particularly significant were a number of lectures in America (at, among others, Columbia, Princeton, Chicago, Michigan, and Illinois), which ended in a series of lectures and conferences at the Graduate School of the U.S. Department of Agriculture, arranged by W. Edwards Deming. They provided a systematic account of his work on hypothesis testing, estimation, and sampling, and included not only formal lectures but also lively discussion.

Information about Neyman's enormously successful Washington performance reached Griffith Evans, chairman of the Berkeley mathematics department, who was looking for someone to develop a statistics program at Berkeley As a result, in November 1937, Neyman received a letter in London from the unknown Evans offering him a position in the mathematics department of the University of California. Neyman hesitated between remaining in England, returning to Poland, or taking the risk of moving (with his wife and two–year-old son) to a completely unknown environment in California. One of the attractions of Berkeley for him was that no statistics program existed there, so he would have a free hand to implement his own ideas. Nevertheless, it was with considerable trepidation that, after some negotiations, he accepted Evans's offer.

The decision to move to Berkeley was a crucial event in Neyman's life and, some believe, in the history of statistics. The great accomplishment of the first (European) half of his life was the development of a new paradigm for statistics. The principal achievement of the second (American) phase was the creation of an institutional platform for the dissemination of these ideas. In that effort too, Neyman was highly successful, in a way that would hardly have been possible had he remained in Europe.

---

[4] See, for example, Neyman (1957).

It led to his development in Berkeley of a statistics department that eventually reached a stable size of about twenty faculty members. By the end of the century, it had graduated more than four hundred Ph.D. students and produced a flood of influential papers and books. Although, of course, he required colleagues for this enterprise (of which I became one), the initial inspiration and energy was his, and for many years the department and its teaching and research reflected his statistical philosophy.

One important part of this development was the series of Berkeley Symposia on Mathematical Statistics and Probability, which Neyman organized at five-year intervals from 1945 to 1970.

During the war, Neyman's energy and that of his lab were devoted mainly to work on a military contract, more specifically the application of probabilistic considerations to determine the best strategies in various bombing situations. Everyone had to pitch in. Briefly (and for the only time in my life), even I found myself plugging away at a calculator.

However, as soon as the end of the war was in sight, Neyman turned his full energy back to science and the development of the lab. As a first step, "to mark the end of the war and to stimulate the return to theoretical research," in June 1945 he proposed a Symposium on Mathematical Statistics and Probability, which took place August 13–18, 1945.

With few exceptions, the speakers came from California, principally from other campuses of the University of California, because Neyman's funds were limited, and some invited speakers had been unable to make it on such short notice. However, since some money was left over after the August symposium, Neyman decided to add a sequel, which took place January 27–29, 1946.

In this second session also, most speakers were local. In particular, Neyman asked me to present a paper. I complied as best I could, but the resulting paper is not one of which I am very proud. However, he gave me another assignment from which I derived great pleasure. The two most distinguished visitors were to be Joe Doob (1910–2004) from the University of Illinois and Will Feller (1906–1970), then at Cornell—the two outstanding probabilists in the U.S.—and Neyman asked me to be their driver.

They were in a relaxed mood, and on a memorable drive to Stanford entertained each other and their chauffeur with various games. My favorite was the discussion of what salary it would take for them to accept a position at Berkeley. The figure would go up and down with the attractions of the surroundings. When we reached the ocean, south of San Francisco, Feller became very enthusiastic and was willing to lower his demand substantially. Not so, said Doob: he would have to raise the salary, since he might be tempted to swim despite the notorious undercurrents and then might drown.

In a report about the symposium to the provost, Chairman Evans was full of praise:

> I cannot help saying that the symposium was an outstanding success, and that the success was due to Mr. Neyman's foresight in seeing its possibility at the time, and to

> his initiative and resourcefulness in planning it. It constitutes a significant page in the history of the University of California. But what is of even more importance, it was convincing evidence of the growing importance of the relation of statistics to experimental work in many branches of science and of the service which the Statistical Laboratory is rendering to the university and to the public. Undoubtedly the demands on the Laboratory from both of these sources will increase continually.

The report reflects the fact that the symposium included papers not only on the theory of probability and statistics, but also on applications arising in such diverse subjects as psychology, astronomy, economics, forestry, meteorology, parasitology, and animal breeding. It also refers to an important activity of the lab, namely responding to requests from both within and outside the university for assistance with statistical problems in an ever-widening variety of fields.

It seems likely that the first symposium was not part of a long-range plan, but was conceived by Neyman on the spur of the moment, as a single event of celebration. However, the meeting was so successful, and Neyman enjoyed so much being host for such a gathering on his own turf, that by 1948 he was beginning to make plans for a second symposium.

The symposia, in fact, continued at five-year intervals, steadily increasing in size, so that the fifth symposium in 1965 had a budget of over $125,000, obtained from multiple sources. In comparison, the budget of the first symposium was $4,000, provided by the university. The proceedings had grown from a single volume of five hundred pages to a five-volume set with a total of three thousand pages. The sixth symposium was even larger and turned out to be the last. The burden of organizing such a mammoth undertaking had become too onerous for a single department.

The symposia were an enormous achievement for Neyman, a testament to his imagination, energy, and organizing ability. During the twenty-five years of their existence, they functioned as the most important international statistics meetings, and put Berkeley on the map as a world center of statistics.

8. Joseph L. Hodges, Jr. (1922–2000)

In the spring of 1944, as the semester (and hence my first graduate statistics course) was nearing its end, Neyman introduced me to a civilian official from the Air Force who told me of a new concept, operations analysis groups, which the 8th Air Force had used with great success in Europe. They consisted of civilian scientists, engineers, and other experts who worked with the military personnel without actually being part of the military. They were thus free to tackle any problems they felt needed attention without going through the chain of command. The visitor was in the process of organizing such a group, and at Neyman's recommendation asked me to join it. In this capacity, I would become a statistical advisor to some Air Force command at a location that could not be divulged. It seemed to me quite unlikely that with my one, very theoretical, graduate course I would be of much use, but refusing did not seem an option. So I agreed to become an operations analyst.

To receive the necessary clearance for secret war work, I received a visit from two FBI agents. Among other things, they wanted to know whether I was a Communist or had even "slightly pinkish tendencies." I had to laugh. No, I told them, I am not a Communist, but yes, I have some pinkish tendencies—as does President Roosevelt. They left soon after, and I received my clearance and was ready for my new job. In preparation, I underwent two training sessions. The first took place at the Pentagon, where my instructor was the chemist and statistician Jack Youden, the inventor of an experimental design known as Youden squares. He began by giving me an important piece of information: it would be my task to track and analyze bombing accuracy, along the lines he had pioneered for the 8th Air Force in England. I read some reports about this work and Jack told me about his experiences. This gave me at least some idea of what was expected of me.

A month at the Pentagon was followed by three weeks at the Air Force Academy in Colorado Springs to acquire some basic military skills. Here for the first time I met the other members of the group. Among them, to my great surprise and happiness, was Joe Hodges, who had been my best friend from Berkeley. Also a student of statistics, he had mysteriously disappeared some weeks earlier, having been asked to keep his assignment a secret. The chief of the group was a physicist, and the group also contained another statistics student, George Nicholson from North Carolina; a more senior mathematician; and a number of engineers and aeronautical specialists—perhaps a dozen in all. We three statisticians had been given different tasks: Joe was responsible for statistical problems wherever they might arise, George for problems related to gunnery, and I for assessing the accuracy of our bombers.

We were now also issued uniforms, but without the usual insignia of rank, although we were given assimilated ranks that, among other things, determined our salaries. Mine was the rank of captain, which seemed to me much too high for a beginning graduate student. A memorable part of our training was the day we were taken to the shooting range to learn how to use a gun. This was the first time either Joe or I had held a gun, much less shot with it. As we were driving to the range, I noticed with some concern that we were being accompanied by an ambulance. This was perhaps a sensible precaution. For when, after several hours of practice, we were tested, most of us, far from hitting the bull's-eye, missed the target altogether.

At the end of this three-week training session, we boarded a military train, its destination unknown. As it worked its way through the landscape, we realized that we were going westward, and soon a rumor spread that we were headed for San Francisco. So we were going to be in the Pacific, rather than the European, theater of war. From San Francisco we flew to Hawaii, and only after the plane left Honolulu were we finally told that our destination was the headquarters of the 20th Air Force on Guam, under the command of General Curtis LeMay.

Hodges and Lehmann in Guam

The island had only recently been taken by the American forces, and nothing was ready for us except the tents that were to be our homes on Guam. The three statisticians were assigned to the same tent, together with a somewhat-older engineer. We were given cots to sleep on but had to assemble them ourselves. I had trouble putting mine together and Joe kindly offered to help. In the process his arm slipped, hit me in the face, and broke my glasses. Fortunately, I had brought along a second pair, but they were darkly tinted. It took three months to get another pair from Berkeley and in the meantime I was mercilessly teased for my Hollywood look.

Guam was the headquarters of the Pacific Fleet under Admiral Chester Nimitz. The navy had arrived earlier than we and as a result was much further along. In particular, they had a mess hall and an officer's club long before we did. We obtained permission to use the facilities of the club, and one Saturday afternoon our section chief loaded us into a jeep and drove us to the naval end of the island. On the way home after a few drinks, he decided to inspect the progress made on building a runway. Once on the runway, he said, "Let's see whether we can take off" and pressed the accelerator to the floorboard. It was beginning to get dark so we could not see very far, and we had no idea when the unfinished runway would end and be blocked by large boulders. I think it was the most dangerous moment of my months on Guam.

One other potential danger occurred somewhat later. Quite a number of Japanese soldiers were still hiding in the dense jungles that covered much of Guam. A radio message was intercepted in which the Emperor of Japan called on these soldiers to stage a suicide attack on our headquarters. As a consequence, all headquarters personnel were ordered to be armed at all times. This, however, did not apply to our group, who as civilians were forbidden by the Hague conventions to carry arms. On the other hand, we were in uniform and it seemed unlikely that attacking Japanese would pause to inquire about our status. Eventually, the decision was left to us. A gun would be issued to anyone wanting it, but we could remain unarmed if that was our preference. Joe and I, and in fact most of us, remembering our performance in Colorado Springs, decided against guns, believing that they would pose a greater danger to our friends than our enemies. In fact, the attack never took place.

The months on Guam were the only time in my life that I had an 8–to-5 job. It involved little statistics but consisted mainly of photo interpretation.

The task assigned to the 20th Air Force was the destruction of Japan's aircraft industry through high-level precision bombing. My job was to record and analyze the results. For this purpose, cameras were installed on the B-29's, which, on each mission, took pictures of the falling bombs, following them if possible until they struck. Our operations analysis group had been given a Quonset hut for its work, in which I had a desk and a viewer for examining the strike photos. At first, I was able to handle the work by myself, but gradually the size of our force increased and I was provided with additional staff. Eventually, my bombing accuracy group consisted of ten people, most of them privates or noncommissioned officers.

The pictures were often unsatisfactory. On a cloudy day they might not show the ground, the motion of the plane could blur the picture, or the timing or placement of the camera might be off. Effecting changes required negotiations with the responsible officers. Because of antiaircraft fire or weather conditions, the bombs were often not released over the target but at some other location. To get an idea of where this was, one had to go to the flight reports. After these difficulties had been resolved as well as possible, it was necessary to record and file the results and to report them, together with summary statistics, to the appropriate departments.

This kind of work was not what operations analysis was originally set up for. Operations analysts were meant to be troubleshooters who would be unfettered by the military command structure, and in this capacity they had had some spectacular successes at the 8th Air Force in England. However, the group that had been organized for the 20th Air Force was ill-suited for this purpose, and seemed in fact intended for more specific routine assignments. Nevertheless, I greatly benefited from the original idea. The civilian status and absence of insignia to indicate rank greatly simplified my work. It made it possible to negotiate directly with the officer in charge of any program, regardless of his rank, without having to go through channels or to be excessively deferential.

From our studies and reports, it soon became evident that the accuracy of the bombing was unsatisfactory, and pictures from later reconnaissance flights showed that in fact the damage to the targeted factories had been relatively slight. The bombing campaign was thus not achieving its mission. A principal cause of the lack of accuracy was the high altitude at which the planes were instructed to fly in order to avoid antiaircraft fire. To see how the situation could be improved, Joe and I were asked to study the likely effects of lowering the altitude, both on accuracy and on vulnerability of the planes.

Whether our study had any effect I don't know,[5] but LeMay decided on a completely different approach, quite outside the range we had been studying. He ordered a surprise attack at a very low altitude for which the Japanese defenses were not prepared. He also made other changes: the attack came at night, the targets were industrial areas of Tokyo, and the bombs were incendiary. The purpose was to start a conflagration, and to do so required a very large force: over three hundred B-29's were used, more than twice the number employed on any previous attack. LeMay realized that he was taking a great risk, and he was not sure whether at the end of the mission he would still have much of an air force. As it turned out, our losses were fairly low.

We did not know about this raid until the next day and then knew little about the appalling toll in Tokyo of over eighty thousand dead. Even so, thinking back I am surprised that we were not more disturbed by such an attack on an urban target. The general attitude was stated brutally by LeMay in his autobiography: in wartime you worry about your own losses, not those of the enemy. And how we did worry about our own! After each mission, we counted the returning planes and tried to learn what had happened to those that had not returned (they were more often lost to engine failure or other malfunctioning than to enemy fire) and whether there was still some hope.

The effect of altitude study was the only major joint military report Joe and I wrote; generally our work took different paths. However, we spent much of our leisure time together. In particular, we found that we shared a love of classical music, and on Sundays would often study (and sing) the late Beethoven quartets, of which somehow we had obtained the scores. Later, Joe discovered a dynamic and interesting protestant chaplain on the Navy side of the island, and on Sunday mornings we would borrow our group's jeep to attend his services.

In June, a new group of bombers came to the neighboring island of Tinian to begin training for the release of the first atomic bomb. It is extraordinary that neither Joe nor I knew anything about these activities until nearly two months later, after the first bomb had hit Hiroshima. It was an amazingly well-kept secret. Two weeks later, after the release of the second bomb, Japan capitulated. The war was over.

Since our group had low priority, I feared it might take weeks for us to get transportation, and then it would be by a slow troopship. At the same time, I felt that my obligations were over and that as a civilian who was not even yet a U.S. citizen, I did not have to wait for orders. So I tried an alternative

---

[5] Comments by former Secretary of Defense Robert McNamara in the documentary film *The Fog of War* suggest it might have.

way of making my escape and left my name at the airport, in case a seat should become available for a flight to San Francisco. And luck was with me. The next night, around 1:00 a.m., I received a call. If I could be at the airport within an hour, space on a flight was available. Without any of the required formalities, I wrote a note to the section chief, asked Joe to turn in my Air Force gear, and packed my duffel bag. When I got to the airport, I heard announcements: "Anyone for the United States? Anyone for the U.S.?" I was told that a plane had been readied to take a group of entertainers back to the States but that they had gotten so drunk that they were unable to fly. The plane was needed in San Francisco and was nearly empty. So hop in. Two days later, I was back in Berkeley.

Joe's return to the U.S. was more complicated. His commitments required him to spend another year at the Pentagon working on matters relating to operations analysis. During his time in Washington, he met, fell in love with, and got engaged to Teddy Long. She too had commitments in Washington, and they made it impossible for her to leave when he was ready to do so. So on his return to Berkeley, he stayed with me and my wife Susanne for the better part of a year.

Joe obtained his Ph.D. under Neyman in 1949 and in the following two years found some of the most important results of his career. In a technical report (with Evelyn Fix), he pioneered nonparametric density estimation. This report was considered so path-breaking that forty years later Bernard Silverman, the editor of the *International Statistical Review,* wanted to publish it with an appropriate introduction. On a visit to Berkeley, since he did not know Joe, he asked me to get his consent. I invited both to lunch so that they would meet personally.

Even more influential was Joe's solution of a long-standing problem. Fisher, in the 1930s, had claimed that maximum likelihood estimates (MLEs) enjoyed the property of asymptotic efficiency—roughly that in large samples their performance could not be improved. Since then, some of the most outstanding probabilists and statisticians had tried to prove this statement but without success. Now Joe produced an extremely simple example in the most standard situation (estimating the mean of a normal distribution) of a "superefficient" estimate—that is, one that improved on the efficiency of the MLE. We finally knew why no one had been able to prove Fisher's claim: It was wrong!

Joe felt that the example was too elementary to publish, so it was only published in 1953 in the Ph.D. thesis of another Berkeley student, Lucien Le Cam, who brought much additional clarity to the issue. He showed that the improvement over the MLE could occur only on a small set of parameter values (technically, sets of Lebesgue measure zero), and that estimates achieving such improvement necessarily had some quite undesirable properties. Although these superefficient estimates thus were not useful in practice, Joe's example changed the landscape and had a profound effect on asymptotic theory.

Between 1950 and 1970, Joe and I carried out much collaborative research and published many joint papers and a book. However, in the mid-1960s he accepted an appointment to the Berkeley Budget Committee, and this was followed by a long period of university service (primarily on personnel matters), which he greatly enjoyed but which left little time for research.

Although our collaboration thus ended, our friendship (which included his wife Teddy and their five children) continued up to the time of his death in 2000. Outside of my family, the relationship with this highly talented and kind (although contrarian) colleague and friend was the closest of my life.

9. Evelyn Fix (1904–1965)

Joe Hodges's coauthor of the fundamental paper on nonparametric density estimation, Evelyn Fix, died in 1965, more than twenty years before its publication by Bernard Silverman in the *International Statistical Review*. It would have been lovely to have Evelyn participate in the lunch I gave for Bernard and Joe and have her savor this triumph.

Evelyn was born in Duluth (Minnesota) and received her B.A. and M.A. degrees from the University of Minnesota in 1924 and 1925, respectively. For the next fifteen years, she taught mathematics in high school. In 1939, she attended a summer session in Berkeley, including two courses in statistics from Neyman. In the process, as Neyman would later say, "she caught the bug."

When in 1941 Neyman found himself desperately shorthanded, he recalled his student from two years earlier, and offered Fix the position of technical assistant. She knew Griffith Evans, the chair of the Berkeley mathematics department, who was a friend of her family; statistics seemed an interesting field; and Neyman a charismatic boss to work for. So, despite the not-very-promising title (for a woman of thirty-seven), she accepted Neyman's offer and quickly became a central figure in the Stat Lab.

Her first big task came in 1942, when Neyman received a contract for bombing research from the National Defense Research Council. The work was computationally very intensive; it was carried out on desk calculators and consumed much time and effort. Evelyn was in charge of the calculations and presided over a hastily recruited, ragtag group of students (of which I was one for a short while) and faculty wives. It was a very demanding job with wartime urgency to get results, and Evelyn was indefatigable.

Her central role became again apparent in 1945 when Neyman suddenly left for Greece, days before the second part of the symposium he had organized. Evelyn was the person keeping things running and on schedule and seeing to the well-being of the guests. By that time, she had been promoted to lecturer and was teaching various upper division courses.

Evelyn obtained her doctorate in 1948 with a thesis titled, "Distributions Which Lead to Linear Regression," supplemented by an earlier report, "The Effectiveness of Several Types of Incendiary Bombs." One aspect of her degree was somewhat awkward for both of us. Since I had received my degree two years earlier and was then the only regular faculty member in statistics besides Neyman, I had to administer the German exam to this friend who had been my supervisor and who was more than ten years older than I. Fortunately, it was a written examination that was not taken very seriously, and it passed without too much embarrassment for either of us.

After her work on density estimation, Evelyn continued working with Joe Hodges, and they published a joint paper on the Wilcoxon test in 1955, as well as another in 1959 on restricted chi-squared tests, of which I was a third coauthor. It showed that great gains could be achieved in chi-squared goodness-of-fit tests by specifying the alternatives of principal importance. That paper, which made crucial use of Evelyn's earlier tables of the noncentral chi-squared distribution, was a contribution to a Festschrift for Harald Cramér, an admired friend of the three of us.

Perhaps Fix's most important paper after her work on nonparametric density estimation was her 1951 paper with Neyman, "A simple Stochastic Model of Recovery, Relapse, Death, and Loss of Patients." Up to that time, survival analysis had considered only length of life. The Fix-Neyman model incorporated health (i.e., quality of life) as a second variable.

Her collaboration with Neyman continued when he asked her to join him for a semester in Bangkok, Thailand, in the fall of 1952. Sponsored by the Food and Agriculture Organization of the United Nations (FAO), their assignment was to organize a training center on survey sampling.

They describe their experiences in a joint paper, "Statistical Adventures in Thailand" (1954).

After that, Neyman's principal collaborator (particularly on problems in astronomy) became Elizabeth Scott, while Evelyn, starting in 1960, collaborated with F.N. David and David Barton on a series of papers on combinatorial problems arising in statistics. Although the total number of her publications was small, their quality was high and, taking into account her many other contributions to the department, she was promoted through the ranks until she attained the professorship in 1964.

Evelyn did not have the forceful personalities of her women colleagues Betty Scott and F.N. David. She was self-effacing and sweet-tempered and uncomplainingly accepted—or more often volunteered for—work from which others shied away. As a prime example, three courses that, though important, were outside the mainstream and were stepchildren of the department became some of her principal teaching assignments and responsibility. These were upper-division courses in survey sampling and in descriptive statistics (the latter required for students taking the actuarial examinations) and a graduate course in experimental design.

Evelyn's life changed greatly when at age thirty-seven she followed Neyman's call to California and shifted to a new profession. It was a life of service, punctuated by significant achievements. She died in 1965, shortly after returning from the banquet of the Fifth Berkeley Symposium, which she had helped to arrange. In her memory, the department established the Evelyn Fix prize, which is annually awarded to the most promising doctoral student in applied statistics.

10. Harold Hotelling (1895–1973)

My return from Guam coincided with the conclusion of the first session of the Berkeley Symposium in August 1945. The talk that had made the greatest impression was the opening talk given by Harold Hotelling of Columbia University on a topic specially requested by Neyman, who five years earlier had heard a lecture by Hotelling that deeply impressed him. The title of Hotelling's earlier talk was, "The Teaching of Statistics," and it raised a basic question:

> The growing need, demand, and opportunity have confronted the educational system of the country with a series of problems regarding the teaching of statistics. Should statistics be taught in the department of agriculture, anthropology, astronomy, biology, business, economics, education, engineering, medicine, physics, political science, psychology, or sociology, or in all these departments? Should its teaching be entrusted to the department of mathematics, or a separate department of statistics, and in either of these cases should other departments be prohibited from offering duplicating courses in statistics, as they are often inclined to do?

Neyman asked Hotelling to continue this discussion at the symposium, which he did with a lecture titled, "The Place of Statistics in the University." He concluded this talk with the following recommendation:

> Organization of the teaching of statistical methods should be centralized and should provide also for the joint functions of research and advice and service needed by others in the institution and possibly outside it, regarding the statistical aspects of their problems of designing experiments and interpreting observations.

Hotelling's remarks carried great weight not only because they addressed problems that many in the audience were experiencing, but also because he was recognized as the outstanding American statistician of the 1930s. He had been the most important early supporter of Fisher in the U.S., who—it seems on his own initiative—reviewed the first (1925) edition of Fisher's *Statistical Methods* for the *Journal of the American Statistical Society* (JASA). His review ended with the statement that, "The author's work is of revolutionary importance and should be far better known in this country." Hotelling was sufficiently enthusiastic that he went on to review also the next six editions of the book as well as the first two editions of Fisher's *The Design of Experiments* (1935).

In 1929, when he was on the faculty of the mathematics department at Stanford University, Hotelling spent six months with Fisher, and then tried to bring what he had learned to the attention of American statisticians through two survey papers in JASA: "British Statistics and Statisticians Today," and "Recent

Improvements in Statistical Inference." However, Hotelling not only put considerable effort into introducing Fisher's work, but he also significantly extended it.

In one of his earliest statistical papers (1929, written jointly with Holbrook Working), Hotelling obtained confidence bands for regression curves several years before Neyman developed his theory of confidence sets. His best known and most influential paper (1931) extended Student's t-test (in both the one- and the two-sample cases) from univariate to multivariate distributions. The resulting test is known as Hotelling's T^2-test. As in the earlier paper, he points out that the tests can be converted into confidence statements, this time for the unknown multivariate mean. He also introduces invariance considerations to simplify determining the null distribution of the test statistic, an idea that entered the mainstream only much later. He continued his contributions to multivariate analysis with, among others, two basic papers on principal components (1933) and canonical correlations (1936).[6]

A paper pointing in quite a different direction was "Rank Correlation and Tests of Significance Involving No Assumption of Normality" (joint with Pabst). Of it, Richard Savage, in his 1953 "Bibliography on Nonparametric Statistics and Related Topics," writes, "Papers related to nonparametric problems were published in the 19th century, but the true beginning of the subject may be taken as 1936, the year in which Hotelling and Pabst published their paper on rank correlation."

Again, invariance considerations are central to the paper, and are used to motivate the reduction to the ranks of the observations. Since invariance played an important role in my own work and nonparametrics was one of my major areas of research, I think of Hotelling as an intellectual godfather, although our personal contacts were very limited.

In 1931, Hotelling moved from Stanford to the economics department of Columbia University (he was an eminent economist as well as statistician). There, he built up an enormously successful statistics program, of which W. Allen Wallis later said,[7] "At the time [i.e., in the 1930s], Hotelling was practically the only person in the U.S. teaching statistics as we think of it today."

The depth of Hotelling's influence can be seen from the fact that the principal early Ph.D. programs in statistics, with the exception of Neyman's at Berkeley, were all started by persons who had learned modern statistics either as graduate or postgraduate students from Hotelling. They were Sam Wilks, who started a statistics program in the Princeton mathematics department in 1936; Al Bowker and Abe Girshick, the founders in 1948 of the Stanford statistics department; and W. Allen Wallis, who was instrumental in establishing a statistics program (in 1949) at the University of Chicago.

These programs, of course, were all preceded by the distinguished statistics group Hotelling built up at Columbia after he went there in 1931, and which

---

[6] A bibliography of Hotelling was published in a Festschrift for him, edited by Olkin et al. (1960).

[7] In Olkin (1991).

included in particular both Abraham Wald and Jack Wolfowitz. He tried to obtain for his group the status of an independent department of statistics. However, the Columbia administration resisted this effort, and persisted in their refusal even in 1946, when Hotelling received an exceptionally attractive offer from the University of North Carolina at Chapel Hill to start a statistics program there with strong external financial backing. As a result, Hotelling left Columbia for Chapel Hill, where he quickly built up a strong department. In the wake of these events, the Columbia administration—afraid that they would also lose Wald—belatedly set up a department of mathematical statistics, with Wald as executive officer.

I had little contact with Hotelling during his lifetime, but unexpectedly found myself in the role of his biographer thirty years after his death. It is a policy of the National Academy to commemorate its deceased members through memoirs of their life and work. A few years ago, since no such memoir had been written for Hotelling, I was asked to find a suitable person for the task. I was unsuccessful and finally decided to write the memoir myself, in collaboration with the Stanford economist Kenneth Arrow.

11. Three Ph.D. Godfathers

Until 1945, Neyman had run the Stat Lab single-handedly, with the help of graduate assistants and occasional temporary junior faculty. But in the summer of 1945, a long-held wish materialized with the arrival of the Chinese scholar Pao-Lu Hsu (1910–1970) as visiting lecturer for the fall term. The next term, he was scheduled to teach at Columbia in Hotelling's group.

Hsu had obtained his Ph.D. under Neyman in London in 1938, and two years later had returned to China as professor of mathematics at Peking University. He suffered much during the war years, but continued his research. After long efforts, Hotelling and Neyman had now succeeded in bringing him to the U.S. It was Neyman's hope that after his Columbia term, Hsu would accept a permanent position at Berkeley.

For me, the most urgent issue after my return from Guam in the summer of 1945 was to find a thesis problem. A possible topic was suggested to me by Hsu after consultation with Neyman. The problem, surprisingly, was in probability theory, but had some application to statistics. By December, I had made enough progress to consider writing up the results obtained thus far. At this point, however, a citation to related work sent me to additional references, and after a few days to the realization that my results were already contained in the work of Russian mathematicians from about fifty years earlier.

Shortly after this collapse of my thesis, Neyman, as an expert in sampling, was asked to join President Harry S. Truman's mission to supervise the upcoming Greek elections. Among the many problems worrying him in the two days before leaving—and possibly being gone for some months—was that of his unfortunate student Lehmann, whose plans for completing his degree by the end of the spring semester were in shambles. So he asked Hsu to give me a new thesis topic.

Pao-Lu Hsu

Within a few days, Hsu presented me with a new possible topic: applying methods of Neyman, Scheffé, and himself to some situations for which they had not been tried before. Hsu then got me started on this line of work. In a letter of January 24 to Neyman, about which I learned only much later, he wrote: "I have passed the problem of testing for independence between successive observations to Erich for his doctoral thesis. Will do all I had done independently, and then add a new part which I have not done. I hope this scheme will meet with your approval, so that Erich can look forward to the degree with certainty."

This was an act of greatest generosity. Hsu made me a present of work he had planned to do himself and on which he had already obtained some results. I had hoped to see him on his return to Berkeley after the term at Columbia. However, this was not to be; in fact I never saw him again.

Hsu announced his decision not to return to Berkeley in the same letter of January 24 in which he informed Neyman about the arrangements he had made for my thesis topic. The letter began:

Dear Neyman,

I do not know what to say to you. I act so like a saboteur that you can hardly be expected to forgive me. The fact is that two-page letter from Hotelling. The letter contained a surprising news about himself—that he is resigning his position at Columbia to organize a new Department of Mathematical Statistics at the University of North Carolina, and a surprising invitation to join him, from July 1, at the rank of associate professorship and a salary of $5,000. Besides, he wanted me to answer immediately to enable him to make an announcement at a statistical meeting on January 24. I accepted him.

Accordingly, Hsu spent the next year-and-a-half with Hotelling at Columbia and North Carolina. Quite unexpectedly, he then returned to his professorship at Peking University. The reasons for this sudden decision are not clear.

Patriotism seems to have been one. This was shortly before the Communist victory and he was looking forward to being part of the new society in his home country. There were also rumors of a failed marriage proposal. (He in fact never did marry.) In China, he suffered much during the Cultural Revolution and in later years from ill health. He died at the young age of 60, after a long illness.

His collected papers, some of them translated from the Chinese, were published in 1983, with introductory material by T.W. Anderson, K.L. Chung, and myself. To quote from this introduction: "Hsu is affectionately remembered by many students and colleagues as a gentle, shy, and modest man who . . . had a strong influence as a teacher and model of a scientist."

We should have added that he was warmhearted, generous, and completely unselfish. I am lucky to be able to count myself as one of his students.

When Neyman left for Greece, he was concerned not only about my thesis topic but also about who, with himself and Hsu both gone, would supervise my thesis work. No one in the mathematics department knew any statistics or even probability theory and would be able to give me guidance. However, it occurred to him that George Polya at Stanford, although not a statistician, had a very broad knowledge of mathematics that included probability theory. The breadth of his interests is indicated by the titles of the four volumes of his collected papers: 1. Singularities of Analytic Functions; 2. Location of Zeros; 3. Analysis; and 4. Probability, Combinatorics, Teaching, and Learning Mathematics.

So Neyman asked Polya, who had helped him out on previous occasions, whether he would take on the supervision of my thesis, and Polya agreed. Thus it came about that during the spring of 1946, every two weeks I would drive to Polya's house, tell him of my progress, and would then be invited to join him and his Swiss wife, Stella, for tea and cookies.

George Polya

At tea we talked not about mathematics or statistics, but rather reminisced about our common experiences. I found out that before coming to Stanford, Polya had taught at the *Eidgenössische Technische Hochschule* (ETH) in Zürich from 1914 to 1940. Since I was a university student in Zürich from 1936 to 1938, I might easily have taken courses from him. However, this did not happen because I was enrolled at the University of Zürich rather than the ETH. It also turned out that both the Polyas and I had left Europe for the U.S. in 1940 and for the same reason: the threat of a German invasion, in their case of Switzerland, in mine of England. We did not want to fall into the hands of the Nazis!

George Polya (1887–1985) was not only an outstanding mathematician but also an exceptional teacher.[8] The year before my sessions with him (although I did not know this at the time), he had published a book, *How to Solve It,* on techniques and strategies for problem solving. It was to become a huge success, particularly after it came out in paperback. Eventually, it sold over a million copies and was translated into eighteen languages.

Unfortunately, I did not take advantage of my meetings with this remarkable man. I was too caught up in the struggles with my thesis, with which I was not very happy. The problem was too special for my liking, the results messy, and their derivation fairly routine. But to my surprise, sometime in April or May Polya declared himself satisfied. When I protested the low quality of the work, he pointed out that there would be plenty of time to do better work later on, and that at the moment the important thing for me was to get my degree. So I wrote up my results in final form and all that remained was my thesis defense. This, however, presented a difficulty, since Polya was not a member of the Berkeley faculty and since no one who was seemed suitable for this examination. The problem found a very unexpected solution, in the form of a telegram from Neyman in Greece saying that he was on his way home. He had been fired for insubordination.

The story is complicated,[9] but basically Neyman believed that the election was rigged and that the mission was not doing anything about it. So he decided to look into the situation on his own, and when asked to discontinue his independent investigation he defied the order. If the government had looked for someone to participate in a whitewash, they had picked the wrong man.

In any case, the mission no longer wanted his services and as a result, Neyman was back in Berkeley just in time for my examination. Thus, in early June I received my doctorate and this event was followed by an appointment to the faculty.

As a result of all these complications, I had three thesis supervisors. The problem was given to me by Hsu, most of the work on it was supervised by Polya, and Neyman presided at the thesis defense. One could hardly have wished for a more distinguished trio of godparents for one's career.

---

[8] For a more comprehensive account of Polya's life, see H. and L. Taylor (1993).

[9] For details, see Reid (1982).

3
Early Collaborators

My first two publications (both appearing in 1947) were written while I was still a graduate student. However, during the five years after my degree, most of my research was collaborative. This was not a deliberate policy on my part but resulted from my delight in being part of a community of congenial colleagues with shared interests. In fact, these professional relations transcended the confines of joint work and became lifelong friendships. I was, of course, extraordinarily lucky in finding such outstanding collaborators as Henry Scheffé, Charles Stein, and Joe Hodges.

The crucial role proximity played in promoting these collaborations is indicated by the fact that no new joint projects developed with either Henry or Charles after they left Berkeley, Henry after a one-year visit and Charles after three years due to political causes. On the other hand, Joe remained in Berkeley and our joint work continued happily for twenty years and ended only when he switched from research to administration.

After the first five years, I began to do more research on my own, but at the same time continued collaborative work, after Joe with my friend and colleague Peter Bickel and still later with my wife, Juliet Shaffer.

In addition to these major collaborations, occasional joint papers with various coauthors came about fortuitously. Two such coauthors, Herman Chernoff and Raj Bahadur, are discussed in this chapter. Other, later, instances resulted from correspondence and conversations with former students: Fritz Scholz, Wei-Yin Loh, and Javier Rojo. Not all such efforts succeeded. On one occasion, David Blackwell and I started to work on a problem but after a while abandoned it. An attempted project with John Tukey suffered the same fate.

Joint work has been a crucial ingredient of my professional life. It has greatly enriched my research and has enabled me to accomplish much more than I could have done alone. At the same time, it has brought me some wonderful, deep, and lasting friendships.

12. Henry Scheffé (1907–1977)

The first time I met Henry Scheffé was in 1946, when he spent a year in Berkeley with a Guggenheim fellowship, on leave from the College of Engineering at the University of California–Los Angeles. His name was of course well known to me, since my thesis had been based partly on his work. It was exciting now to meet him in person.

Henry was born of German parents living in New York. His father, who had for many years worked as a baker for the same firm, lost his job during the Depression and was reduced to selling apples at a street corner. The memory of this injustice and of his father's suffering remained with Scheffé throughout his life.

Henry, who was ten years older than I, had obtained his degree in pure mathematics with a thesis on differential equations. However, he decided that the field of mathematical statistics promised more interesting opportunities for research, and in 1941 went to Princeton to study statistics under Sam Wilks. After some years of war work at Princeton, he taught statistics for a year at Syracuse University and from 1946 to 1948 was on the engineering faculty of UCLA. It was the first of these three years that he spent in Berkeley.

Despite the image of a prize fighter conjured up by his broken nose, Henry turned out to be a very nonbelligerent, rather shy person with interests in art,

music, and literature. We quickly took a liking to each other and on long walks discussed statistical issues as well as literature, music, and the state of the world. I was impressed by his hatred of prejudice. He once told me that when he heard an anti-Semitic remark he tried to silence the speaker by stating that he was Jewish (which was not the case).

His attitude toward religion emerges from a story he told of his daughter being asked in school about the family's religious affiliation. He told her that they were atheists. The next day, she returned with an additional question: "Yes, but are we Protestant, Catholic, or Jewish atheists?"

One of his best bon mots concerned our two introductory statistics courses. He explained that the more theoretical course (Stat 1) was for students who wanted to understand statistics but were not planning to use it, while the methods-oriented, cookbook-style course (Stat 2) was suitable for students who planned to use statistics but did not need to understand it.

Our statistical conversations led us to discuss a unifying concept that tied together many different situations we had been considering, which we called completeness. For models possession this property, it turns out that both testing and estimation become particularly simple. The reason, it seems, is that in such models one can discard all parts of the data that by themselves carry no information about the unknown parameters (for details, see Lehmann, 1981).

The basic idea was not new; it had been used by various authors in a number of special cases. However, isolating the basic underlying concept and formulating it abstractly turned out to be very fruitful, and made possible a host of new applications. We published a preliminary report in 1947 in the *Proceedings of the National Academy,* but a full exploration of the concept (which we called completeness) took us several years. Eventually, we gave a comprehensive account in two long papers in 1950 and 1955. Completeness has become a staple of statistical theory.

By the time Henry left Berkeley at the end of his Guggenheim year, the outline of the work was clear, and it was possible to elaborate the details by correspondence and occasional visits back and forth. On the other hand, Henry was very busy in new positions, first at UCLA and after 1948 at Columbia. In addition, Henry's interests were shifting, partly under the influence of his friend, the applied statistician Cuthbert Daniel. As a result, we did not start any new projects and our collaboration gradually petered out. It was not even resumed when in 1953 Henry joined our Berkeley department. In bringing him to Berkeley, Neyman had hoped that Scheffé, with his strong interest in applications, would assist him in the administration of the laboratory, and Henry's original appointment was as professor of mathematics and assistant director of the Statistical Laboratory. However, the arrangement did not work out—Scheffé was too independent—and the additional title was dropped after the first year. Henry remained in Berkeley as professor of mathematics until his retirement, serving as department chair from 1965 to 1968. During his term of office, he had to contend with great unrest on campus, the result of what became known as the Free-Speech Movement.

Different groups of both faculty and students in the department had violently opposite attitudes, and Henry was in the middle, trying to hold the department together and to keep the atmosphere pleasant. His fair-mindedness gained him the respect and affection of all members.

It was due to the prodding of Cuthbert Daniel that Henry wrote what is probably his best-known paper, "A Method for Judging All Contrasts in the Analysis of Variance" (1953). Daniel wrote later[1] that he takes great pride "in the fact that [my] copy is inscribed, 'To the guy who hounded me into this.' This required listening to long disquisitions throughout more than a year, on how messy the distribution was, climaxed one evening at 11:30 with, 'Guess what, it's the F-distribution.'" Henry had found a very elegant solution to what seemed to be a quite intractable problem.

In addition to his research, Scheffé is particularly remembered as the author of an outstanding book, *The Analysis of Variance* (1958), written during his Berkeley years. The feature that makes this book so special and caused it to be the standard account of the subject for decades is its combination of the theoretical and applied points of view. It is rigorous, the formulations are general, but at the same time it is full of practical insights. Especially noteworthy in this regard is the last chapter, "The Effects of Departures from the Underlying Assumptions."

After his retirement in 1974, Scheffé accepted a three-year appointment to the mathematics department at Indiana University. In June 1977 he returned to Berkeley, where he was planning to prepare a second edition of his book. Unfortunately, he was not able to carry out this project. On July 5, 1977, he died as a result of a bicycle accident.

Henry Scheffé was my first collaborator, and I found our joint work very satisfying. It filled a need that had once been touchingly described by Neyman in an early letter to Pearson. Discussing plans for their continued collaboration, Neyman wrote, in his still very imperfect English:

> Possibly it is no need to work out everything together or even publish things in joint papers. *Only what I would like is to have a sort of companionship in the work.* [Emphasis added.]

This companionship is what I too was seeking, and I was lucky to find it in Henry and in several later collaborations.

13. Charles Stein (b. 1920)

By the fall of 1947, Henry had left Berkeley and I would again have been without the hoped-for companionship, if a new faculty member had not just then joined our group.

---

[1] In Daniel and Lehmann (1979).

Charles Stein had come to Neyman's attention through a remarkable paper (1945) he had written as a graduate student. In it he had solved a problem that had long been of interest to Neyman. The power of the t-test of the hypothesis H: $\theta = 0$ for the mean θ of a normal distribution is a function of θ/σ, where σ^2 is the variance of the distribution. It is easily seen that as σ becomes arbitrarily large, the power against a fixed alternative θ tends to its value at 0, that is, the significance level α.

Neyman's first American student, George Dantzig (who later became famous for his work on the simplex algorithm for linear programming), proved that in fact no test can exist that for fixed θ and all possible values of σ has power bounded away from α, regardless how large the sample size. This is intuitively plausible, since two normal distributions with means 0 and θ, respectively, and the same very large σ are practically indistinguishable.

In his paper, Stein gave not only a very simple proof of this result, but showed that fixed power greater than α, independent of σ, against a final alternative θ, can be attained by a sequential two-stage procedure. An initial sample is used to estimate σ, and the size of the second sample is determined by the value of this estimate. The larger the estimate, the larger the sample size at the second stage, which becomes arbitrarily large as the estimate of σ does.

Stein's solution was not only very original but also extremely elegant. It elicited Neyman's enthusiasm and resulted in Charles becoming a member of our faculty in the fall of 1947. Having just completed his degree at Columbia, he brought with him not only his great talent but also familiarity with Wald's decision theory, the hot topic of the day.

His appointment caused one small problem: our group was growing but we had not been given any additional space. So Charles was assigned to share an office with Evelyn Fix (Neyman's principal assistant during the war years), Joe Hodges, and me. The office was so small that it barely accommodated our desks when they were arranged as a square block in the middle of the room. This forced proximity of four congenial people with common interests led to many interchanges of ideas and to some joint papers. In particular, Charles and I wrote four joint papers over the next two years, dealing with four quite distinct and unconnected problems. A common feature was that they were all theoretical, concerned with optimality and related issues.

One of the most important ideas that I learned from Charles was not part of Wald's decision theory (but had earlier been used by Hotelling in some special cases). It was that of invariance of a hypothesis testing problem under some group of transformations and the related property of invariance of tests of this hypothesis. The principal result arising from these considerations was the Hunt-Stein theorem, which states that when the group satisfies certain conditions, there exists a "maximin" test (i.e., that maximizes the minimum power over an invariant class of alternatives), which is invariant. It thus greatly simplifies the usually difficult problem of determining a maximin test. This is particularly the case if there exists a best invariant test that then automatically is also maximin. Rather surprisingly, Hunt and Stein did not publish this important result.

Charles later told me the reason. Since they were unable to prove the result in full generality (i.e., for all groups), they investigated it for special classes of groups, and were able to prove it for Abelian groups and for compact groups (where it is obvious). This was enough to cover the case of analysis of variance and more generally of the univariate linear hypothesis. However, despite much effort, they could not prove it for the group of all linear transformations, which was needed for Hotelling's T^2. Charles found it embarrassing not to be able to include such a simple case, and decided to delay publication until he could do so.

Several years later, he found a simple counterexample showing that the theorem did not hold for all problems invariant under the group in question. By that time, I was working on my book on hypothesis testing, and Charles gave me permission to include both the theorem and the counterexample, an act of great generosity. Thus, it came about that the Hunt-Stein theorem made its first public appearance when my book came out in 1959.

Of our four joint papers, I shall mention only one: "Most Powerful Tests of Composite Hypotheses" (1948). As the title indicates, the problem was to determine a level α test that would maximize the power against a specific alternative. Its purpose was to fill a gap in the classical Neyman-Pearson theory. This theory showed that many standard tests, for example the t-test, maximize the power among all unbiased tests. (A test is unbiased if its power against all alternatives is greater or equal to α.) But does this optimum property still hold when the restriction to unbiased tests is dropped and all level α tests are permitted to compete?

We developed some general theory for this problem that naturally suggested itself as an adaptation from decision theory, and followed this by examining a number of classical testing problems. In some examples, the standard test retained its optimality against this wider competition; in others it did not. What was needed for these results was the construction of a "least favorable" weighted average of distributions in the hypothesis H as close to the alternative as possible. This least favorable distribution was often suggested by intuition, and then all went swimmingly.

However, this turned out not to be the case when we came to the most interesting example, that of the t-test. We conjectured that the least favorable distribution would concentrate all its probability on a single point, but then intuition deserted us. We saw no way of determining this point and were quite frustrated. A few days later, Charles told me that he had solved the problem. Although not determining the point explicitly, he showed by a careful analysis that for $\alpha < 1/2$ such a point exists and gives the right test, which is quite different from the t-test. It has better power in the neighborhood of the specific alternative for which it was designed but lower power elsewhere. For $\alpha \geq 1/2$, the situation turned out to be much easier, and in that case the t-test cannot be improved.

In the aftermath of this work, I began to realize that Charles had insight, power, and intellectual courage that far surpassed mine. Despite this disparity, he seemed satisfied with our collaboration, and it probably would have continued if political events at the university (the requirement of a loyalty oath) had not caused him to leave Berkeley after two years, first for the University of Chicago and then for Stanford.

The qualities that Charles showed in solving this problem led him later to deep and influential results. Particularly striking is his discovery of a very surprising phenomenon, now called Stein estimation.

Suppose that $\bar{X}$ is the average of several measurements of some unknown quantity θ (a height, temperature, blood pressure, . . .), and that $\bar{X}$ has a normal distribution with mean θ and variance 1. If we want to estimate the unknown value of θ, the obvious estimate seems to be the average $\bar{X}$. This estimate is not only natural but also possesses various good properties. In particular, suppose that we measure the loss resulting from the fact that $\bar{X}$ differs from θ by the square of the error, that is, $(\bar{X} - \theta)^2$ and the resulting risk by the expectation of this quantity (which is a measure of the accuracy (or rather inaccuracy) of the estimate $\bar{X}$. Then it is known that there exists no other estimate that improves on the risk of $\bar{X}$ uniformly, that is, for all θ. We say that $\bar{X}$ is admissible.

Consider now the case that we wish to estimate s unknown quantities θ_1, . . ., θ_s on the basis of s means $\bar{X}_{(1)}, \ldots, \bar{X}_{(s)}$, distributed independently with means $\theta_1, \ldots, \theta_s$ and common variance 1. Since $\bar{X}_{(i)}$ is the best estimate of θ_i for each i intuition tells us that the set of estimates $(\bar{X}_{(1)}, \ldots, \bar{X}_{(s)})$ is optimal for the set $(\theta_1, \ldots, \theta_s)$.

It therefore came as a great shock when Stein (1956) showed that the performance of this "obviously" right estimator can be improved when s is 3 or greater and when the overall loss is measured by the average of the individual losses. And the improved estimator has the strange property that the estimated value of the ith component θ_i depends not only on the ith average $\bar{X}_{(i)}$, but also on the completely unrelated average measurements of the other θ's.

When Charles first told me of this result, I rather rudely said, "I don't believe it," to which, somewhat offended, he replied, "But I proved it." And so he had. After all efforts of finding a hole in his proof had failed, a large literature sprung up in which the phenomenon was explored for different loss functions and in different settings. Eventually, it became clear that in the formulation of the problem stated above, the s component problems, despite their independence, were linked through the loss function, which combines the individual losses into a single average. And indeed, it turns out that although the Stein estimator does better than $(\bar{X}_{(1)}, \ldots, \bar{X}_{(s)})$ on the average, its performance for the individual components can be quite unsatisfactory. Thus, for example, if the $\bar{X}$'s are the average test results for s patients sent to a common laboratory, the Stein estimate would be desirable from the laboratory's point of view, but it would not protect an unusual patient from a very erroneous assessment.

While Stein's innovation therefore has some drawbacks in addition to its advantages, it nevertheless opened up a whole new area of possibilities, which was explored in a large and very interesting literature. Perhaps the most surprising later discovery relates to the fact that Stein's improvement is possible when the number of unknown means is 3 or greater but not when it is 1 or 2. A distinction between the cases "3 or greater" and "1 or 2" prominently occurs also in a completely different field, the theory of random walks and diffusion. In an extraordinary paper in 1971, L.D. Brown showed that there exists a completely unexpected but in fact quite close connection between these two theories, by establishing a correspondence between estimators and diffusion, with the estimators being admissible if and only if the corresponding diffusion is recurrent (see Section 49).

Surprisingly, fairly late in his career, Stein made influential contributions not only to statistics but also to probability theory, when in 1972 he published a completely new approach to the classical problem of obtaining good approximations and limit theorems for the distribution of sums of dependent random variables. He developed his method further in his book, *Approximate Computation of Expectations* (1986), and it was later expanded by others, for example in the book, *Stein's Method: Expository Lectures and Applications* (Diaconis and Holmes, eds., 2004).

This and his other work showed Charles's outstanding originality. His writings inspired many later authors to mine the rich veins he had exposed.

14. Hodges–Lehmann I: Parametric Inference

After Charles left in the fall of 1949, another collaboration developed, this time not with a newcomer but with my friend, tentmate on Guam, and now officemate, Joe Hodges. He had just completed his Ph.D., with a thesis written under Neyman's supervision, and had then joined the faculty. As a consequence, he was now free to consider other problems, and we began a collaboration which, in the years 1950 to 1970, resulted in fifteen joint papers and an elementary text. Later, Joe accepted a number of high-level administrative positions that left him no time for research. Thus, our collaboration ended, although our friendship continued.

Our joint work covered two different areas. The early papers (to be considered in the present section) dealt with problems arising in the then-standard parametric situation in which the form of the probability distribution is assumed known (usually normal) but involves some unknown parameters. Later (see Section 40), our principal interest centered on an alternative (nonparametric) methodology.

Hodges and Lehmann

Our first three papers, one each in 1950, 1951, and 1952, were concerned with concepts of Wald's new decision theory—with minimax and Bayes procedures and their admissibility. Our first paper was motivated by the fact that Wald's work, while an imposing abstract edifice, contained practically no examples. So, piqued by curiosity, we asked ourselves what the minimax estimator would look like in the simple problem of estimating a binomial probability p under squared error loss. According to the general theory, the minimax estimator should be a Bayes solution. Unfortunately, Bayes solutions are difficult to determine explicitly. In fact, the only situation we saw how to handle was that of a beta prior. In that case, the Bayes solution turned out to be a linear function $aX + b$ of the binomial variable X. Since a Bayes estimator is minimax if it has constant risk, we next found that for suitable a and b the Bayes estimator $aX + b$ has constant risk, and the problem was solved.

So far we had been lucky, but now our luck deserted us. Our minimax solution turned out to be a very poor estimator that, despite its minimax property and being admissible, on the whole was much inferior to the standard estimator X/n.

Admissibility of the minimax estimator in the binomial example follows from the fact that any unique Bayes solution is automatically admissible, that is, that there then exists no other procedure that is better for all parameter values. However, minimax procedures often are not Bayes solutions but only limits of Bayes solutions, and then cannot be guaranteed to be admissible.

So for our next project, Joe and I looked for a different method of proving the admissibility of such estimators. We found such a method by considering a certain differential inequality related to the so-called Cramér-Rao inequality.

Our third paper again grew out of our interest in minimax and Bayes procedures. The latter assumes complete knowledge of the a priori distribution, a requirement that seemed rarely satisfied in practice. On the other hand, the minimax procedure corresponds to the prior distribution (or sequence of distributions) that is least favorable, which may not be at all close to the investigator's assessment of the situation. We proposed a compromise between these two extremes: namely, to put an upper bound on the maximum risk so that—even though not minimum—it could not be too large, and subject to this restriction to minimize the Bayes risk. The resulting paper developed a general theory of such "restricted Bayes procedures" and provided a number of examples.

Of the remaining parametric papers I shall mention only one, "Testing the Approximate Validity of Statistical Hypotheses" (1955). In the classical Neyman-Pearson theory, the hypothesis $H{:}\theta = \theta_0$ completely specifies the value of the parameter being tested. Frequently, it is more reasonable to consider instead the hypothesis $H'{:}\,|\theta - \theta_0| < \Delta$ for some $\Delta > 0$. We worked out a number of examples, the most interesting (and rather complicated) being the case of a normal mean. The paper did not find much resonance, but the problem was later revived. It became known as "testing for bio-equivalence," however with the hypothesis and alternatives interchanged so that the hypothesis being tested was: $H': |\theta - \theta_0| > \Delta$.

In our joint work, Joe and I approached problems from very different points of view. Mathematicians are often characterized as problem-solvers or system-builders. In this categorization, Joe was a pure problem-solver. He seemed to have little interest in the context in which a problem arose, but considered each problem entirely on its own merits—a hard nut that it was his job to crack. And he was superb at that task, bringing to it great ingenuity and intelligence. My own attitude was just the opposite: problems attracted me because they constituted irritating gaps in our systematic knowledge, and I was more interested in how the answer increased our understanding than in the process of solution.

As had been the case in my joint work with Henry and Charles, much of the work with Joe was also done on walks in which our conversation was not confined to statistics. A favorite diversion on these occasions was the composing of limericks. One of Joe's says something about our taste in music, which at the time appreciated only Bach, Mozart, and Beethoven:

The music of Johannes Brahms
Has strange ineluctable charms
And sometimes it seems
It might lapse into themes
But alas, they are all false alarms

Another time, we challenged each other to produce a limerick on a colleague named Neustadter. This eventually resulted in the following joint effort:

A student named Siegfried Neustadter
Lost all his pertinent data
He thus could not cram
For his final exam
Which exam was crammed full with errata

Clearly we had fun.

These three collaborations and the lifetime friendships they engendered are some of the greatest rewards my profession has brought me.

15. Herman Chernoff (b. 1923) and Raj Bahadur (1924–1997)

The previous sections of this chapter covered my collaborations with Henry Scheffé, Charles Stein, and the first phase of my work with Joe Hodges. These joint investigations with Berkeley colleagues were the result of nearly daily conversations in our offices or on walks, over an extended period. This section is motivated by one joint paper each with two colleagues at other

Herman Chernoff

universities, which came about more or less accidentally by correspondence. Both Herman Chernoff and Raj Bahadur were outstanding statisticians whose work I admired and with whom I kept in contact through occasional encounters at statistical meetings or on brief visits to their departments.

Born and raised in New York, Herman Chernoff obtained his B.S. in mathematics in 1943 from the City College of New York. Herman's decision to become a statistician was strongly influenced by his encounters with two fundamental papers. The first occurred during his studies at City College, which included a couple of courses in statistics. At one point, he was assigned to read the 1933 paper in which Neyman and Pearson developed their theory of hypothesis testing. Chernoff was blown away. In an interview with Bather, he said: "It was quite a traumatic experience. It took me a long time to realize that it was as simple as it seemed to be. It required a complete reorganization of my brain cells to adapt to it and I was quite profoundly impressed."

Chernoff did his graduate work at Brown University in applied mathematics but, as he says, "When I was at Brown, Henry Mann had shown me Wald's 1939 paper on decision theory and that again was another revelation to me, but it was easy to absorb after having had contact with the Neyman-Pearson paper." As a result, after completing all the requirements for a Ph.D. at Brown except for the thesis, Chernoff went to Columbia in 1947 to write his thesis under Wald.

Wald suggested a number of possible thesis topics, of which Chernoff chose an asymptotic version of the Behrens-Fisher problem. This difficult problem concerns testing the equality of two normal means when the corresponding (unknown) variances are not necessarily equal. The task was to find a test that, under the hypothesis, would have a constant probability of rejection. Following Wald's suggestion, Chernoff did not attempt an exact solution (later work of Linnik proved that a smooth exact solution does not exist), but instead showed how to construct tests that approximate this ideal to any given degree of (asymptotic) accuracy.

After completing his degree, Chernoff spent a year-and-a-half at the Cowles Commission in Chicago, followed by three years in the mathematics department of the University of Illinois. In 1951, he moved to the Stanford statistics department, where I first met him when I spent the year 1951–52 as visitor at Stanford. He remained at Stanford for twenty-three years, and in 1974 left for the Massachusetts Institute of Technology to develop a statistics program there. However, when it became clear to him that his program was not succeeding, he accepted an offer from Harvard to join their statistics department.

Chernoff's research spans many different areas. Much of his early work dealt with sequential problems, and is summarized in his monograph, *Sequential Analysis and Optimal Design*. One very unusual paper that attracted much attention was titled, "The Use of Faces to Represent Points in k-Dimensional Space Graphically" (1973). The face is determined by up to eighteen features, each corresponding to one coordinate of the sample point. Two, for example, are the length and curvature of the mouth (represented by the arc of a circle), two others the size and separation of the eyes (reported by ellipses whose eccentricity constitutes a third feature), and still another the length of the nose (a line segment). The use of such a representation is illustrated by a number of examples, one of them a cluster analysis in which faces are grouped together by their resemblance to each other.

I shall mention only two other of Chernoff's papers, both of them connected to my own work. One of these (joint with Richard Savage) arose from a conjecture that Joe Hodges and I had published in 1957. We believed that a certain nonparametric test (based on normal scores) was asymptotically as efficient as Student's t-test against translation alternatives in the normal case and more efficient for all other distributions. The following year, Chernoff and Savage not only proved this conjecture but, in their paper, also established the asymptotic normality of a large class of rank statistics, a key result and the basis of much later work.

The other paper in question is a joint paper by Chernoff and myself (1954), which concerns Karl Pearson's goodness-of-fit statistic and came about as follows. It was well known that Pearson's statistic obtained by grouping the data, and with unknown parameters obtained by maximizing the likelihood of the frequencies, has a limiting chi-squared distribution. But what if the original (ungrouped) observations are available, so that the parameters can be estimated more efficiency from the original data? I discovered that the limit distribution then no longer is chi-squared, and had worked out the limit distribution for a number of examples.

When I mentioned my results to Herman, who was an expert in this kind of large-sample work, he told me that he too had noticed this phenomenon and was in fact in the process of writing a paper on it. Although his results

Raj Bahadur

were more general than mine, he generously offered to make it a joint paper by the two of us, and the resulting paper appeared in the 1954 volume of the *Annals of Mathematical Statistics*.

In recognition of his work, Chernoff was elected to both the National Academy of Sciences and the American Academy of Arts and Sciences. He was invited to give both the Fisher and Wald Lectures, and in 1983 a festschrift was published in his honor, edited by Rizvi, Rustagi, and Siegmund.

My other collaborator, Raj Bahadur, was born and educated in India. After receiving an M.A. in 1945 from the University of New Delhi, he went to the University of North Carolina for further graduate study and obtained his Ph.D. in 1950 with a thesis suggested to him by Hotelling. He then joined the statistics faculty at the University of Chicago but returned to India in 1956, where for the next five years he held a professorship at the Indian Statistical Institute. In 1961, he returned permanently to Chicago.

Bahadur's two most influential contributions are mathematically too complex to fully explain here. The first, a short note of only four pages (1966), establishes what is known as the Bahadur representation of quantiles. It represents the sample quantile as a sum of i.i.d. (identically independently distributed) random variables plus an error term that tends to 0 as the sample size increases, at a rate that Bahadur determines. The result exhibits a relation between sample quantiles and order statistics that has proved useful in many applications (see, for example, section 2.5 in Serfling, 1980).

Another major contribution is the concept and theory of Bahadur efficiency, a comparative (asymptotic) measure of the efficiency of different tests or estimators. The great advantage of Bahadur's efficiency measure over the earlier measures of Edwin Pitman, Chernoff, and Hodges, and Lehmann is its much broader applicability, including, for example, the Kolmogorov-Smirnov and the Wald-Wolfowitz run test. On the other hand, Bahadur's measure may not always be as accurate in approximating the actual finite-sample efficiency as, say, Pitman efficiency.

Still another important line of work was his clarification of the concept of sufficiency in sequential analysis. A paper that I particularly liked and to which I have often referred in my own writing is the joint work of Bahadur and his Chicago colleague Jimmy Savage (1956). It concerns tests of the mean such as Student's t-test and shows that if the form of the distribution is unknown, it is not possible to control the size of such a test. More specifically, for any given sample size, there exist distributions for which the size of the test is arbitrarily close to 1. This result provides a warning not to be over-confident about the well-known asymptotic robustness of the t-test.

My own joint paper (of 1955) with Bahadur came about as part of his early work on sufficient statistics and subfields. In response to a question raised by him in a paper of 1954, I made some suggestions; he replied, and after one or two more letters we wrote up the conclusions we had reached.

A complete list of Bahadur's publications up to 1993 is provided in a festschrift for him edited by J.K. Ghosh, S.K. Mitra, K.R. Parthasarathy, and B.L.S. Prakasa Rao.

4
Mathematical Statistics at Other Universities

The idyllic situation in which I found myself in the late 1940s—teaching and research among a group of congenial colleagues—was disrupted in 1949 by a political event, the requirement of the faculty to sign an anti-Communist loyalty oath. This led to turmoil and bitterness, which made it difficult to work. It seemed a good time to leave Berkeley for a while, and to broaden my horizons through visiting appointments at other universities.

Fortunately, Berkeley was not the only university with a good program in mathematical statistics. Centers for this new field had been started at Columbia, Princeton, Stanford, and Chicago, and the Berkeley group had close relations with all four of them. As a result, I was able to obtain visiting appointments for the fall of 1950 and the spring of 1951 at Columbia and Princeton, respectively, and for the following year at Stanford. At the same time, Joe Hodges spent a year at Chicago.

For the sake of completeness, I should mention that by 1950 another outstanding program in mathematical statistics had been developed by Harold Hotelling at the University of North Carolina. After he left Columbia for Chapel Hill in 1946, he quickly assembled a distinguished faculty that included, among others, Herb Robbins, Wassily Hoeffding, and R.C. Bose. However, Berkeley had little contact with this group.

Even with North Carolina included, the above list of early statistics programs is quite one-sided. In addition, other, actually even earlier, statistical centers existed that had a more applied or methodological orientation. Among the most prominent of these were H.L. Rietz's program at the University of Iowa, George Snedecor's at Iowa State, and Harry Carver's at the University of Michigan. However, they were on the fringes of my statistical world, and I had no direct interaction with them. An account of their history is given in a paper by Harshbarger (1976).

16. Abraham Wald (1902–1950)

Nineteen thirty-eight was a banner year for American statistics. It brought not only Neyman to the United States but also Wald, who in some sense completed Neyman's mathematical formulation of statistics.

Unlike Neyman, Wald arrived in America not as a statistician, but as a geometer and econometrician. He had been schooled at home, not able to go to the gymnasium, because as a Jew he would not attend school on Saturday. After graduating from the University of Cluj (Romania), his hometown, he was, after some difficulties, admitted to the University of Vienna in 1927 to study mathematics. There he quickly came under the influence of Karl Menger and became a frequent contributor to Menger's geometric program. He also worked on von Mises' theory of collectives and in particular proved that it was free of inconsistencies.

Since an academic career was essentially impossible for a man of Wald's background, Menger advised him to work also in applied mathematics. In 1933, in pursuit of this possibility, he approached Oskar Morgenstern, then director of the Austrian Institute for Business Cycle Research. As Morgenstern writes in his 1951 obituary of Wald in *Econometrica,* "Like everyone else I was captivated by his great ability, his gentleness, and the

extraordinary strength with which he attacked his problems," and, like Menger, Morgenstern became not only an admirer but also a lifelong friend.

Wald became an associate in Morgenstern's institute and, in this capacity, made important contributions to econometrics, which are described in Morgenstern's article. (They also brought him into contact with some statistical issues.) In 1938, he accepted an invitation to join the staff of the Cowles Commission for Research in Economics in Colorado Springs, and left Vienna just in time to escape the fate of his family, most of whom were murdered by the Nazis.

In the fall of 1938, Wald went to Columbia University on a fellowship from the Carnegie Corporation, and there undertook a year of intensive study of statistical inference under Hotelling. It is extraordinary that during this first year with Hotelling, while he still knew little of the details of modern statistical theory, he conceived of a wholly new unifying approach to statistical inference, which he published in a long paper in 1939. He stayed at Columbia as a Carnegie Fellow until 1941, when he became a regular faculty member in the economics department, rising from assistant professor to professor in 1944.

In the meantime, war had come to the United States. In 1942, a statistical research group was set up at Columbia, with W. Allen Wallis as director of research and Hotelling as principal investigator. The group had an outstanding membership, including Jack Wolfowitz, Milton Friedman, Abraham Wald, Albert Bowker, Jimmie Savage, Abe Girshick, and Fred Mosteller. It dealt with a great variety of problems.[1] One area of special interest was sampling inspection for quality control of the huge amount of military material that was being produced for the services. In this context, the question arose whether the efficiency of the sampling process could be improved by using not a fixed sample size but sampling sequentially, that is, by considering after each observation whether, in light of the information obtained up to that point, it was worth going on, or whether sampling should be stopped.

The problem was suggested to Wald, who, after some initial reluctance, agreed to take a look. He soon became convinced that the idea was worth pursuing, and he grew enthusiastic both about the statistical problems this involved and the promise the approach held for substantial savings. Sequential analysis became his principal concern, and for several months he did little else. The story is told that each morning, Wallis called up Wald to inquire how he had slept. If Wald had slept well, Wallis's reaction was, "Too bad!" because it meant that Wald had not made the progress that he would have made during hours of sleeplessness.

Despite occasional restful nights, Wald did develop a substantial body of theory. The centerpiece was a sequential procedure for testing a simple hypothesis against a simple alternative, the sequential probability ratio test. It took its clue from the Neyman-Pearson lemma (discussed in Section 7),

[1] For a more detailed account, see Section 20.

which, for a fixed sample size, found that the best test rejects the hypothesis when the likelihood ratio is sufficiently large and accepts it in the contrary case. Wald now proposed to compute the likelihood ratio, say r_n, successively for $n = 1, 2, \ldots$ observations, and to continue the process of observation as long as these ratios took on intermediate values, which strongly supported neither the hypothesis nor the alternative, that is, as long as they satisfied $a \leq r_n \leq b$ for some specified limits a and b. The process is stopped the first time the ratio falls outside these limits, and the hypothesis is then accepted or rejected as $r_n < a$ or $r_n > b$. Wald also found formulas for a and b which approximately yield given error probabilities α and β.

The results of this work were published after the war in a long report in the *Annals of Mathematical Statistics* (1945) and in Wald's book, *Sequential Analysis* (1947). In the following year, Wald and Wolfowitz showed how good Wald's intuition had been. They proved that among all tests with the given error probabilities, the sequential probability ratio minimizes the expected number of observations both under the hypothesis and under the alternative.

As reported in Section 10, in 1946 Hotelling left Columbia and Wald was appointed executive head of the new Department of Mathematical Statistics. He immediately appointed his friend and close collaborator Jack Wolfowitz to the faculty, as well as a recent Princeton Ph.D., Ted Anderson, who shared his econometric interests. In addition, he made offers to Jerzy Neyman and Joe Doob, but both decided to remain at the homes they had made for themselves. In 1948, Wald did succeed in adding another senior member to his faculty—Henry Scheffé. It was a stellar group (with which I was to hold a visiting appointment in the fall of 1950).

The first time I met Wald was in the summer of 1948 on a visit to my friend and collaborator Henry Scheffé, who had just moved to Columbia. Rather surprisingly, Henry told me that Wald would like to meet me. The reason, it turned out, was a short note that I had written while still a graduate student, and that had been published the previous year. The note pointed out that typically there is no clear choice for "best" procedure. Instead of making a specific recommendation, which inevitably is somewhat arbitrary, I suggested it might sometimes be preferable to present a list of the available possibilities from which the user could then make a choice. What procedures such a list should contain is most easily explained by stating the procedures it would not include: namely any procedure A for which there exists a procedure B that is uniformly better, that is, better in all circumstances. The list would consist of all procedures not eliminated by this criterion. (Such a list would later be called a "complete class.") I then worked out this list for a particularly simple class of hypothesis-testing problems.

Wald at that time had resumed work on the general theory of statistical inference he had outlined in his 1939 paper. He found that my suggestion fit well into his general framework, and he magically transformed it into a theorem of great beauty and generality, which became one of the principal pillars of his decision theory.

I was to see much more of Wald in the near future, since he spent the year 1948–49 in Berkeley on a sabbatical, during which he hoped to complete his book on statistical decision theory without the burdens of his Columbia position. On visits to his Berkeley home, one was likely to find him in the garden at a card table he had set up under a tree, working on his manuscript.

A highlight of this visit occurred during the summer of 1949 before his return to New York, when Charles Stein, Joe Hodges, and I asked him to join us on a four-day hiking trip in Yosemite National Park. It was a loop trip of the High Sierra camps: May Lake, Tuolumne Meadows, Vogelsang, and Glen Aulin. The first day was the most strenuous: a climb of about 6,000 feet over a twenty–mile distance. As preparation, we had taken a hike on Mount Tamalpais, but the present climb was more than we had bargained for.

The next day, Charles was not feeling well and we decided not to go on. Since at that point we were close to the road, Joe and I were commissioned to hitch a ride down to the valley where our car was parked. We would then drive up to where Charles and Wald were resting, and return home. Joe and I, neither of us experienced hitchhikers, had no success, and we decided to try our luck one at a time. Eventually, a car stopped for me and the two women in it opened the door for me to get in. At that moment Joe, with his big frame and height of 6'4", came lumbering out of the bushes. The women screamed, slammed the door shut and sped off.

We gave up the effort for the night, which turned out to be lucky. The next morning Charles was feeling all right, and that day's hike turned out to be the most beautiful. In particular, crossing Vogelsang Pass at about 11,000 feet to the flower-studded meadows below showed us a scene that was unforgettable.

This Yosemite hike also provided an opportunity to get to know Wald, who had in a sense brought Neyman's approach to statistics to completion, and whose book on the subject was being eagerly awaited. Despite his accomplishments and fame, Wald was completely unpretentious and easy-going. Much of our conversation was about statistics, but he was also quite interested in our surroundings. He prided himself on his ability to estimate distances, heights, and speeds. At the foot of one peak we were about to climb, he estimated the rise to be 1,500 feet. When we got to the top, he looked down and proclaimed, "Actually, it was 1,450 feet, so I was pretty close."

These four days in spectacular scenery, with three wonderful companions, live in my memory as one of the high points of my life. Considering how little time was left to him, I can only hope that Wald (or Dan, as he permitted us to call him) enjoyed them as much as we did.

To explain the circumstances of my next, and as it turned out last, encounter with Wald, I must go back to the fall of 1946, when I was appointed to the faculty of the Berkeley mathematics department. The appointment of a department's own students immediately upon obtaining their Ph.D.'s violated university policy. Neyman overcame this hurdle by arguing that he was the only one training students in his new approach to statistics, and that he needed them in order to build a cutting-edge statistics group, for which they constituted the best-qualified candidates. As a result, he was allowed to retain not only me but also over the next years a number of his other students. However, we were given to understand that before long we should spend a year at some other university in order to broaden our experience.

As a result, I made plans to spend the year 1949–50 at Columbia, where Wald had offered me a visiting position. But Neyman asked me to postpone this leave since he himself was going to take a European sabbatical that spring. I thus was in Berkeley during the academic year 1949–50, which became known as "the year of the oath."

The oath in question was a result of the anti-Communist hysteria gripping the country at the time. The California Legislature was threatening to take over ensuring the loyalty of university employees, particularly the faculty. To prevent this, after lengthy negotiations with the president and leaders of the faculty, the Regents voted to impose an anti-Communist loyalty oath.[2] This provoked a much stronger reaction than they had anticipated. The oath was opposed not only by liberal members of the faculty but also by influential conservatives, who considered it a threat to tenure.

The great majority of the faculty eventually decided to sign the oath, and this included Neyman and the rest of our group, with the exception of Charles Stein, who resigned and accepted a position at the University of Chicago. After a year of political turmoil, the thirty-one faculty members who had refused to sign were dismissed from their positions. They sued for reinstatement and two years later won their suit in the California Supreme Court.

The bitterness of the debate at endless meetings poisoned the atmosphere and I was happy at the prospect of spending the next year at Columbia. However, it then turned out that Sam Wilks was going on leave in the spring semester, and he suggested that I come to Princeton for that period to take over some of his teaching. To make the best use of the year, I therefore spent the fall term at Columbia and the spring term at Princeton.

During the five years since Guam, I had been a member of the Stat Lab, a small, tightly knit group clustered about Neyman at the center. I enjoyed the sense of community; at the same time—despite some newcomers and visitors—the atmosphere was a bit claustrophobic, and I was looking forward to the change.

The Columbia statistics department was a lively place at that time, with the faculty consisting of Wald, Wolfowitz, Scheffé, Ted Anderson, and Howard Levene. Wald's eagerly waited book on statistical decision theory came out that fall (and I was happy to be given an inscribed copy). In addition, social life in the department was active and we were invited to dinners with Wald

[2] The details are complicated. They can be found, for example, in Gardner (1967).

and Wolfowitz and their families. And of course I saw much of Henry Scheffé and his family.

However, what started out on such a positive note ended in tragedy. As had been planned for some time, Wald and his wife left for India, where he was to lecture on his new decision theory. A few weeks later, a rumor began to circulate in the department that an Indian plane had crashed on which the Walds might have been passengers. After a few days of uncertainty and great anxiety, the Indian government finally confirmed that the Walds—parents of two young children whom they had left in New York with relatives—had been killed in a plane crash on their way to Nepal.

Wald's death left a great void; within a few years the faculty he had assembled dispersed, and the students who had planned to work with him had to find new advisers. (In fact, two of them, Alan Birnbaum and Jack Laderman, asked me to take them on and to provide them with suitable problems. Thus, it came about that two of my early Ph.D. students got their degrees at Columbia rather than at Berkeley.) However, the loss was felt not only at Columbia but by the whole profession. Wald was considered by many as the leader who had provided the field with a new unifying paradigm and who would on this basis move the subject into new directions.

What Wald had accomplished in his relatively short life (he was only forty-eight at the time of his death) is indeed remarkable. He had started a successful career in Vienna in geometry and econometrics. When he came to America in 1938, under the influence of Hotelling he switched to statistics. And in the short period of twelve years that remained to him, he had changed the field. He had made a number of seminal contributions, but the one that brought him fame was the creation of a new framework for statistics. Up until that time, only problems of testing and estimation had been considered. Now Wald's sweeping formulation encompassed any kind of statistical inference that had a probabilistic basis.

The Institute of Mathematical Statistics (IMS) honored Wald's memory in a number of ways. It dedicated the 1952 volume of the *Annals* to Abraham Wald,

> who contributed vitally to the advancement of mathematical statistics through his broad and fundamental research which will continue to influence the development of statistical theory and practice, and who will long be remembered as an inspiring and esteemed teacher and colleague.

The March issue of the 1952 *Annals,* in addition to this dedication, carried commemorative articles on Wald by Wolfowitz, Menger, and Tintner, followed by a list of Wald's publications.

In 1955, the IMS sponsored a volume, Wald's *Selected Papers in Statistics and Probability,* edited by Anderson, Freeman, Hodges, Lehmann, Mood, and Stein, with discussion of the papers by the editors. The institute also set up the program of Wald Lectures, typically two or three talks on the lecturer's current research. These prestigious lectures have been given annually since 1957.

17. Jacob (Jack) Wolfowitz (1910–1981)

Wald's best friend and close collaborator was Jack Wolfowitz, whom Wald met in 1938 when he moved to Columbia to study with Hotelling. They soon started working together, with their first paper appearing the following year, and they jointly published thirteen papers in the next decade.[3] In 1946, Wolfowitz became a faculty member at Columbia, but after Wald's death he left for Cornell (in 1951).

The first Wald and Wolfowitz papers dealt with nonparametric problems (the term *nonparametric* is due to Wolfowitz [1942]), followed by a series on sequential analysis. This included the 1948 proof of the optimality of the sequential probability ratio test, a stunning result. Wolfowitz's interest in these areas continued even after Wald's death.

However, Wolfowitz also branched out into many new directions. One of the most important was large-sample theory. In particular, he developed

[3] Since the authors of joint statistical papers were typically listed alphabetically, it was jokingly said that Wald had looked long and hard to find a collaborator whom he preceded in the alphabet.

(jointly with Lionel Weiss) his method of maximum probability estimation summarized in their book, *Maximum Probability Estimators and Related Topics* (1974). Beyond statistical inference, Wolfowitz became interested in information and coding theory, and his work in this area led to his influential book, *Coding Theorems of Information Theory,* which went through three editions (1961, 1964, and 1978).

My first acquaintance with Wolfowitz occurred during my visits to Columbia, and particularly the semester I spent there in the fall of 1950. From that period, I recall being invited to sit in on the thesis defense of Wolfowitz's student Jack Kiefer (who much later became my Berkeley colleague). I was surprised by the aggressive manner in which Wolfowitz raised questions and objections, quite different from what I was used to in Berkeley, and admired the calm and unruffled way in which Kiefer defended himself.

My interaction with Wolfowitz increased considerably after I became editor of the *Annals* (in 1953). Crucial for the success of a journal is the choice of associated editors, who arrange for the refereeing of manuscripts and eventually make recommendations to the editor regarding their disposition. One obvious choice for me was my friend and colleague Joe Hodges, with whom I would be able to discuss any problems that might arise. I also wanted to appoint Jack Wolfowitz, whose scientific standing was very high but who had the reputation of being severe in his judgments. Although I was warned that I would find him difficult to work with, I decided to take the risk, believing that he would take his responsibilities seriously. And it turned out well. I got no more complaints concerning the cases he handled than about those handled by other members of the editorial board.

Jack's appointment did lead to one unusual incident, however. A problem editors face is how to handle their own papers. The natural solution is to ask one of the associate editors to take charge of those situations. In my case it seemed only fair to ask Jack, as the toughest of the associate editors, to take on this job. Accordingly, I submitted a paper to him and in due time received his report. While not enthusiastic, it was mildly favorable and recommended acceptance of the paper. However, it was impossible not to notice that several passages in the report had been crossed out, but in such a way that they could still be read without much effort. In this way, he let me know his true negative opinion without seeming to be impolite or disloyal. I thought it was a neat trick, withdrew the paper and published it elsewhere.

My next encounter with Wolfowitz was indirect. In 1970, I was surprised to learn that he had published a paper, "Reflections on the Future of Mathematical Statistics" (in a festschrift for S.N. Roy), which prominently mentioned my 1959 book on hypothesis testing. In it, he took stock of the enterprise of mathematical statistics as it had developed during the preceding twenty-five years and evaluated it in terms of two criteria. It should either

(i) meet the needs of science and technology; or
(ii) be interesting when viewed as mathematics per se.

One section of the paper criticized the Bayes approach not on philosophical grounds but for violating the second of these criteria. Wolfowitz quoted Jimmy Savage, who had launched the Bayesian paradigm on its postwar path, as writing: "There is a lot of exciting work to do that is relatively easy." To this, Wolfowitz responded with disdain:

> How can any scientific endeavor which is "relatively easy" be "exciting" or hold out much prospect as a research discipline? . . . According to the Bayesian point of view, one has only to determine the a priori distribution and then compute the a posteriori distribution. Can the study of this engage for long the serious efforts of first-rate minds?

The other principal target of the paper is hypothesis testing, and Wolfowitz condemns it for both reasons (i) and (ii). Concerning the first, he says that it poses the wrong problem, since the null hypothesis is never exactly true. (Another strong supporter of this view was John Tukey.)

Regarding criterion (ii), the subject is examined in the light of my book on hypothesis testing, because of "the great influence this book has and is bound to have." The assessment is very negative: "One comes away," Wolfowitz writes, "with a general impression of relatively few deep and difficult theorems, and of many clever and ingenious examples, mostly involving the binomial, Poisson, and other distributions of the exponential family. So many ingenious tests about the latter have been studied, and so few problems of practical interest solved."

After impugning my motives in publishing a book, some faults of which I admitted in the Preface, Wolfowitz concludes:

> I agree enthusiastically that this book should have been published and that it is a distinguished book . . .. But I would consider it a disaster for statistics if this book should determine the direction of research for any appreciable period of time.

In this paper, Wolfowitz questions not only the work of most of the authors discussed in the present book, but beyond it the whole discipline of mathematical statistics. It essentially denies the validity of a statistical theory as a separate field that uses mathematical tools and language but whose concepts and issues are of interest in their own right, quite apart from the mathematical sophistication needed for their investigation. Wolfowitz considered this paper an important contribution. In fact, when Jack Kiefer planned to omit it from a volume of selected papers of Wolfowitz he was putting together, the latter insisted that it be included.

The paper is of interest also in the light it throws on the personality of its author. Wolfowitz was a complex and conflicted person who seemed uncomfortable with himself as well as with others. In the paper, he acknowledges that he too has contributed to the kind of research the paper chastises. Surprisingly, he continued to do so after its publication.

His relations with colleagues were complicated further by his extreme political views. Like many refugees from Eastern Europe at the time (he came from Poland to the United States as a ten-year-old with his parents in 1920), he was violently anti-Communist and very conservative.

Wolfowitz died in 1981, following a heart attack. During his lifetime he received many honors, including an honorary doctorate from the Technion in Haifa, Israel, election to the National Academy of Sciences and the American Academy of Arts and Sciences, and presidency of the Institute of Mathematical Statistics. A volume of his selected papers, edited and with a very useful introduction by Kiefer, and including a bibliography, appeared in 1980, a year before his death.

18. William Feller (1906–1970)

As mentioned in Section 16, for the spring semester of 1951 I had accepted a visiting appointment at Princeton. So in late December 1950, I moved from New York to Princeton, where I was installed in Sam Wilks' spacious office. My assignment was to teach one of Wilks' undergraduate courses, together with a graduate course on topics of my choice. If my goal for this year was to broaden my experience, I certainly was achieving it. At Columbia, an urban university, I had to teach one of my courses in the evening so that it could be attended by older students who were working during the day.

Now, at Princeton, the students were treated like children. For the only time in my life, I had to call roll at the beginning of each lecture and report the results to the administration.

Since Wilks was in Europe, the only statistical faculty member at Princeton at the time was John Tukey. However, his position was divided between Princeton and Bell Laboratories, so he was frequently not available when I needed help with some unfamiliar situation. Fortunately, assistance was always available from David Wallace, the head teaching assistant (later professor at the University of Chicago). His friendliness and common sense were of great help throughout the semester. I also received moral support from another source: the probabilist Will Feller, who a few years earlier had been my passenger at the first Berkeley symposium.

Feller, who had only recently joined the Princeton mathematics department, was a native of Zagreb. After receiving the equivalent of a master's degree from the University of Zagreb, he continued his graduate work at Göttingen, where he came to the attention of Richard Courant, the Director of the Mathematical Institute. As Constance Reid reports in her Courant biography:

> At the beginning of the term in 1925, [Courant's assistants] were delighted to discover that the answers of a new student from Yugoslavia were invariably correct and that there was no longer any need to solve the problems themselves. They promptly alerted Courant to the presence of Willy Feller . . .. After Feller was "discovered," he was an accepted member of the "in group" which gathered around Courant.

Feller obtained his Ph.D. in 1926, but remained in Göttingen for another two years before moving to Kiel, where he served as Privatdozent until 1933. When the Nazis came to power, he lost his job. After a year in Copenhagen, he spent the next five years at Cramér's Institute in Stockholm. Of this period, Cramér recalls[4]:

> In the fall of 1934, our group had the good fortune to receive a new member from abroad. It was during the bad days of the Nazi regime in Germany, when so many outstanding scientists were leaving the country. Will Feller, who had been turned out from the University of Kiel, came to join our group, and stayed on in Stockholm for five years. He made a great number of Swedish friends, collaborating with economists and biologists as well as with the members of our probabilistic group. He had studied in Göttingen and was well initiated in the great traditions of this mathematical center. We tried hard to get a permanent position for him in Sweden, but in those years before the war this was next to impossible, and it was with great regret that we saw him leave for the United States, where an outstanding career was awaiting him.

With Courant's help (who by that time was well established at New York University), Feller found a position as associate professor at Brown

[4] Cramér (1976).

University and as the founding executive editor of *Mathematical Reviews*. Of his work in the latter position, Doob states, in a memorial article[5]:

> The only current review journal *[The Zentralblatt]* was then becoming corrupted by Nazi ideas. Much of the success of *Mathematical Reviews* has been due to the policies initiated by Feller.

In 1945, Feller moved to Cornell, and in 1950 to Princeton (with an additional appointment as permanent visiting professor at the Rockefeller University), where he remained until his death twenty-five years later. Feller was a probabilist with little interest in statistics, so I won't say much about his work except to mention his famous proof, in 1935, of the necessity of the Lindeberg conditions (with a slight addition) for the Central Limit Theorem, the solution of an important problem of long standing. The result was also obtained at about the same time by Paul Lévy. Although Feller's version was the first of the two to appear in print, Lévy had obtained the result slightly earlier, and Feller, in a further paper two years later, acknowledges it[6]:

> I am happy to note, according to a kind communication from Mr. P. Lévy, that his paper, although published later, was submitted and presented to the Société Mathématique de France substantially before mine (October 1934 versus May 1935).

One can imagine the gnashing of teeth that accompanied this expression of happiness.

To statisticians, Feller is best known for his *Introduction to Probability Theory and Its Applications* (Vol. 1, 1950, 1957; Vol. 2, 1966). Many enthusiastic reviews of this work have been written. I shall here quote Mark Kac about volume 1[7]:

> [It] is a book with few peers in scientific literature. It is a treatise and a textbook, a masterpiece of exposition and a credo of methodology, a sweeping panorama of a subject and a collection of exemplary jewels. No wonder it has appealed to an audience so wide as to border on the incredible, no wonder that no other book on the subject, not even Volume 2, can match its luster.

Feller was a man of enormous vitality and boundless enthusiasm. His friend Joe Doob (in the article quoted above) remembers him

> most for his gusto, the pleasure with which he met life, the excitement with which he drew on his endless fund of anecdotes about life and its absurdities, particularly the absurdities involving mathematics and mathematicians. To listen to him deliver a mathematics lecture was a unique experience. No one else could generate in himself as well as in his auditors so much intense excitement. In losing him, the world of mathematics has lost one of its strongest personalities as well as one of its strongest researchers.

[5] Doob (1972).
[6] Translation quoted from Le Cam (1986).
[7] Kac (1972).

When I arrived at Princeton, Feller showed a side not reflected in Doob's portrait: his kindness and thoughtfulness. Realizing my isolation, he proposed that we meet for lunch once a week, and each week on the appointed day I would go to his office. There, I always found him lying on his couch—he claimed to be able to think only in a horizontal position—and we would wander over to the faculty club.

Since Feller knew little about statistics, he would sometimes, at these lunches, ask me to tell him about some statistical concepts. I recall talking about sufficiency and the power of tests, but these ideas and their context seemed quite foreign to him and not very congenial, and these "tutorials" were not successful.

One very different conversation impressed me greatly. Feller expressed his deep regret of not being a better mathematician. When I demurred and mentioned how much he had accomplished, he brushed me aside. Yes, he said, he was aware of all that, but it still left him far inferior to Gauss.

However, measured on a less demanding scale, Feller was extraordinarily successful and his achievements were widely recognized. In 1947, he served as president of the IMS. He was elected to the three main American academies (the American and National Academies and the American Philosophical Society), as well as a foreign member of the Danish and Yugoslav Academies. In 1969, when he was already terminally ill, he was awarded the National Medal of Science by President Nixon, which cited him for "original and definitive contributions to pure and applied mathematics, for making probability available to users, and for pioneering work in establishing *Mathematical Reviews*."

19. Albert H. Bowker (b. 1919)

The three most modern programs in statistics before the war were those at Columbia (started by Hotelling in 1931), at Princeton (Wilks in 1936), and at Berkeley (Neyman in 1938). They were joined shortly after the war by Stanford, largely at the initiative of W. Allen Wallis (then on the faculty of the economics department) and with the help of funds from the Office of Naval Research (ONR). The choice to lead the Stanford program was Al Bowker, who was known to Wallis from his work as a member of the Statistical Research Group during the war.

Bowker's initial appointment was in the mathematics department. However, the attitude of the department's chairman, Gabor Szegö, toward statistics was very different from that of Evans at Berkeley. While Evans insisted that statistics was part of mathematics and fought a long battle to keep the program, Szegö's position is described by Bowker[8] as being just the

[8] Olkin (1987).

opposite: "The mathematics department received me with a certain detachment," Bowker says. "Although he became a great supporter of statistics, Gabor Szegö was then chairman of the mathematics department, and explained to me very nicely that while what I did was very interesting, it wasn't mathematics. So we moved rather quickly to a separate department."

And thus it came about that Al Bowker, formally still a graduate student at Columbia (although by then his thesis had been completed), in 1948 became chairman of the fledgling statistics department, where he was soon joined by an earlier student and wartime colleague from Columbia, Abe Girshick.[9]

In the summer of 1950, before I left for Columbia and Princeton, the oath controversy was still unsettled. I was sufficiently worried about the future at Berkeley that I approached Al Bowker to ask whether there might be a possibility for me at Stanford. It turned out that at the time an offer was out to David Blackwell, who was spending the year at Stanford and who had not yet decided whether to stay there. However, in October Bowker wrote to me at Columbia that Blackwell had decided to return to Howard University: "Consequently, we are now in a position to talk turkey with you and I am writing to inquire about your current thinking." He went on to review the

[9] For an account of Girshick's career, see Section 36.

situation at Berkeley, with the conclusion: "My own wild guess is that some kind of arrangement will be made so that Neyman can stay on and I suppose that a number of people would stay on with him."

He then explained, "The real reason of my long digression upon the situation at Berkeley is that one of my axioms is that you would not be interested in coming to Stanford if there were a possibility of staying at Berkeley under circumstances which were honorable and which were congenial from a professional point of view."

The letter concluded with a description of the position and the duties it would entail. The crucial sentences were: "We feel that our major need at the moment is an appointment in theory and you are our choice for this appointment. You are not expected to engage in any applied work." The last statement clearly was in answer to a concern I must have expressed.

Since the situation in Berkeley continued to be very uncertain, I raised the question of whether it might be possible to postpone the decision for a year, and in the meantime to spend the year 1951–52 at Stanford on a visiting appointment.

The Stanford department was agreeable to the suggestion, but Bowker felt that at this point he should get Neyman's reaction to what was going on. He told Neyman that during the year, while the oath controversy had been going on and Neyman had been in Europe, several members of the Berkeley group had asked about the possibility of jobs at Stanford, and that now, for the first time, a permanent position was open. He explained that the circumstances were exceptional and that they would ordinarily not expect to compete with the Berkeley lab. Neyman's reply, as Bowker reported to me, was that "he was delighted to have Stanford make offers to people on his staff, that he never made any objections or felt personally insulted when that happened. In fact, he felt rather flattered and his usual procedure in such cases was to scream like hell to the administration to better the conditions of the man in question." And so it was agreed that I would spend the 1951–52 academic year at Stanford on continued leave from Berkeley.

At the end of that year, I had to decide whether to stay at Stanford or return to Berkeley. By then the loyalty oath had been rescinded and was no longer an issue. Thus, I was in the wonderful position of making a free choice between what seemed to me the two best positions in statistics in the country. In the end, the most important consideration was that after much wandering Berkeley had become my home and I had a close collaboration and friendship with Joe Hodges. I also preferred a public university to an expensive private one where most of the students came from wealthy homes and where it was said that you could distinguish the faculty from the students by their clothes: if they were well dressed, they were students.

In making this decision, I did not try to use the Stanford possibility to increase my Berkeley salary or speed up my promotion. However, I did take advantage of it to improve my situation at Berkeley in one respect: An important activity of the lab was the consulting service that provided help for faculty members in other departments with their statistical problems. Neyman handled some of these problems himself; others he passed on to members of the staff. He considered it one of our obligations to accept such assignments. Although I recognized the importance of this service and its appropriateness, my difficulties with applied work persisted and it made me uncomfortable. Since the Stanford offer had explicitly stated that no applied work would be required of me, I now asked Neyman for a similar dispensation. He agreed, although rather grudgingly. In exchange, I offered to teach an occasional extra course, but he never took me up on this offer.

Over the next years, Bowker built up a first-rate department. In 1956, after Girshick's early death, the faculty consisted of Arrow, Chernoff, Karlin, Lieberman, McNemar, Moses, Parzen, and Stein. Several of these were joint appointments (with economics, psychology, engineering, and public health), a deliberate policy to give the department, and particularly its teaching, a broad base within the university.

The department had close contact with the Stat Lab at Berkeley through the Berkeley–Stanford Colloquium, which was as much a social as a scientific event. It is still functioning today, more than fifty years later, although at a somewhat reduced schedule.

For the year 1955–56, toward the end of his chairmanship, Bowker took a sabbatical leave at Columbia, during which he wrote two papers on multivariate analysis. As he wrote later,[10]

> It was a year of stock-taking, and I had to decide whether I saw my future mainly in statistics or whether I would go into more general administration.
>
> After thinking it over and talking to Fred Terman at Stanford, I decided to return to Stanford first as his assistant (by now he was Provost of the university) and later, when it became available, as Graduate Dean . . .. And I made, I guess implicitly, a decision that I would look for my career in university administration. Although there was a high element of chance in all of these decisions.

It was a gamble that paid off. For in 1961, Bowker became chancellor of the City University of New York (CUNY), where he remained for eight years. During his tenure, he greatly expanded the system, from four senior colleges and three community colleges to twenty institutions. Perhaps his best-known and most controversial initiative was the adoption of an open admissions policy, which offered a place to every high school graduate in New York. In the interview quoted above, Bowker explains his reasons for making this change and why it caused such fierce opposition:

> The academic excellence of the City College, in particular, was at its height in the 1920s and 1930s. They had more or less a monopoly on the children of the Jewish

---

[10] Olkin (1987).

immigrants in New York. After the war, the bright Jewish kids had lots of opportunities elsewhere, but many people look back on those days as to what City College ought to be. It just isn't appropriate to run an elitist institution that is primarily white in the middle of Harlem, in my view anyway.

During his New York period, I never saw Al, although we of course heard about some of his activities. Then in 1971, very unexpectedly, at least for me, he came to Berkeley in a new role: he was appointed chancellor of the Berkeley campus.

As chancellor, he lived (with his wife Rosedith Sitgreaves, also a statistician and a faculty member, first at Teacher's College, Columbia University and then in the School of Education at Stanford University) on campus in University House. It was the only time in my long Berkeley career that I had a personal relationship with the chancellor, and it was fun to be invited fairly frequently not only to university functions but also to birthday parties and other private events.

On the other hand, as a matter of policy Bowker was not involved in the business of the statistics department. I know of only one exception. At one point, we got into serious difficulty with our dean. Things had gotten so bad that he refused to even talk to us. I was delegated by the department to appeal to Bowker. He agreed to receive me—it was the only time I saw him in his official capacity—and he intervened and resolved the problem.

One of Bowker's principal achievements during the nine years of his chancellorship was to institute a major fund-raising campaign to make the campus less dependent on the vagaries of the state budget. The other—partly due to him and partly to the changing times—was to restore Berkeley's reputation, which had been badly damaged in the 1960s as a result of the Free Speech Movement, Vietnam protests, and Reagan's attacks during his 1966 gubernatorial campaign. As Bowker later summed it up:

When I first went there, for example, people from most central valley towns wouldn't come to Berkeley, a reaction to student violence and so forth. Now Berkeley is incredibly popular all over the country. Its reputation for violence and protest has changed to that of a major cultural center and hub of Bay Area politics.

On the whole, the campus was calm during this period. However, there were occasional protests, sit-ins, and takeovers of administrative offices over local issues. The following story concerning one such incident (which I did not witness myself but which made the rounds of the campus) may give some idea of Bowker's style:

A delegation of protesters demanded to see the chancellor. He opened the door that led to his suite of offices, stood in the doorway and asked what they wanted. They had a list of demands. "Let's hear them," Bowker said. The leader of the delegation read the first demand, and Bowker said, "Nope." The second demand: "Nope." And so on. After he said "nope" to the twelfth and last demand, he closed the door and went back to his offices. The students were so perplexed, they did not know what to do and left. Crisis averted.

Bowker resigned the Berkeley chancellorship in 1979 to become assistant secretary of education for post-secondary education in the Carter administration, but this position soon terminated when President Jimmy Carter was defeated for reelection. He then worked for a number of years for the University of Maryland, first as founder of the School of Public Affairs, then as executive vice president. He returned briefly on a part-time basis to the City University of New York, and after a remarkable career retired to Berkeley where he now has an office as emeritus chancellor and emeritus professor in the statistics department.

20. W. Allen Wallis (1912–1998)

The person most responsible for initiating a program in mathematical statistics at Stanford, and for the choice of Bowker to lead the program, was W. Allen Wallis, then on the faculty of the Stanford economics department. The careers of Wallis and Bowker, who became lifelong friends, ran along remarkably similar lines. Both received their statistical training from Hotelling and, having made early contributions to statistics, spent much of their careers in university administration and achieved great success in that

area (Bowker as chancellor in New York and Berkeley, Wallis as chancellor and then president of the University of Rochester). And both were later appointed to high office in the federal government (although Bowker served only briefly).

Wallis worked in statistics mainly from 1942 to the late 1950s, in a wide range of activities. He contributed a number of papers on statistical methodology (the best known perhaps being the Kruskal-Wallis test), principally on nonparametric subjects, and in 1956 (jointly with Harry Roberts) published an innovative elementary text that emphasized statistical thinking (in the context of interesting examples) rather than mathematical formulas.

One of Wallis's most important contributions to the development of the field of statistics was made during the war, when from 1942 to 1945 he served as director of research (with Hotelling as principal investigator) of the Statistical Research Group (SRG). He was asked to take on this position in the spring of 1942 by Warren Weaver,[11] a director of the Rockefeller Foundation who at the time was the head of the Fire Control Division of the National Defense Research Committee and a few months later of its successor, the Applied Mathematics Panel (AMP). This panel, which was basically in charge of all war-related mathematical research, consisted of Richard Courant, Griffith Evans, Samuel Wilks, Thornton Fry (of Bell Laboratories), and three more pure mathematicians (Lawrence Graves, Marston Morse, and Oswald Veblen).

The group that Weaver, Wallis, and Hotelling assembled included—to list only names that have been mentioned in earlier sections—Bowker, Girshick, Hotelling, Mosteller, Wald, Wallis, and Wolfowitz. Most of them were young and unknown at the time but after the war became leaders of the profession. Their participation in the work of the SRG for many constituted an important part of their statistical training. This is one of the ways in which the SRG made a major contribution to the postwar development of the field.

The other was through the many problems it solved (contained in 572 reports) and the new techniques it developed. This proof of the usefulness of statistics to the war effort greatly enhanced the reputation of the subject after the war. This greater credibility of a new and somewhat suspect field assisted its development in universities, in the government, industry, and many other areas of application. An offshoot of this work is a volume, *Selected Techniques of Statistical Analysis* (edited by Eisenhart et al., 1947), which "discusses a series of problems that occur frequently in planning, analyzing, or interpreting quantitative data."

An area that received a great deal of attention, and in which the group was particularly successful, was that of sampling inspection. Concerning this

---

[11] For an account of the life and achievements of this enormously influential and charismatic man, see his autobiography, *Scene of Change* (1970). (It also explains the strange term *fire control.*)

work, which included the development of sequential analysis, Warren Weaver comments (on pp. 88–89 of his autobiography):

> Under the auspices of the Applied Mathematics Panel were developed powerful new statistical techniques which improved the efficiency and lowered the cost of testing our own war material. In just one such instance, involving improved testing of the propellant for rockets, the financial saving—not to mention the improvement of the material—was so great that within a few months it was sufficient to pay the cost of the total program of the Applied Mathematics Panel throughout the war.

The sampling work also led to a book, *Sampling Inspection* (edited by Freeman et al., 1948). The preface explains that it is "intended as a systematic account of certain of the best current inspection practices, together with tables and detailed instructions for carrying out these practices."

In its totality, the work of the group was a most remarkable achievement for which Wallis deserves much of the credit.[12]

After leaving the SRG in 1946, Wallis spent a year at Stanford and then went to the University of Chicago, where in 1949, jointly with two other members of the group (Milton Friedman and Jimmy Savage), he founded what amounted to a statistics department. However, the chancellor, Robert M. Hutchins, did not permit it to be called a department, and so it was a statistics group until 1951, when Hutchins resigned and it became an official department with Wallis as chair. Among the early members were Bill Kruskal, Raj Bahadur, David Wallace, Murray Rosenblatt, and Leo Goodman. Wallis resigned as chair in 1956, when he became dean of the Business School.

One other service to the statistical profession should be mentioned. From 1950 to 1959, Wallis served as the editor of the *Journal of the American Statistical Association* (JASA). After leaving Chicago in 1959, he moved away from statistics. In fact, as president of the American Statistical Association in 1965, in his presidential address he refers to himself as "a former statistician."

Personally, I had little contact with Wallis. However, during the oath controversy, Joe Hodges spent a year in Chicago and Charles Stein took a position with Wallis's group after resigning from Berkeley, but shortly left for Stanford. I only met Wallis later, and fondly recall a dinner he hosted as chairman at his house on the occasion of a talk I gave in the department. (On my later visits to Chicago, Wallis had left and I was the guest of Bill Kruskal or Steve Stigler. Still later, these contacts with the department led to my getting an honorary degree from the University of Chicago in 1991.)

Wallis's later career included twenty years (1962–82) as chancellor and then president of the University of Rochester, his service from 1982 to 1989 as Undersecretary of State for Economic Affairs, and other high government

[12] A more detailed history of the SRG is given in Wallis (1980).

appointments.[13] Surprisingly, his work for the federal government included one more important contribution to statistics. President Nixon created the President's Commission on Federal Statistics and appointed Wallis its chair. The work of the commission led in 1971 to a two-volume *Report on Federal Statistics*, and on its recommendation to the establishment in 1972 of the Committee on National Statistics.

Allen Wallis died in 1998, and to today's statistical community his name is known primarily through the Kruskal-Wallis test. But we should remember him for the profound and broad-based effect he had on the field of statistics as director of research of the SRG, founding chair of the Chicago Statistics Department, longtime editor of JASA, and chair of the Federal Commission on Statistics.

[13] For details, see Olkin (1991).

5
The Annals

The *Annals of Mathematical Statistics* was founded in 1930 as an outlet for papers that were too mathematical for the statistics journals of the time. The first four editors were Harry Carver, Sam Wilks, Ted Anderson, and myself. At that time, the editor was responsible not only for the contents of the journal but also for the production and business side. As the size of the *Annals* grew to over 1800 pages, this became too much of a burden. Consequently, in 1964 the editor, Joe Hodges, persuaded the Institute of Mathematical Statistics (IMS) to split the job and appoint a managing editor, leaving the editor with responsibility only for the content of the journal.

This change concerned the administrative structure of the *Annals*. However, in 1972 the journal underwent a more radical change that profoundly altered its character. Up to that time, the *Annals* had published not only papers in mathematical statistics, but also had been one of the main outlets for papers in probability theory. Now the editor, Ingram Olkin, felt that the theory of probability had developed into a subject that deserved its own journal. He persuaded the IMS to create a new journal, the *Annals of Probability,* and at the same time to broaden the scope of the old *Annals* by dropping the limiting adjective "mathematical," so that it would become more welcoming to applied work. The first of these two endeavors was wholly successful, the second less so. Despite its new name, the *Annals of Statistics* continues to be extremely mathematical. (Since then, both the *Annals of Probability* and the *Annals of Statistics* have split again.)

21. Samuel S. Wilks (1906–1964)

The increasingly mathematical orientation of statistics as a result of R.A. Fisher's work in the 1920s and that of Neyman and Pearson in the 1930s caused difficulties for statistical journals, most of whose readers had little mathematical background. (It is remarkable that as late as 1936, the editor of *Biometrika,* Neyman's friend and collaborator Egon Pearson, rejected Neyman's paper on confidence intervals as too long and too mathematical.)

The principal American journal, the *Journal of the American Statistical Association* (JASA), solved the problem by creating a separate journal, the *Annals of Mathematical Statistics,* for the more mathematical material. As an editorial in the first issue (of February 1930) explains:

> For some time past it has been evident that the membership of our organization [the American Statistical Association] is tending to become divided into two groups—those familiar with advanced mathematics, and those who have not devoted themselves to this field. The mathematicians are, of course, interested in articles of a type which are not intelligible to the nonmathematical readers of our journal. The editor of our journal has, then, found it a puzzling problem to satisfy both classes of readers.
>
> Now a happy solution has appeared. The Association at this time has the pleasure of presenting to its mathematically inclined members the first issue of the *Annals of Mathematical Statistics,* edited by Professor Harry C. Carver of the University of Michigan.

However, in 1934 the American Statistical Association decided to discontinue its financial support of the new journal. Generously, Carver stepped in and financed it privately until 1938, when the recently founded IMS took over financial responsibility and appointed Wilks of Princeton University as editor. During his twelve years as editor, Wilks transformed the journal from its modest beginnings to an internationally recognized journal of the first rank.

Samuel (Sam) S. Wilks, after studying topology with R.L. Moore and statistics with E.L. Dodd at the University of Texas, obtained his Ph.D. in statistics under H.L. Rietz at the University of Iowa, with a thesis on a distributional problem in multivariate analysis. He spent the next two years on fellowships, first with Hotelling at Columbia and then in England at the University of London and at Cambridge University. There he got to know Karl and Egon Pearson, Fisher, and Neyman, and published several more papers on sampling problems in multivariate analysis.

In 1933, at the end of his fellowship he was appointed to an instructorship in the mathematics department of Princeton University, and he remained there for the rest of his life. It seems a surprising appointment, considering the very theoretical orientation of that department and the very negative attitude most pure mathematicians then had toward statistics and even probability. We owe the details of the story to an account by Churchill Eisenhart (1989), a student of Neyman's in London and son of Luther Pfahler Eisenhart, the powerful chairman of the Princeton mathematics department, who at the time in question was also dean of the faculty and chairman of the University Committee on Research.

Like his counterpart Griffith Evans in Berkeley, L.P. Eisenhart (who worked in differential geometry) had an early interest in statistics. Over the years this had been kept alive by Hotelling, who had been one of his students (with a thesis in topology). After Eisenhart became chair of the mathematics department in 1928, the department in 1931 for the first time offered a course in probability theory. This was quite unusual at the time and even later. As Doob (1988) points out:

> The basic difference between the roles of mathematical probability in 1946 and 1988 is that the subject is now accepted as mathematics, whereas in 1946, to most mathematicians, mathematical probability was to mathematics as black marketing to marketing . . . . And the fact that probability was intrinsically related to statistics did not improve either subject's standing in the eyes of pure mathematicians.

It took unusually broadminded and farsighted mathematicians such as Evans and Eisenhart to appoint statisticians to their departments.

Wilks was brought to Eisenhart's attention by Hotelling. Knowing of Eisenhart's interest in building a program in mathematical statistics and probability at Princeton, Hotelling suggested to him that Wilks, with his training in mathematical statistics and his excellent publication record, was one of the most promising young men in the field. Stressing the long-term advantage to Princeton and Wilks' desperate situation (his fellowship had run out and, because of the Depression, he had been unable to find a position), he appealed to Eisenhart to give Wilks a chance. And despite the nearly unanimous opposition of his faculty, Eisenhart did offer Wilks an instructorship for the year 1933–34. Wilks remained at Princeton for the rest of his life, even turning down—to the amazement and outrage of his Texas family and friends—an offer of the presidency of the University of Texas.

Since at the time of his appointment some statistics courses were being offered in the economics department, Wilks did not introduce his own first courses—one semester undergraduate, one graduate—until 1936. By then, according to Churchill Eisenhart,

> The division of territory between the Department of Mathematics and the Department of Economics and Social Institutions had been resolved. The latter would be restricted to instruction in statistical theory and methods pertinent to the economic and social sciences; and the basic undergraduate course(s) in statistical theory, and the graduate courses in advanced mathematical statistics would be the province of the Mathematics Department.

This agreement and Wilks' promotion to assistant professor in 1936 gave him a fairly free hand, but Wilks expanded the program only very slowly, adding a third one-semester upper-division course in 1939. He also did not try to build up a group; however, he acquired a colleague fortuitously. This was John Tukey, a topologist in the mathematics department since 1939. During the war Tukey became involved in statistics, and by 1945 considered himself a statistician rather than a topologist. Wilks' program was further strengthened in 1950 by the appointment of Will Feller, although Feller was a probabilist with little interest in statistics.

Despite a minimal course program, Wilks was very successful in training a substantial number of graduate students, who included, among others, Ted Anderson, George Brown, Will Dixon, David Votaw, Alexander Mood, and Fred Mosteller. They learned primarily not through courses but by participating in Wilks's many statistical activities. This system served a dual purpose: the students learned to become statisticians, and Wilks obtained the help he needed.

His activities included a great deal of applied work, both during and after the war, but I shall discuss only two major projects here.

One of Wilks's most influential achievements was his editorship of the *Annals of Mathematical Statistics* through the crucial period from 1938 to 1949. He appointed an editorial board of great distinction, consisting of A.T. Craig and Neyman as coeditors, the other members being Carver, Cramér, Darmois, Deming, R.A. Fisher, Fry, Hotelling, von Mises, E.S. Pearson, Rietz, and Shewhart. One is struck both by the international nature of this group and by the breadth of interests it represents. But he did not—as was done later—put the board members in charge of refereeing, but kept this crucial editorial process in his own hands. Some papers he sent out to referees of his choice, others were refereed in-house by his students and presented by them in his seminar. Although such a practice would not be considered appropriate today, it was very convenient and provided a wonderful learning experience for the students. They were drafted also to help out with other aspects of the *Annals*. Fred Mosteller, one of these students, reports in his obituary of Wilks, entitled, "Samuel S. Wilks: Statesman of Statistics" (*The American Statistician,* 1964):

> Between classes, travels, committee meetings, and long-distance phone calls, one could rarely catch Wilks doing his own work, but a glimpse of him getting out final

copy for an issue of the *Annals* may provide some insight. Since the Wilks family loved to give hospitality, on a typical evening a visiting fireman would have been encouraged to stay on for yet another train (because Sam had no plans at all for the evening) and the guest was finally taken to Princeton Junction about 10 p.m. As the train pulled out, Sam would begin to express uneasiness about the need to get out the next issue of the *Annals*. He would wonder whether he shouldn't spend a few minutes on that yet tonight, and conviction would grow in him that he should, indeed. He supposed that his graduate assistant would not care to join him because the hour was so late. Surely a half hour or so would do the whole thing. Driving to the office, he would begin to list dozens of little matters that needed attention. And finally, after a furious half-night's work, the packages would be mailed at the Princeton Post Office around 3 a.m.

When Wilks took over the *Annals*, it had about 150 individual subscribers and its four issues ran to a total number of 230 pages. Ten years later, at the end of his editorship, these numbers had increased to 1,200 subscribers for a volume of over 600 pages. From a small and somewhat provincial publication, it had become the foremost, and internationally recognized, journal in mathematical statistics.

While Wilks' establishment of the *Annals* was perhaps the achievement of his that had the greatest influence, at least one other major project should also be mentioned. In 1943, Wilks published *Mathematical Statistics,* the first modern graduate text in the field. By "modern," I mean that it centered on the approach to statistical inference created by the Fisher, Neyman, and Pearson revolution.

The difference becomes clear by a comparison of Wilks' text with the standard American prewar text by Rietz (Wilks' thesis supervisor), also entitled, *Mathematical Statistics*. It was published in 1927, with a fifth printing in 1947. What strikes a reader today about Rietz's book is the complete absence of statistical inference. Neither the terms *estimation* nor *hypothesis testing* are mentioned. The statistics being offered, such as correlation and regression, is basically nineteenth century material. Surprisingly, not even Pearson's test for goodness of fit is included.

In contrast, after some preparatory chapters, statistical inference occupies the entire second part (slightly more than half) of Wilks' book. It covers point and interval estimation and the Neyman-Pearson theory of hypothesis testing, together with their applications to analysis of variance, regression, and multivariate analysis. As Wilks states in the preface:

> Most of the mathematical theory of statistics in its present state has been developed during the past twenty years. Because of the variety of scientific fields in which statistical problems have arisen, the original contributions to this branch of applied mathematics are widely scattered in scientific literature. Most of the theory still exists only in original form.

To pull these various contributions together and present them in a unified, coherent account, combined with the necessary mathematical and probabilistic preparation, was a major achievement. The book could well have served as the standard graduate introduction to the field, but it never got its due.

This is partly the result of its having been published in wartime, when the profession had different concerns, and partly that Wilks considered it not sufficiently polished and he published it with a soft cover by a photographic process rather than regular print. Immediately after the war, competing books appeared, and its opportunity was gone.

As had been the case with his editing the *Annals*, in writing this book Wilks heavily involved some of his graduate and postdoctoral students. He acknowledges this in the last paragraph of the preface:

> Finally, the author wishes to express his indebtedness to Dr. Henry Scheffé, Mr. T.W. Anderson, and Mr. D.F. Votaw, Jr. for their generous assistance in preparing these notes. Most of the sections in Chapters X and XI were prepared by these men, particularly the first two.

Of course they based their writing on his lectures and notes.

These two major projects—editing the *Annals* and writing a graduate text—were only a small part of Wilks's activities, which, besides teaching, consulting and much influential committee work, also included statistical research. Much of this was in multivariate analysis (including Wilks's lambda-criterion, a multivariate generalization of the F-statistic) and some early nonparametric work. One of his best-known results was the asymptotic distribution of the likelihood ratio criterion.

However, Wilks did not give research the prominent place that most academics do. Ted Anderson, in his obituary of Wilks, reports that Wilks told him that he thought a mathematician should not go through life concentrating on research, but should take on broader responsibilities. Anderson adds: "I think Wilks made a deliberate choice to give up mathematical research in favor of taking on other duties of import in defense, government, mathematics generally, natural and social sciences, and education."

Summing up Wilks' achievements in the *Yearbook of the American Philosophical Society,* 1964, pp. 147–154 (to which Wilks was elected in 1948), John Tukey writes:

> When the totals are entered in the last book of record, it is likely that the largest amount to Sam Wilks' credit will be for his work as a committeeman and adviser . . . . He was the chairman of the committee charged with a scientific report as to why the election polls of 1948 had not been followed by Thomas E. Dewey's election to the Presidency. He was a key member of the committee appointed by the National Academy of Sciences in the famous ADX-2 battery additive case. It would be hard to find two other committees which combined political pressures and statistical issues to as great a degree.

My first contact with Wilks occurred in 1946 in his capacity as editor of the *Annals*. Shortly after I had submitted my student paper (mentioned in Section 16) to the *Annals*, Neyman showed me a letter he had received from Wilks. It said that Neyman's student Lehmann had submitted a paper to the *Annals* but had omitted acknowledging Neyman's supervision of the work. Was that all right? Neyman replied that he had nothing to do with the paper, and it was published the following year.

Soon Wilks began sending me papers to referee and in 1948 listed me as one of about twenty "cooperating" members on the masthead of the *Annals*. Then, in 1950, he wrote to say that he was going on leave in the spring semester of 1951, and asked whether I would like to spend the semester in Princeton to teach one of his undergraduate courses together with a graduate course on topics of my choice. As a result, I spent the semester in Princeton as described in Section 18. During that time I never saw Wilks, who was already gone when I arrived. In fact, I got to see something of him only once, when he spent several days in Berkeley during the Fourth Berkeley Symposium, only four years before his sudden death at the age of fifty-eight. I am sorry that I did not get to know him better. Remarkably modest and self-effacing, yet vigorous and highly effective, he was dedicated to the profession of statistics and to the service he was able to render.

22. Wilks' Successors

When Wilks resigned from the editorship of the *Annals* in 1949, a new constitution of the IMS put the editing on a more formal basis, which relied heavily on a small board of associate editors. They would see to the refereeing of the papers and then make recommendations to the editor. To succeed Wilks, the council of the IMS selected Wilks's student T.W. (Ted) Anderson (b. 1918). I was pleased when Ted asked me to be one of his associate editors, the others being Bose, Feller, Girshick, Mood, and Tukey.

At the end of Ted's term, at his recommendation, I was asked to succeed him. Although I had been involved with the *Annals*, both as referee for Wilks and associate editor for Anderson, I was reluctant to accept the editorship, since I was quite unfamiliar with the administrative side and also feared the demands it would make on my time. In those early days, the editor had to get the manuscripts prepared for the printer, handle galley and page proofs, and negotiate various publishing details with the printing company in Baltimore.

However, Neyman strongly encouraged me to accept the job, which would bring prestige to the lab, and he was willing to give me the substantial support that Anderson had received from Columbia. This involved reducing my teaching load to half-time and providing the salary and space for an editorial assistant, who would take care of the voluminous typing, filing, and marking of the manuscripts. And so I agreed.

My first task was the selection of a set of associate editors. The four mathematical statisticians I picked—Blackwell, Hodges, Hoeffding, and Wolfowitz—are all subjects of this book. The remaining two, Madow and Mood, represented more applied interests. I had, of course, asked Ted Anderson to be one of the group, but he had declined. As he explained, having been the ultimate decision maker, he did not want to take on a position in which he no longer had this authority. After the termination of my own editorship, I felt quite differently and I served as associate editor under all but one of the next five editors.

In fact, I found the position of associate editor more congenial than that of editor. It is the associate editors who do the scientific work of evaluating the referees' reports and making recommendations to the editor, which are only rarely questioned or overruled. In addition, they tend to deal with papers in their general areas of interest instead of being responsible for material they know very little about.

And even in the setting of broad policies, the power of the editor is limited. This is illustrated by a phone call from John Tukey that I received shortly after assuming the editorship. Is it true, he wanted to know, that I planned not to accept any Bayesian papers? I reassured him that nothing could be further from my mind. "Good," he said, "because otherwise I would have asked the council to find a new editor!"

At the end of my fairly uneventful three-year term, the institute asked whether I would be willing to continue for another term. Since I did not feel strongly one way or the other about continuing, I asked Neyman whether he was willing to continue the previous arrangement. He agreed, so I accepted the appointment for a second term. However, a few weeks later, perhaps because of financial and other pressures regarding the forthcoming Third Berkeley Symposium, Neyman reversed himself. Without his support, I could not continue and had to inform the institute of my inability to serve. A great brouhaha ensued; there was even a move to boycott the third symposium. The details are recounted in Constance Reid's Neyman biography (1982). But although I was nonplused by Neyman's action and embarrassed at having to renege on my commitment to the institute, it seemed to me that the issue did not warrant such an uproar and I did what I could to calm the waters.

The institute appointed the probabilist Ted Harris in my stead, and he was succeeded by Bill Kruskal, who was followed by Joe Hodges. By then, the *Annals* had grown to three times the size of the six hundred pages it had been when Wilks retired. Joe persuaded the institute that the editor's workload had become unmanageable and that the institute should appoint a separate managing editor who would deal with the publishing aspects. From then on, the job of editor was much less demanding.

23. Ingram Olkin (b. 1924)

One big change was still ahead of the *Annals*, which occurred in 1972 under the editorship of Ingram Olkin.

Ingram Olkin obtained his B.S. degree from the City College of New York. From there he went to Columbia, where in 1949 he took a master's degree in

mathematical statistics, and he then followed Hotelling to North Carolina and received his Ph.D. two years later. His first faculty appointment was at Michigan State University (from 1951 to 1960), followed by a year as chair of the statistics department at the University of Minnesota. Finally, in 1961 Olkin moved to Stanford with a joint appointment in statistics and education. From 1973 to 1977, he chaired the statistics department.

Olkin has published more than two hundred papers, many of them in multivariate analysis and, more recently, meta-analysis. In addition, he is the coauthor of several books. Particularly noteworthy is *Inequalities: Theory of Majorization and Its Applications,* coauthored with A.W. Marshall (1979), which has become a classic and has been translated into Russian. His book with Hedges, *Statistical Methods for Meta-Analysis* (1985), has also been very influential. As the first book-length statistical treatment of meta-analysis—the methodology for combining findings from repeated studies—it has become a primary source for this important subject.

However, perhaps Olkin's greatest impact on the statistical community has been through some of his editorial activities. As editor of the *Annals of Mathematical Statistics* in 1971–72, he realized that probability had become too big a subject in its own right to be covered by a statistical journal, and he persuaded the council of the sponsoring society (the IMS) to split off an independent *Annals of Probability*. He also proposed a broadening of the *Annals of Mathematical Statistics* toward applications by dropping the adjective "mathematical" from its title, and then became the first editor of the new *Annals of Statistics* (1972–1974). In a recent letter to me, he explained:

> The rationale was not only size and growth. There was some tension between probability and statistics in that the probability authors felt that there was a preference for statistical papers in the *Annals*, and that they had to publish in mathematical journals, but that they wanted more connection with statistics . . . . So another part of the motivation to split [besides the fact that the *Annals* was getting too big] was an attempt to bring probability more into statistics rather than have them move into the mathematics camp.

Olkin also played a key role in founding a new journal for IMS, *Statistical Science*. Quoting again from his letter, his proposal was for

> a general journal that most statisticians could read. This was not to be a journal that carried much technical material. We had to recognize that there are about 4000 IMS members and 20,000 ASA [American Statistical Association] members . . . . So part of the goal was to attract a wider readership. We believed that historical and biographical articles would be of interest (there was no repository for biography) and also articles of an intellectual nature.

Statistical Science made its debut in 1986, with Olkin as one of three associate editors. The new journal admirably realized Ingram's vision. Particularly, the series of "conversations" provide living history that would have been lost otherwise. These interviews (quite a number of them conducted by Ingram) have been an invaluable source for many sections of this book.

A third journal, which was initiated by Olkin jointly with the educational statistician Mel Novick, was motivated by his interest in statistical work in education. It was intended to be, as Ingram wrote, "similar to technometrics, biometrics, and so on." The result was the *Journal of Educational Statistics,* which began publication in 1976 under the editorship of Mel Novick.

However, as Ingram admits, "This journal has not fully succeeded. We had lots of good editors and lots of good papers but it is not as popular as I would like." To broaden its base, the journal changed its name in 1994 to *Journal of Educational and Behavioral Statistics*. In this new incarnation, it was hoped, the journal might form a bridge between the social and behavioral sciences and the statistical concepts and methods they require for their work.

Olkin has had an important influence not only on statistical journals but also on the publication of books in our field. He has been a longtime advisor to the "Springer Texts in Statistics," which published my three principal books (on hypothesis testing, point estimation, and large sample theory). As statistics editor of the Society for Industrial and Applied Mathematics (SIAM's) reprint series, "Classics in Applied Mathematics," he was instrumental in the recent republication of my long-out-of-print elementary text with Hodges, *Basic Concepts of Probability and Statistics*.

Among Ingram's many honors are the Wilks Medal and the prestigious Founders Award of the American Statistical Association; a Lifetime Contribution Award from the American Psychological Association; the Elizabeth Scott Award from the Committee of Presidents of Statistical Societies (COPSS); and an honorary doctorate from DeMontford University (England). He has now been a Stanford colleague and friend for more than forty years, and he continues to be very active.

6
The Berkeley Statistics Department I: Establishment and First Generation

In 1938, Griffith Evans, chair of the Berkeley mathematics department, brought Jerzy Neyman to Berkeley to develop a statistics program. He presumably thought of two or three undergraduate courses, and a similar number of graduate courses taught by Neyman and perhaps one or two younger people. That things turned out very differently was due to two factors: Neyman's ambition and energy, and the explosive development of the field of statistics in the wake of World War II.

As a result, in the decade from the end of the war in 1945 to 1955, Neyman was able to assemble a faculty consisting of five professors, two associate professors, and four assistant professors, augmented by five visitors to teach an extensive program of courses. At the same time, he achieved a steadily increasing degree of independence for his laboratory until in 1955 (after Evans retired as chair) he reached his goal: a separate Department of Statistics.

A year later, the new department faced a crisis. Dissension developed and Neyman resigned as chair. His decision came as a great shock to his colleagues, but the group weathered the storm thanks to good will on all sides, and the tactful and wise management of David Blackwell, the new chair.

Although this change made little difference on the surface, it profoundly affected the way the department was run. It had moved from a one-man operation—a benevolent dictatorship—to a democracy. The chair had become the servant of the department rather than being its master. According to general university policy, the chair served a nonrenewable term of three to five years, and gradually most of us took a turn. After Blackwell came Lucien Le Cam, Henry Scheffé, Elizabeth Scott, and myself.

By the time I became chair in 1973, the faculty had reached a size of slightly over twenty, and there it has remained since then. So large a group was justified by the large number of students from all over the campus who were taking statistics courses and the great number of Ph.D.'s the department was graduating. The reputation of the department resulting from the many research papers and books it produced was of course also helpful.

24. Neyman's Struggle

As a result of the rapid growth of statistics after the war, the teaching and organization of the subject became a pressing issue in many universities. In the previous chapter, I briefly sketched the difficulties encountered in the development of four of the major early programs in mathematical statistics, at Columbia, Princeton, Stanford, and Chicago. This describes in more detail how it played out in Berkeley.

The Berkeley statistics program started in 1938, when Evans appointed Neyman as professor of mathematics. Evans considered statistics to be a subdiscipline of mathematics such as algebra or differential equations that would be represented by a single professor. During the next three years, Neyman established a skeleton program of basic courses and a small temporary staff to assist with the teaching, most of which he did himself. In addition, he engaged in statistical consulting with faculty members in other departments. His organization was the Statistical Laboratory (the Lab), of which he was the director.

Further development of the program was halted by the war, during which Neyman's energy and that of his lab were mainly devoted to war work. There was much coming and going, as temporary staff members, as soon as they had received some training, left for military duties and had to be replaced.

During the first part of 1946, Neyman was in Greece, as a member of President Truman's mission to supervise the Greek elections (see Section 11), and the fall semester of that year he planned to spend at Columbia with Wald. This presented him with a difficulty. He had counted on Hsu to teach his graduate course while he was gone, but Hsu had accepted Hotelling's offer and had left Berkeley. He then tried Polya, but Polya could not free himself from his Stanford obligations. Having failed with both Hsu and Polya, Neyman gave up on a senior appointment and fell back on an in-house solution. I was just completing my Ph.D. and was available. So I was given a faculty appointment as instructor for 1946–47, with the principal assignment of teaching Neyman's graduate course. But there was an additional task. At this point, I was the only member of the statistics group with a regular faculty position and was therefore appointed acting director of the Statistical Laboratory.

The glory of this position was somewhat diminished by the instructions that accompanied the appointment. I was told that although I had the authority, I was to take no major steps without first consulting Professor Evans. A timid instructor, who had graduated only a few weeks earlier, I was hardly the person who on his own would engage in bold new initiatives, but in any case, anyone concerned about such a possibility had little reason to worry, for another reason: The moment Neyman left Berkeley, he began to bombard me with a stream of instructions:

> See to it that Miss Fix and Joe Hodges complete their papers. Please check again the table of contents [of the symposium proceedings] and take all the manuscripts to the press with an appropriate covering letter. Oh, before doing this, mention it to Professor Evans.

Sometimes the letters were minutely detailed:

> It would be preferable [on some other publication issue] to have a joint talk between you, Professor Evans, and Professor Bernstein so that the latter has no doubt that Professor Evans approves of the idea. The thing would be to talk to Professor Evans while Professor Bernstein is sitting at his desk.

Neyman's semester at Columbia led to unexpected repercussions in Berkeley. It turned out that Wald, the chairman of Columbia's newly established Department of Mathematical Statistics, was eager to gain Neyman as a colleague and, in January 1947, made a very favorable offer. Neyman, in a long letter to President Sproul of the University of California, pointed out some of the great advantages that Columbia offered, but also stated his attachment to Berkeley and the Statistical Laboratory.

The most important aspects of the offer, in Neyman's view, were not the personal advantages such as better salary and retirement benefits, but that he would be a member of a group of congenial colleagues in a separate statistics department. Comparing this with the Berkeley situation, he raised some general issues concerning the relation of statistics and mathematics.

Similar discussions were to take place during the next years at many American universities.

In his letter to Sproul, Neyman wrote:

> During the recent decades the theory of statistics made tremendous advances and from the position of not-quite-recognized secondary mathematical subject developed into a wide independent science having innumerable contacts both with pure mathematics and with various experimental fields. As a result, no single man is able to give adequate instructions in mathematical statistics . . . .
>
> As far as I can see, the only way in which the instruction and research in statistics can be brought up to a desirable status is through the organization of an entirely independent Department of Statistics, with an adequate staff including several associate and full professors.

Evans responded with a "Memorandum on Statistics," in which he stated:

> I believe that our present organization of statistics is sound and promises most for the development of the subject, if personnel and equipment are allowed to increase in proportion to demand. The pressure for separation from mathematics comes from a personal bias, wherein there is an overestimation of the administrative position of chairman.

Evans was undoubtedly correct in attributing Neyman's drive for an independent department partly to "personal bias"—that is, his passion for doing things his way, with as little interference from others as possible. However, Evans had been his staunch ally, using whatever power or persuasive ability he had for Neyman's support. Thus, the obstacle Evans presented was not so much practical as symbolic; what was at stake was a matter of principle. Neyman did not want to have to ask permission for what he wanted to do, even when he could assume that this permission would be granted.

Next, Evans argued forcefully against a B.A. degree in statistics, since it would require "practically the whole of the upper division time, and would be essentially nothing but an undergraduate professional degree." Interestingly, for graduate study in statistics he would not insist on a major in mathematics but would also admit a degree in a substantive field.

At the heart of the disagreement was the question of whether statistics is a subfield of mathematics or a new and separate discipline. Evans believed that

> probability and statistics are essentially one subject. Probability is pure mathematics, as much so as geometry, or theory of sets, or any branch of mathematics . . . . Theoretical statistics is a further specialization of the theory of probability . . . . It is true that theoretical statistics has developed methods which are specialized in a great extent to it. But this is also true of any branch of mathematics . . . . In fact, every branch shows the same characteristics—mathematical specialization, mathematical development and application by means of significant approximations. A division between mathematics and statistics would be purely artificial.

Neyman did not really want to leave, nor did Evans or Sproul want to lose him. So a compromise was negotiated. The most important aspect involved a split of the budget. It separated research and teaching by assigning research appointments (even if they involved some teaching) to the budget of the Statistical Laboratory, which would be submitted by the director of the lab directly to the university president. On the other hand, instructional activities remained within the mathematics department. In addition, the agreement authorized two new appointments, one a position of tenure grade, the other at the rank of instructor. Neyman referred to this document as the Magna Carta.

If Evans thought this would settle the matter, he was mistaken. A year-and-a-half later, Neyman used a minor disagreement with Evans and the appointment of a new dean to reopen the issue:

> Dear Dean Davis: This is to request that steps by taken to investigate the desirability of establishing the present Statistical Laboratory as an entirely independent Department of Statistics with full responsibility for both instruction and research.

This was followed a few months later by another letter:

> Dear Dean Davis: With reference to my letter of December 1948, this is to submit a new argument in favor of establishing an independent Department of Statistics, and to outline a tentative plan whereby such a department could be established by separating the Statistical Laboratory from the Department of Mathematics.

This request was turned down by Davis, but Neyman kept up the campaign. Going above Davis's head, he wrote a year later:

> Dear President Sproul: You may be aware that since the beginning of my appointment in this university in 1938 I have advocated the creation of a separate Department of Statistics . . ..

Shortly before this last letter, a major obstacle to Neyman's effort had been removed by the retirement of Evans as chair of the mathematics department in 1949. His successor, Charles Morrey, did not share Evans' vision of a broadly based mathematics department. He may, on the contrary, have felt that the growth of statistics had come at the expense of pure mathematics and that his department would be better off without Neyman's constant demands for more positions and increased funding. In any case, he recommended that the university recognize the merits of Neyman's position and grant his request for a separate department. As a result, a committee was formed to study the problem.

However, the process was slow, and in January 1953 Neyman wrote, somewhat impatiently:

> Dear Chancellor Kerr[1]: This is to enquire whether or not we can expect in the near future any action on the report of the committee about the desirability of transforming

[1] In 1952, Clark Kerr had been appointed Berkeley's first chancellor while Sproul remained president of the university, i.e., of all campuses.

this laboratory into a Department of Statistics, separate from the Department of Mathematics . . .. I most sincerely hope that a final decision can be made without much further delay . . ..

Finally, in the summer of 1954, Chancellor Kerr recommended to President Sproul "that the Mathematical Statistical Laboratory be redesignated the Department of Statistics as soon as possible in the fiscal year 1954–55."

A summary of the long history of the issue was prepared for Sproul by an assistant who, without much enthusiasm, recommended approval of the de facto independence:

Here, a willful, persistent and distinguished director has succeeded, step by step over a fifteen year period, against the original wish of his department chairman and dean, in converting a small "laboratory" or institute into, in terms of numbers of students taught, an enormously expensive unit; and he then argues that the unit should be renamed a "department" because no additional expense will be incurred.

One can sympathize with the irritation of administrators at Neyman's relentless pursuit of his goal. It is also true that the total of 364 students enrolled in statistics courses in 1954–55 was rather small for a faculty of twelve, even if one takes into account the additional responsibility for consulting. On the other hand, the report ignores a crucial element: the development of the field of statistics during the fifteen years since Neyman's arrival in Berkeley, and what this portended for the future. History has sided with Neyman. The number of students rose to about 2,500 by 1964 and to twice that number in another decade. Gradually, most major universities established departments of statistics.

Sproul's final approval of the department came on October 24, 1954.

The struggle to convert a one-man appointment as professor of mathematics into a substantial separate department of statistics did not, of course, take place in a vacuum. It required the acquisition of a faculty, the associated office and laboratory space, a corresponding expansion of the course program, and, as justification for such an enterprise, an increased enrollment of students taking these courses. Neyman not only carried out these tasks with great skill and unflagging energy, but he also expanded the research program and the resulting financial support for the work of the group. In addition, through symposia and a new series of publications, he created a national and international reputation for his laboratory.

The first order of business in building a statistics program at Berkeley was to assemble a faculty. After my appointment in 1946, the Magna Carta provided for two additional positions. Neyman filled one of these with Charles Stein, who had just completed his Ph.D. at Columbia with a highly original solution of a problem that had long interested Neyman. Charles would also bring with him first-hand knowledge of Wald's new decision theory, a natural development of Neyman's own work. For the other position, Neyman obtained the French probabilist Michel Loève, who was to take charge of the probability side of the program.

Gradually, over the next seven years, Neyman appointed some more of his students as they completed their degrees: Edward Barankin (in 1947), Evelyn Fix and Elizabeth Scott (in 1949), Joe Hodges (in 1951), and Lucien Le Cam (in 1953). A faculty that has mostly been trained by the founder of the group faces two dangers: the in-breeding is likely to result in a certain narrowness, and—in the opposite direction—conflicts may arise as former students become independent colleagues with ideas of their own.

In the present case, the first of these dangers was mitigated by the very strong outside appointments Neyman made in addition to those of his own students. These included not only Stein and Loève, but Scheffé (in 1953), who had interests and expertise in applications, and Blackwell (in 1955), a specialist in game theory and dynamic programming. Nevertheless, a certain narrowness did result. There was a lack of attention to Fisherian and Bayesian ideas. (No course on Bayesian statistics was introduced until 1969.) In general, the program reflected the Neyman-Pearson-Wald point of view so strongly that this approach was sometimes simply referred to as "Berkeley."

This weakness was at the same time a source of strength. It resulted in a congenial group that shared a basic point of view and engaged in much collaborative work. At one time or another, joint papers were written by Blackwell and Hodges, Fix and Hodges, Hodges and Le Cam, Lehmann and Scheffé, and Lehmann and Stein. In addition, long-term collaborations developed between Hodges and Lehmann and between Neyman and Scott.

Crucial for the development of the program was the question as to who should have the responsibility—or the right—to teach statistics courses. The obvious answer was that this was the task of the statisticians. But elementary statistics courses were being taught in economics, education, forestry, psychology, sociology, and a number of other disciplines. And the instructor was often the most junior member of the department, who might have little background in statistics. Despite these shortcomings, the other departments were very reluctant to give up their courses. For one thing, they argued, they could motivate their students better by basing the instruction on examples from their particular subject matter.

In addition, economic issues were involved. The sections of the large lower-division courses, particularly in economics and psychology, gave employment as teaching assistants to a substantial number of graduate students, a source of support not easily relinquished. After lengthy negotiations, Neyman was able to work out a compromise. The Statistical Laboratory would teach the lower-division courses but would not object to other departments offering more advanced courses tailored specifically to the needs of their students. He also agreed that, at least for a number of years, he would employ qualified graduate students from other departments as teaching assistants for the lower-division courses.

When on July 1, 1955, statistics became at last an independent department, it had a faculty of eleven members: five professors (Blackwell, Lehmann, Loève, Neyman, Scheffé), two associate professors (Barankin, Hodges), and three assistant professors (Fix, Le Cam, Scott), augmented by some visiting faculty. A substantial course program was in place. The department's future seemed assured. However, the following year it was to be shaken by a crisis that endangered its existence.

25. David Blackwell (b. 1919)

The crisis that quite suddenly descended on the new department in its second year was the completely unexpected resignation of Neyman as department chair. It was quite incomprehensible: Why would he take such a radical step?

One precipitating event was a change of deans. Throughout the ten-year postwar effort to build a statistics group, Neyman had enjoyed the support of the same dean, with whom he had established a good relationship. Now a new dean had taken over and had immediately questioned some of Neyman's arrangements. Clearly, from now on the sailing would be much rougher.

A second cause had its roots in an incident the year before. A vacancy had occurred on the statistics faculty, and several of us felt that the candidate Neyman was proposing as replacement would not meet our principal needs at the time, and we expressed our disagreement with his choice.

I believe this opposition to his wishes came as a shock to Neyman. In principle, he wanted to run the department democratically. He thought this would be easy, since he expected us to agree with his views. Furthermore, he undoubtedly felt, rightly, that the department was his creation and that it was he to whom we owed our appointments. Our opposition to his plans thus came as a surprise and seemed to him black ingratitude. He once indicated his feelings to me by telling me about a certain bird. If the eggs in its nest were touched or tampered with, it abandoned the nest. He now was disgusted with a situation in which he encountered interference from both above and below and, like the bird in his story, considered starting all over again, perhaps on another campus of the university.

However, another issue that played a role had its roots in his personal situation. Neyman's great scientific results, which had made his name, had been obtained more than twenty years earlier. Since coming to Berkeley, most of his energy had been consumed by the demands of the new situation: consulting, war work, the symposia, building a department, and the constant struggle for funding and space these activities required. As a result, his research had suffered. He was now sixty-two; if he wanted to return to major research, this was his opportunity. And so an accommodation was found.

The university administration granted Neyman an independent laboratory with him as director. It would be a research organization unconnected with the instructional activities of the department, but in charge of all research grants and contracts. This arrangement was not without risk. The research budget under Neyman's control was about equal to the department's budget, and they supported the same group of students and faculty. The divided authority provided plenty of opportunity for friction. Many in the profession thought that the Berkeley department would fall apart (as had been the case at Columbia after Wald's death). The credit for this not happening belongs to the man whom the department now asked to take charge and who agreed to do so—David Blackwell.

Blackwell's early career was largely determined by the fact that he was African-American and the racial attitudes of the time. When as a graduate student at the University of Illinois he was awarded financial support, it could only be for research, not for a teaching assistantship. (It is instructive to compare this with Teichmüller's letter to Landau on the teaching of German students by Jews, reported in Section 1.) Asked later[2] whether discrimination against blacks had affected his education or his career after the Ph.D., he explained:

---

[2] De Groot (1986).

It never bothered me. I'll put it that way. It surely shaped my expectations from the very beginning. It never occurred to me to think about teaching in a major university, since it wasn't in my horizon at all.

After getting his Ph.D. in 1941 at the University of Illinois with a thesis on Markov chains, supervised by Joe Doob, Blackwell spent a postdoctoral year at the Institute for Advanced Studies in Princeton. He followed this with a year each on the faculties of two black colleges, first the Southern University in Baton Rouge, Louisiana, and then Clark College in Atlanta. From there he went to Howard University in Washington, D.C., of which he wrote later that "it was the ambition of every black scholar in those days to get a job at Howard University. That was the best job you could hope for." He stayed at Howard for the next ten years, serving as head of the mathematics department from 1947 to 1954.

In Washington, Blackwell formed a friendship with Abe Girshick, who was then working in the Department of Agriculture. Later, they spent some months together at the Rand Corporation. After Girshick joined Bowker at Stanford in 1948, Blackwell spent the year 1950–51 as visiting professor at Stanford. However, he turned down an offer of a permanent position there for family reasons. Since Berkeley had a black middle class that Stanford lacked, he decided instead to accept an offer from Neyman. After a visiting year (1954–55), he became a permanent member of the Berkeley faculty in 1955.

Although he had thus been with us for only two years when Neyman resigned as department chair, we had all known David for much longer, and for a number of reasons he seemed the obvious choice to lead the department in this crucial transition period. He had an easy and comfortable way of dealing with people, including, most importantly, Neyman. As a relative newcomer, he had the advantage of not having been involved in earlier conflicts. And of course he had an outstanding scientific reputation.

Among Blackwell's highly original contributions at the time were a new proof, under weaker conditions, of a famous equation in sequential analysis due to Wald; his work on the comparison of experiments; the discovery that an estimator can be improved by conditioning it on a sufficient statistic; and a very influential paper (joint with Arrow and Girshick), "Bayes and Minimax Solutions of Sequential Decision Problems" (1949), which initiated the method of backward induction. Later, Blackwell also made significant contributions to probability theory, game theory, dynamic programming, and information theory. One of the contributions, for example, is the use of game theory as a tool for working on measure theoretic problems. In 1954, jointly with Girshick, he published a very innovative book, *Theory of Games and Statistical Decisions*.

David's chairmanship from 1957 to 1960 was remarkable not for any great innovations but (like the absence of barking in the Sherlock Holmes story of the *Hound of the Baskervilles*) by what did not happen. There were no fights, controversies, even friction, but just a smoothly running operation settling into a new pattern. This success was largely due to David, but Neyman greatly contributed to it by going out of his way to cooperate. He participated in the business of the department like any other faculty member, neither boycotting it nor making any effort to dominate.

One slight inconvenience during Blackwell's chairmanship was that much of the time he did not have a home telephone. (The rumor at the time was that his pregnant wife was bothered by so many calls from colleagues, so he ripped out the phone. However, David denies this version.) One day, Henry Scheffé urgently needed to reach David on some departmental matter and bemoaned the fact that he was unable to call him. But suddenly he brightened. "Oh, but I can," he exclaimed, "David is in Washington."

Blackwell's originality as a mathematician is mirrored in the independence of his thinking on other subjects. After experiencing the painful process of denying tenure to persons who for years had been colleagues, he decided that he would no longer serve on tenure committees; he did not want to play God. His solution: all appointments should be made at a level that carried tenure. Another example is his refreshing attitude toward research. "I'm not interested in doing research and I never have been," he has said,[3] and then amplified with, "I'm interested in understanding, which is quite a different thing."

In recognition of his accomplishments, Blackwell has received a nearly unprecedented number of honors. He is a member not only of the National Academy of Sciences and the American Academy of Arts and Sciences, but also of the American Philosophical Society, the oldest of the American academies and one that rarely elects mathematicians to its membership. He has received honorary doctorates from many colleges and universities: Illinois, Michigan State, Southern Illinois, Carnegie-Mellon, Lesotho, Amherst, Harvard, Howard, Yale, Warwick, Syracuse, and Southern California. In addition, he has served as president of the Institute of Mathematical Statistics, and of the Bernoulli Society for Mathematical Statistics and Probability, and as vice president of the American Statistical Association, the International Statistical Institute, and the American Mathematical Society. It is an amazing record.

David Blackwell has now been my colleague and friend for over fifty years. We once embarked on a joint paper that, unfortunately, did not materialize, and we usually drive together to Stanford when the Berkeley–Stanford Colloquium meets there. I have often dropped by his office just to chat for a few minutes, to get his views on some topic of common interest or advice on some problem that was bothering me.

Of nearly the same age, we are now the last survivors of the original Stat Lab group assembled by Neyman.

---

[3] From Albers and Alexanderson (1985).

26. Lucien Le Cam (1924–2000)

In contrast to Blackwell, who kept a low profile and tried to avoid conflict and controversy, his successor as chair, Lucien Le Cam, was flamboyant and enjoyed making provocative statements to the department, the university administration, and the statistical community.

As an example, here are some excerpts from a memorandum (of 1958) to the statistics department regarding a proposal by the probabilist Loève to strengthen the probability part of a basic introductory course.

> The proposed revision seems to arouse such violent opposition that the inarticulate undersigned feels obligated to communicate his feelings on the subject by the present memo.
>
> Loève's proposal seemed at first so innocuous and so gentle that I did not expect much reaction to it from any side, except possibly that practical people (are statisticians supposed to be practical?) might desire even more emphasis on applicable probability theory. As of now I consider the differences of opinion arising in our midst are irreconcilable and due to such basic differences of understanding of what is and what should be probability theory and how it should be taught that no useful purpose will be derived by arguing any further in the same direction. Therefore the present memo will not propose any solutions but only try to generate some heat on controversial matters.

Our teaching of Probability and consequently Statistics is hopelessly inadequate. As far as I can tell, the people who struggle through [our basic courses] do not even get a knowledge of probability remotely comparable to the knowledge imparted by J. Dubourdieu in his evening lectures to candidates to the Actuarial examination in Paris.

In case one should object that Probability Theory per se is not a worthy subject of study, I shall make my next point: The statisticians who are going to make the headlines in the future are not those who can in a twinkling give an analysis of variance for a Latin Square or a three-way classification. Statistics is basically much more complicated than Probability, would it be only because where the Probabilist has only one measure to cope with, the statistician has a family of measures. There is of course plenty to do in statistics without using complicated machinery. It just requires brains. This last commodity we cannot dispense to the students, but we can give them tools.

If we could give our students a good background in mathematics and probability, we might be able to teach them more, not less, statistics in a shorter time. Otherwise we are bound to produce Ph.D.'s in Statistics who cannot even read the statistical papers of our Symposia, not to mention the sundry applied papers to be found in the same Symposia.

If this memo seems unreasonable to you, I will gladly restore it to its original strength and triple the emphasis on the necessity of teaching probability theory as a major part of our task and not as an undignified accessory to some statistical arguments.

Le Cam, who became the most mathematical of all my statistical colleagues, had started his career as an applied statistician at the Electricité de France. A chance meeting with Neyman at a seminar in Paris led to an invitation to spend the year 1950–51 in Berkeley. There he found a statistical atmosphere quite different from what he was used to. As he later explained[4]:

My statistics was of the applied type. At Electricité de France one did not worry about proofs or such niceties. But at Berkeley everything was full of measure theory and other fanciful mathematics. I had no formal training in such things, only a superficial knowledge gathered in odd ways. Whatever I knew of abstract mathematics had been learned from Bourbaki books. Those I read, carefully at times, having eventually a "subscription" to them.

At the end of the year, Neyman suggested that Le Cam stay in Berkeley another year and get his doctorate. So in 1952 he obtained his Ph.D. with a spectacular thesis, which examines the asymptotic theory of maximum likelihood estimates and, in particular, proves the results on superefficiency mentioned in Section 8.

After obtaining his degree (and getting married), he did not return to France, but became a member of the Berkeley faculty, and continued the investigations started in this thesis. Particularly noteworthy is his 1960 paper, "Locally Asymptotically Normal Families of Distributions." In it, he introduced the LAN families indicated in the title and the fact that such families

[4] Quoted from Albers, Alexanderson, and Reid (1990).

can be closely approximated by families of normal distributions. The LAN assumption has become the standard setup in much if not most asymptotic work. The paper also introduced the concept of contiguity of two sequences of distributions, and the important results concerning contiguity known as Le Cam's three lemmas.[5]

In this paper, Le Cam also states a topic to which he would recur repeatedly, his mistrust in the principle of maximum likelihood:

> This author is firmly convinced that a recourse to maximum likelihood is justifiable only when one is dealing with families of distributions that are extremely regular. The cases in which m.l. estimates are easily obtainable and have been proved to have good properties are extremely restricted. One of the purposes of this paper is precisely to deemphasize the role of m.l. estimates. Since, however, the m.l. estimates seem to exert a quasi-hypnotic attraction, a comparison of the results obtained herein with those obtainable for m.l. estimates is given below.

Starting in 1966, Le Cam gave a graduate course in asymptotic theory based largely on his own work. The course was mathematically so advanced that students would audit it, sometimes more than once, before daring to take it for credit. It took Le Cam another twenty years before, in 1986, he published the definitive account of his approach in a massive (740 pages) book, *Asymptotic Methods in Statistical Decision Theory*. The difficulty of the course was shared by the book, which, under the influence of his Bourbaki background, treated the theory in the greatest possible abstraction and generality. The situation was summarized perfectly in the concluding paragraph of a review by Lawrence Brown (in the 1988 volume of JASA):

> This is a book for serious study. The mathematically or statistically unprepared reader or the prepared but casual reader will likely get nothing from it but a headache. But the prepared and diligent reader will find a gold mine, from which can be distilled an effective and powerful understanding of statistical asymptotics.

In addition to his principal asymptotic project, Le Cam worked on many smaller issues, often in collaboration with others. Most of these collaborators were Berkeley colleagues, visitors, or students. These joint papers reflected the fact that in his office, the door of which was always open, Le Cam was visited by a steady stream of callers who wanted to discuss their problems with him. Beyond these sporadic joint efforts, he was also involved in three deeper and more long-range collaborations.

The first of these, with the Czech statistician Jaroslav Hajek, was not a collaboration in the usual sense. The two authors never wrote a joint paper, and although Hajek twice spent several months in Berkeley, Le Cam was very busy both times and the two had only limited contact. However, they worked

---

[5] A very clear overview of Le Cam's many contributions is given in van der Vaart (2002), which is followed by a list of Le Cam's publications.

on the same asymptotic problems. Sometimes one would publish a new idea and the other would develop it further, sometimes the order was the opposite, and on still other occasions they would publish similar results simultaneously. As one consequence of this "collaboration" or friendly competition, two important theorems bear their joint names: the Hajek–Le Cam asymptotic minimax theorem and the Hajek–Le Cam convolution theorem.

The special relation with Hajek's work was commemorated by Le Cam in a paper,[6] "Recollection on My Contacts with Jaroslav Hajek," which concludes:

> Hajek and I had precious little chance for collaboration. In spite of that our work, originating from different considerations, overlapped to a noticeable extent. I clearly benefited from his ideas, and he used some of mine.
>
> He was a very good friend. I deeply regret his untimely demise. [Hajek died in 1974 at the early age of forty-eight from a longstanding kidney disease.]

A real collaboration was Lucien's joint work with his student Grace Yang. It started with a suggestion she made in 1966–67, which Le Cam mentions in his asymptotics book as having been "most valuable." In 1988, their work led to a joint paper in the *Annals of Statistics*. Most importantly, they collaborated on a book, *Asymptotics in Statistics,* which came out in 1990. It presented some of the basic ideas of Le Cam's theory on a level at which they were more accessible than in his earlier book.

In 1999, Grace interviewed Le Cam for *Statistical Science*. After Lucien's death in 2000, she wrote a memorial article on him for the *Annals of Statistics,* which dedicated its June 2002 issue to his memory.

A third very different collaboration arose from the illness of Le Cam's 12–year-old daughter, Linda. In 1972, she was diagnosed with osteogenic sarcoma, a rare and usually fatal disease. After amputation of a leg and removal of a lung, it became necessary to decide on a follow-up treatment. The standard treatment of radiation and chemotherapy was tried but nearly killed Linda. So Lucien contacted Vera Byers, who, with her husband A.S. Levin, had developed a yet-untried new approach, immunotherapy. It turned out that Lucien and Linda's two brothers were suitable donors of white blood cells, so the treatment was started and proved successful. It saved Linda's life.

An unexpected consequence of Linda's treatment is described by Vera Byers[7]:

> It was only somewhat later that I found out Lucien was a statistician. I was describing to him what we were doing and he said, "Well, you know, maybe I can help you a bit."

The upshot was that Le Cam did all the statistical work for the project, which over a period of several years led to six joint papers.

---

[6] In Hajek (1998).
[7] Albers, Alexanderson, and Reid (1990).

In a minor way, I too collaborated with Lucien. In 1974, we wrote a joint paper for Neyman's eightieth birthday, in which we tried to highlight Neyman's great accomplishments. The paper appeared in the May 1974 issue of the *Annals,* which the Institute of Mathematical Statistics dedicated to Neyman.

Some time after Neyman's death in 1981, while preparing a memoir on Neyman for the National Academy of Sciences, I came across two unpublished manuscripts of his that still seemed to be of interest. I asked Lucien to join me in editing them for a special volume of the Polish journal *Probability and Statistics,* to be published to commemorate the one-hundredth anniversary of Neyman's birthday. We also each wrote a paper for the volume, Lucien on "Neyman and Stochastic Models" and I on "Neyman's Statistical Philosophy."

It was natural for me to turn to Lucien for this task, not only because he had done much organizational and editorial work for Neyman, but also because he was one of the members of our department to whom I felt closest. I would often stop by his office to get help with a technical point or just for a short chat. We shared an interest in the history of statistics. In this connection, he occasionally asked my advice on some German text while I required his assistance with French, particularly when studying Laplace.

For Le Cam's seventieth birthday on November 18, 1994, he received a festschrift edited by Pollard, Torgersen, and Yang (1997). I contributed a paper, "Le Cam at Berkeley," which carried this dedication:

> Written in appreciation of the pleasure and many benefits I have received from over forty years of friendship and collegiality with Lucien Le Cam.

Lucien died in April 2000, after a period of deteriorating health.

27. Elizabeth Scott (1917–1988)

After the chairmanship of first Blackwell and then Le Cam, the burdensome task of chairing the department continued to rotate among its senior members. The next chair (1965–1968) was Henry Scheffé, the subject of Section 12. His tenure was marked by great unrest on campus, the result of what became known as the Free Speech Movement.[8] Different groups of both faculty and students had violently opposite attitudes and Henry was in the middle, trying to hold the department together and to keep the atmosphere pleasant. His fair-mindedness gained him the respect and affection of all members.

Scheffé's successor was Elizabeth (Betty) Scott (1968–1973), who had to deal with a very different kind of problem—the planning for, and eventual move to, Evans Hall, which, after our many moves, was to serve as permanent

[8] For details, see Kerr (2003).

home to both the mathematics and statistics departments. She handled the details and decisions that such a project entails with great energy and efficiency, and we were grateful that she did so without involving the rest of us.

Betty had started her career not in statistics but in astronomy, the field in which she obtained her Ph.D. in 1949. She first became interested in statistics as a tool for analyzing her data. But while she continued to work in astronomy throughout her career, statistical issues gradually began to dominate. Two reasons caused this change of emphasis.

One was the discrimination in astronomy against women, who, for example, were forbidden to use the telescopes at the Mount Wilson Observatory. There was no hope for a woman to obtain a faculty position in astronomy. On the other hand, Scott was appointed lecturer in statistics in 1948 (before even having completed her degree) and steadily advanced in rank, becoming professor in 1963.

The second reason for the greater involvement with statistics was that she came under the influence of Jerzy Neyman. She audited an upper-division course from him in 1938–39, his first year in Berkeley, and, although only an auditor, turned out to be the best student in the class. As a result, when, the following year, the university provided Neyman with a research assistant, he chose Betty. In 1942, she became a member of the staff he recruited for a contract in bombing research, and for the next three years she was primarily occupied with war work.

During the first postwar years, Scott published several papers in astronomy and, in 1948, a first joint paper with Neyman, "Consistent Estimates Based on Partially Consistent Observations." The paper became famous as providing the first example to show that in certain circumstances maximum likelihood estimates were not necessarily consistent.

In 1951, C.D. Shane, the director of the Lick Observatory, approached Scott about a large-scale project on galaxies for which he needed statistical help, and she referred him to Neyman. This led to a longtime collaboration, with Scott providing the bridge from Shane's data to Neyman's statistical concepts. Later, Neyman referred to this collaborative work as one of "three emotional involvements in research." The first was his enthusiasm when he encountered Lebesgue's theory of integration, the second his seminal work with Egon Pearson, and the third "Certain problems of astronomy—C. Donald Shane and E.L. Scott." Neyman (1970) recalled:

> The initiative for cooperation in astronomical studies came from C.D. Shane. Some years before his first visit to the Statistical Laboratory he embarked on a project which impressed me by its time scale . . . . [It] was to make a complete photographic survey of the part of the sky accessible to the telescopes at the Lick Observatory, to store these photographs and to hope that, half a century later, one of his successors at the observatory will do the same. Then, the superposition of corresponding photographs of the two sets would reveal some of the intricacies of the structure of our galaxy.
>
> The inspection of the plates brought to Shane's attention certain fancy features of the distribution of the many images of galaxies visible on the plates . . . . What he hoped [the statisticians would supply] was some kind of general stochastic model of the distribution of the galaxies . . . .
>
> Once we [Neyman and Scott] learned a little of the current astrophysics, there arose a large number of exciting problems which we tried to solve, occasionally with a degree of success, and for more than a decade, we were deeply involved in them.

As a result, between 1952 and 1964 there appeared twenty-six papers on galaxies, most under the joint authorship of Neyman and Scott, and occasionally with Shane or some other astronomer as additional coauthor.

During this period, Neyman and his wife, Olga, separated and Betty became his constant companion and frequently acted as hostess at dinner parties at his new house, although she continued to live with her mother at the other end of town. She was the kind of partner he needed because she was as strong-willed as he and stood up to him. He submitted much of his writing to her criticism and this allowed him to be himself, to write as he felt in the secure knowledge that she would let him know when he stepped over the line. This sometimes led to noisy arguments ("You can't do this, Jerry!"), but in the end he would usually accept her advice.

Although Scott had come to statistics as an aid to her work in astronomy, her statistical interests gradually broadened in the environment of Neyman's laboratory, and she became an accomplished applied statistician. That is, she did not study statistical methods for their own sake but rather investigated subject matter problems in different areas that needed statistics for their resolution. In particular, she devoted much effort to three such areas: weather modification through cloud seeding (with Neyman), the causes of skin cancer, and inequities in the salaries of academic women.[9]

The recognition Scott's work received both nationally and internationally can be seen from the numerous positions to which she was elected: president of the Institute of Mathematical Statistics (1977–78) and of the Bernoulli Society (1983–85), and vice president of the American Association for the Advancement of Science (1970–71) and of the International Statistical Institute (1981–83). In addition, she served on many panels of the National Academy of Sciences and of other scientific organizations.

My own relations with Betty were friendly but never close, since I was not part of the Neyman–Scott inner circle. Like other members of the department, I was a frequent guest at parties at her house or hosted by her at Neyman's. Both she and Neyman were enormously generous and treated the department like family, of which they were the parents. On the other hand, Betty tended to come down hard on anyone whose actions displeased her, regardless of whether they were students, faculty, or deans. But I was lucky and don't recall her ever taking me to task. Nevertheless, at one point she did significantly affect my life—it is a story that will be told in the next section.

28. E.L. Lehmann (b. 1917) I: Department Chair

In the spring of 1970, toward the middle of her tenure as chair, Betty Scott was going to be on leave for a semester and asked me to fill in for her as acting chair. Knowing of my aversion to administration, she told me that this would involve little work, since she had made all the necessary preparations. All that remained, she assured me, was to sign documents from time to time. What she could not know was that this was to be "Cambodian Spring," during which American troops invaded Cambodia. As a result, a few days after Betty left, the campus exploded. Many students, teaching assistants, and faculty members went on strike, and our department again was deeply split, with some members refusing to teach on campus while others wanted it recorded that they had met their classes in the usual way.

In normal times, the chair acts principally as an agent of the department in its negotiations with the administration. However, under extraordinary circumstances such as those prevailing at the time, the chair also serves in the opposite direction as conduit for instructions from the administration to the department. In case of conflict, the chair is in the middle and has to follow his or her best judgment.

[9] For more on these activities, see Billard and Ferber (1991).

A difficult issue of this kind arose when the administration asked me for detailed information on how each faculty member and teaching assistant had met his or her classes. Some members of the department wanted me to honor this instruction, others to refuse it. Since we had been told that the information would be used only for statistical purposes, I decided on an intermediate course. I provided summary statements that gave the needed statistical information but I refused to report the behavior of individuals. I was asked to appear before a council of deans and was told that I was disobeying orders. But I stuck to my position that under the university's claim to use the information only for statistical purposes, I was providing them with all that was needed. Next, I was summoned to a meeting with the vice chancellor and told that I was one of only three chairs who were not in compliance. He threatened serious consequences for my career, and that was the last I ever heard of the matter.

However, my service as acting chair during this tumultuous semester did have other consequences for me. When, two years later, Betty's term came to an end, it had become natural for me to succeed her, and I agreed to do so.

In many departments, the position of chair is coveted and often bitterly fought for by competing candidates. No one on our faculty felt that way. Most of us did not particularly enjoy administration, but rather considered it a chore leaving little time for research and teaching, which interested us much more.

For most purposes, the chair is the servant of the department rather than its master. That this was the way the position was seen by colleagues was forcibly brought to my attention on the first day of classes. One of my colleagues who was in charge of the introductory course that had an enrollment of more than one thousand students and that employed a dozen teaching assistants, came to my office and barked, "I want twelve bodies by 5:00 this afternoon," and left. I was stunned. Up to then we had been on friendly terms, but now he obviously saw me in a different light—as an administrator. I told him that if my colleagues were now going to treat me in this way, I would resign immediately. He apologized, explaining that he had not realized how abrupt he had been, and we remained friends.

That colleagues saw (or treated) you differently as department chair was also seen in a change of my relation with Neyman. He had always called those of us who were his former students by our first names, while we continued to address him as Professor Neyman. Now, the first written communication I received from him about some minor administrative detail was signed, "Jerry."

The aspect of chairing the department I disliked the most was the overcommitment of our resources that it was necessary to make each year. The administration provided us with a certain number of graduate assistants, but when at the specified time we sent out our offers of support for incoming graduate students we knew that not all of them would come to Berkeley. So in order to fill our slots with good candidates, we had to send out considerably more acceptances than were authorized. But what would happen if the number of acceptances exceeded our allowance? Presumably nothing—the administration would reprimand us and bail us out. But the practice went so completely against the way I had been brought up and conducted my personal life that it caused me much anguish.

Not everyone reacted that way. Each year, the chairs of the physical science departments (which included mathematics and statistics) met with the dean and reported on the events of the year. At my first of these meetings, the chair of one of these departments reported overspending the equipment allowance by a huge amount. I expected the sky to fall, but the dean's reaction was quite mild: "All right," he said, "we'll make it up this time, but don't let it happen again." But it did happen again, exactly the same way, the next year, and the third (my last). I apparently could have saved myself a lot of worry.

On the whole, the three years of my tenure as chair were calm, and my principal recollections are of festive occasions and memorable visitors. Perhaps the most outstanding event was the celebration of Neyman's eightieth birthday. To mark the event, I asked the two statisticians of my generation whom Neyman admired the most, Herb Robbins and Charles Stein, to give lectures on their work. They both accepted, and there was enough interest in Neyman and enough publicity to fill the principal auditorium, Wheeler Hall.

The lectures were followed in the evening by a banquet hosted by Al Bowker, who was then chancellor at Berkeley. Among the many speeches and toasts, there was a variation of Neyman's favorite toast: "To all the ladies present and some of those absent," which the speaker changed, perhaps under the influence of too many drinks, to the memorable, "To all the ladies absent and some of those present."

An event planned for the second year of my term to which I was looking forward with great excitement was an extended visit by Andrei N. Kolmogorov, considered by many to be the greatest living mathematician. Among other seminal contributions, he had proposed the now commonly accepted foundation for probability theory, and his broad mathematical interests included statistics. Neyman knew Kolmogorov well and had repeatedly tried to bring him to Berkeley for a visit, without success. This time, the situation looked very promising. In fact, the university catalogue for the year 1974–75 lists Kolmogorov among the visiting faculty. What made me so confident was that some months before he was due to arrive, Kolmogorov had sent a vanguard in the form of his young colleague, Igor Zhurbenko, whose assignments were to become fluent in English, get a driver's license, find suitable housing, and generally prepare the ground. All these preparations went well, but unfortunately at the last moment Kolmogorov experienced severe health problems (we were later told that it was a breakdown from overwork) and had to cancel the visit.

Although this was a great disappointment, we had in this year a number of other stimulating visitors. One was Bob Bohrer, who came on a sabbatical from the University of Illinois and taught a course in the analysis of variance.

He was already suffering from the diabetes that later resulted in complete blindness and years of much suffering, which he bore with admirable grace and fortitude. He and his wife, Joyce, became lifelong friends, and after his death I gave the first Bohrer Memorial Lecture (in 1999) at Illinois.

We owed the possibility of another visitor to the generosity of the university's Miller Institute for Basic Research. One of its most helpful programs provides funds for extended visits by distinguished researchers at other institutions. During their stay, they are expected to be available for consultations and to offer a number of public lectures. I asked Fred Mosteller of Harvard whether he might be interested in such an appointment, and as a result he spent the year 1974–75 in Berkeley as Miller Professor.

At the time he came to Berkeley, he was studying the effectiveness of social and medical innovations. His lectures on this subject were fascinating. They showed that the enthusiasm with which innovative procedures were carried out (for example, in surgery) were often not matched by their usefulness. However, it required careful study to arrive at this realization.

One of Fred's closest collaborators for many years had been John Tukey, and Fred thought it would be useful if we could arrange for a Tukey visit to Berkeley. Fortunately, a perfect vehicle existed for this purpose, the Hitchcock Lectures, which bring distinguished persons to the campus for a period of three to four weeks, during which time they give a number of lectures. The first Hitchcock Lectures in statistics had been given by R.A. Fisher in 1936 because he was being considered for a position. The visit had not been a success, and two years later the position went to Neyman. In contrast, Tukey's visit (which was not a job interview) was very enjoyable, and provided a look at his new work on data analysis. Having both him and Mosteller in Berkeley was a great boon to our department.

The term for chairing a department was typically three years (although in some cases it was extended to five), and I was very happy when after three years I was able to return to full-time teaching and research. In a certain sense, the end of my term as chair in 1976 marked the end of a period. It had now been twenty years since statistics had become a separate department, and some years earlier the department had attained the stable size of about twenty members, which it still has today. After Blackwell, Le Cam, Scheffé, and Scott, I was the last chair of my generation. (Some others who would also have been suitable, for example Hodges and Loève, refused to take on this job.)

The department continued to flourish under the next generation of younger chairs, and for many years now Berkeley and Stanford have been ranked as the two top statistics departments in the United States, with the top spot sometimes going to one and sometimes the other. The department is teaching over five thousand students a year and continues to produce Ph.D.'s, books, and research papers in great numbers. Its development, starting with Neyman's appointment as professor of mathematics in 1938 and driven by his vision and energy, has been a remarkable story.

29. E.L. Lehmann II: Teaching and Writing

When as a high-school student I was living with my parents in Zürich, my father was worried about my future. His concern led him to seek assistance from an unusual source. Without my knowledge, he sent a sample of my handwriting to the Swiss graphologist Max Pulver, asking for an analysis. As my mother told me many years later, Pulver's report consisted of vague generalities, with one exception: he claimed to have discovered a talent for teaching. Whatever may have been the basis for this conclusion, teaching did become my profession.

I began as a teaching assistant with courses in remedial algebra (which is high-school material), analytic geometry, and first-year calculus. Later, I taught statistics courses at all levels from lower-division introductions to advanced seminars, and all with enthusiasm, with one proviso: the class had to be small enough (not to exceed about forty) so that I could get to know the students individually, or at least to know their names. Lecturing to classes of hundreds of students, involving no personal contact with most of them, did not appeal to me, and I was lucky enough to be able to avoid such courses throughout my career.

Fortunately, we offered a very theoretical introductory course (Stat. 1), which attracted only thirty to forty students and which I taught regularly (and for which in the 1960s I wrote a text, jointly with Joe Hodges). The department generously accepted this as fulfilling my lower-division obligations.

One year, this course netted me a gift. At the last meeting of the semester, one of the students (who was the quarterback of the football team that semester), in the name of the class, presented me with a small jeweler's box. I opened it and found that it contained a nickel. Not quite knowing what to make of it, I thanked the class and was about to pocket the coin when a cry went out, "Don't put it away, look at it." The nickel, manufactured by the students in an engineering lab, turned out to be two-headed. It memorialized a favorite example involving such a coin (how many uninterrupted heads before you should become suspicious?).

Another course led to a different kind of "present." Once, when correcting a final as a teaching assistant, I found a blue book containing a five-dollar bill (worth about fifty dollars in today's currency), the only time I recall being offered a bribe. A less-benevolent student action occurred in a graduate course. A student failing all his courses filed a suit against me and three colleagues for $1.5 million, for violating his civil rights. My particular crime was to have coached other students in the class for the final but to have excluded him from this preparation. Although the various allegations were entirely a product of his imagination, and despite the dismissal of the case by one court after another, he managed (without the benefit of lawyers) to continue appealing the case to higher courts until one day I received a document from the U.S. Supreme Court stating that it too had dismissed the suit against me.

While I eschewed very large courses, I loved the teaching that occurred at the other end of the spectrum. Working on a one-on-one basis with Ph.D. students was, for me, the most enjoyable and rewarding aspect of teaching. At the same time, it was an extension of my research, since these students would help me explore areas in which I was working at the time.

In addition to classroom instruction and supervision of Ph.D. students, there exists another form of teaching that I found particularly congenial, namely the writing of textbooks. Although this may not sound like a very exciting activity, developing an integrated account of a beautiful body of work, finding a unifying point of view, searching for the best illustrations and most useful applications, and striving for the greatest clarity all present challenges. I enjoyed trying to meet them, and book-writing became a constant companion throughout my professional life and eventually resulted in five books.

The first, *Testing Statistical Hypotheses,* was the result of my occasional early teaching of the first-year graduate course for which no text existed at the time. The book had a dual purpose. On the one hand I wanted to present the theory of this branch of statistics as it had been developed by Neyman and Pearson and augmented by the later ideas of Wald and Stein. But what gives these theoretical results their interest is that they provide justification for much of the standard statistical methodology. For this reason, the book gave a fairly full account of these methods as applications of the general theory, and it was the combination of these two aspects that constituted the essence of the volume. The students were introduced to the basic statistical methods, but not as a bag of clever tricks coming out of the blue but as being derived systematically from a body of general theory.

The book appeared in 1959 as a volume in the Wiley Publications in Statistics, where it joined, among others, Wald's *Statistical Decision Functions* and Feller's *Introduction to Probability Theory* (both published in 1950), Doob's *Stochastic Processes* and Cochran's *Sampling Techniques* (of 1953), Anderson's *Multivariate Analysis* (1958), and Scheffé's *Analysis of Variance* (1959).

After the book was published, I of course wanted to use it as a text for my own course. However, it was not clear to me how best to do this. It seemed a waste of time to go through in detail in class what I had labored hard to express as clearly as possible in print. So I proposed a different scheme: At each meeting of the class I would outline the next section and then ask the students to read it carefully and be prepared to discuss any difficulties they had found at the next meeting. After this discussion, I would assign some problems. This seemed to me a great way to proceed, but at the end of the first week a delegation of three members of the class came to my office. They told me that the book was much too difficult to read on their own, and that the whole class would drop the course unless I returned to the usual method of detailed lectures.

While the experiment was thus a failure, the availability of the book greatly facilitated teaching the course to a class of diverse backgrounds. It was now possible to omit some material (for example, the measure theoretic aspects or some particular application) and to ask interested students to work through that material on their own.

Once a book is published, it takes on a life of its own. Errors are discovered, reviews appear (not all of them favorable, although rarely as disparaging as that of Wolfowitz mentioned in Section 17), and translations may be undertaken (in this case into Russian, Japanese, and Polish). A somewhat unusual development resulted from the more than two hundred problems given in the book. Many of them dealt with extensions of the theory and some were quite difficult. In addition, they were not always stated with sufficient precision, and the given hints were sometimes misleading. To correct the situation, a group of Dutch statisticians went systematically and painstakingly through the whole collection and, in 1984, published the detailed solutions in a book of 310 pages, nearly as long as the text itself.[10]

When my book on testing first appeared in 1959, twenty-six years after Neyman and Pearson had put forth their approach (and less than 10 years after Wald's book on decision theory), it contained all the theory concerning hypothesis testing that existed at the time—or at least all of which I was aware. For this reason, the book served not only as a textbook but also as a reference work. But, of course, the subject was not standing still. There was a constant flow of new results and ideas, and gradually the book became out of date. An updating was called for, and in 1986 I published a second, much-enlarged edition in which the text had grown from the original 380 to 600 pages. When, fifteen years later, a third edition seemed desirable, I enlisted the help of a younger coauthor, Joe Romano of the Stanford faculty, and a third edition by the two of us appeared in 2005, a volume of 780 pages, nearly twice the length of the original. The principal new material consisted of five chapters on large-sample theory.

Like the testing book, my second text also had the purpose of meeting the needs of a particular course. Joe Hodges and I had taken turns teaching the theoretical introductory course Stat. 1, which we both enjoyed. However, we did not find any of the existing books suitable as a text. Most of them were of the "cookbook" variety and devoid of theory. The exception, Neyman's *First Course in Probability and Statistics* (1950), was too complicated and difficult for our audience. In addition, Neyman's book did not include many of the topics we wanted to cover, for example, sampling, rank tests, and point estimation. We therefore decided to write our own version of a rigorous introduction at the precalculus level. We thought that such a book would be particularly suitable for liberal arts colleges, where at the time such courses were being taught by mathematicians rather than statisticians.

---

[10] Kallenberg (1984).

Joe and I found working together on this project very enjoyable. We debated each section intensely and hammered out the details. Then Joe, having better command of English, would go home and take a first stab at getting things down on paper. But what he showed me the next day often bore little resemblance to what we had agreed upon. When I confronted him with this discrepancy, he would explain that it was not his fault: when he had started writing, his pen had taken over and this is what it had produced. Sometimes I would accept the new version; at other times I would take it home to see what my pen would come up with.

At the time I thought that Joe was just being facetious. However, in light of my own experience with writing since then, I now see that he really meant what he said. Over and over I have started to write down what I had carefully planned and thought about, only to find that, as Joe put it, "my pen took over." As I would write, new ideas would come rushing in and would divert me into a different direction. I cannot explain why the act of writing exerts such a strong influence, but I admit that it is so, and in retrospect apologize to Joe for not having taken his explanation more seriously.

Eventually, we were able to complete the manuscript, and the book finally appeared in 1964 under the title, *Basic Concepts of Probability and Statistics*. It was quite unconventional in replacing the standard tests by rank tests, and by including some results on optimal experimental design.

Although the mathematical level of the book was elementary in the sense of requiring no calculus, its use of mathematics was rather sophisticated and, together with the theoretical orientation, made it unsuitable for most introductory courses. We thus did not expect it to become a bestseller. Nevertheless, for a number of years it did not do badly. It was also translated into Italian, Danish, and Hebrew, and more recently into Farsi. Unfortunately, the publisher of *Basic Concepts* (and of a statistics series I was editing for him) had to declare bankruptcy. As a result, in 1991 the book went out of print, but it has recently been republished, with a new preface, by SIAM in its series, "Classics in Applied Mathematics."

In 1952, I introduced a course into our curriculum that was to acquaint our students with the new methodology of nonparametric inference. The course was intended primarily for students in the master's program, but it was also suitable for seniors majoring in statistics. After having taught this course for a number of years without a suitable text, I began to develop course notes that eventually grew into my third book, *Nonparametrics—Statistical Methods Based on Ranks*. It was published in 1975 in the series I was editing for Holden-Day, and therefore—like *Basic Concepts*—went out of print in 1991 when the company folded. It has now been republished by Springer.

Unlike my two earlier, theory-oriented, books, *Nonparametrics* emphasized methods rather than theory. It thus seemed important to illustrate the methods with real-life data. Since I was not personally doing any applied work, I had no examples available, and hence spent a summer in the library looking for suitable material. The search turned out more difficult than expected. As I explained in the preface:

> Authors do not publish their data, and when a set of published data is potentially suitable, it usually turns out that the sample size is too large or too small, there are too many or too few ties, the results are too obviously significant or too obviously not, or that the design or sampling procedure is not what is required to illustrate the particular point in question.

As a result of this difficulty, the examples I found often came from out-of-the-way journals such as *Psychosomatic Medicine,* the *International Journal of Clinical and Experimental Hypnosis,* or the *American Journal of Physical Medicine*. The publication of these data had a curious consequence. I sometimes came across references to my book in quite unexpected places. On checking, it turned out that the references were not to some of my text but to one of these data sets.

These three books were eventually followed by two more, both written at the urging of my wife, Juliet Shaffer. I shall return to these in Section 59. However, I was not the only member of the department publishing textbooks. Early texts at one level or another were written by Blackwell, Brillinger, Hodges, Loève, Neyman and Scheffé. Perhaps the most influential were the lower-division introduction, *Statistics,* by Freedman, Pisani, and Purves (1978), and the graduate introductory text, *Mathematical Statistics,* by Bickel and Doksum. Books such as these have helped to define the subject and to enhance the reputation of the department from which they emanated.

30. F.N. David (1909–1993)

Berkeley, though a wonderful place in which to live and work, suffered from one disadvantage: its isolation because of its great distance from the East Coast and Europe. In the 1950s and 1960s, flying was not as easy and as common as it is today, and a train from coast to coast took two-and-a-half to three days. To alleviate the resulting insularity, Neyman arranged frequent visiting positions for a summer session, semester, or year. Among such visiting faculty were, for example, Cramér, Grenander, Robbins, and Wald.

A different kind of visitor was Neyman's old student F.N. David, who, starting in 1970, for a number of years regularly taught a course for us on the history of statistics.

Florence Nightingale David (who detested her first and middle names and insisted on being called David) was born in 1909 in Ivington (England) and received her bachelor's degree in mathematics in 1931 from Bedford College for Women. She wanted to become an actuary, but no positions were open to women. Since she had heard that Karl Pearson had done some actuarial work, she went to his office on a whim and he agreed to take her on as a graduate student and research assistant. When Pearson retired in 1933, he moved

to the department of zoology and David went with him. For two years, as she wrote,[11] she had his sole attention.

In the wake of Pearson's retirement, his department was split between the Department of Eugenics under Fisher and the Department of Applied Statistics, of which Pearson's son Egon was the head. Egon brought Neyman to University College as a reader, and Neyman took an interest in David and persuaded her to get her doctorate. (She later claimed that this had been a waste of twenty pounds, the fee she had to pay for the degree.) Her appointment as an instructor in Egon Pearson's department was interrupted during the war when she worked for various government agencies, but after the war she returned to University College with a promotion to a readership.

When Egon Pearson retired in 1960, David was the natural person to succeed him. However, prejudice against women prevented her appointment and instead an outsider, Maurice Bartlett, was brought in to succeed Pearson. After seven years, Bartlett left University College for Oxford, and David was finally offered Egon Pearson's chair. However, by that time she had committed herself to take a position at the University of California's Riverside campus, and she left for the United States.

[11] Laird (1989).

After a year of giving statistics courses at Riverside, she became the head of a new department of statistics. At the same time, she developed a close association with the Berkeley statistics department, and in 1969 began to teach a regular course in Berkeley as visiting professor. She divided her work between the two campuses, which are several hundred miles apart, by flying to Berkeley each Thursday evening, teaching a two-hour course on Friday, and returning to Riverside Sunday night. She had two cars, one at each place, and eventually also bought a house in Berkeley, together with Evelyn Fix of the Berkeley statistics department. She retired from Riverside in 1977, but remained active with work in forestry in Berkeley, work that had started in 1958 when she had come to Berkeley for the summer and had become a consultant to the Forestry Service.

David was a prolific author, with over one hundred papers, and was author or coauthor of nine books. Her early work was largely computational, resulting in her book, *Tables of the Correlation Coefficient,* computed under the direction of Karl Pearson, who insisted on twenty–figure accuracy. A strong interest of hers was combinatoric problems arising in probability theory. Between 1951 and 1968, she wrote about thirty papers on the subject, some jointly with Colin Mallows and some with David Barton. Some of this work was summarized in her book with Barton, *Combinatorial Chance,* which dealt with runs, matching, occupancy problems, symmetric functions, and related problems. Her next book, *Symmetric Function and Allied Tables* (1966), was jointly written with Kendall and Barton and continued this combinatorial line of work.

David also wrote a book in a very different area, the history of probability. In the preface to *Games, Gods, and Gambling* (1962), she explains its relation to the standard work in the field, Todhunter's *History of Probability*. "From the point of view of development of ideas," she writes, "he does not start soon enough. He notes the mathematical arguments fairly and with precision, but this is like embarking on a river when it has become of respectable size, and paying no attention to the multitude of small streams and tributaries of which it is the united outcome." Accordingly, the book stresses the early history and covers the development of probabilistic ideas from antiquity to De Moivre.

David had hoped to later write a monograph on Laplace, but that did not happen. This is a great pity, as is the fact that she did not write about the period she had herself witnessed, that of Karl Pearson, Fisher, Gosset (Student), Neyman, and Egon Pearson. Her sense of history made her a perceptive observer of the contemporary scene, and the following comments from her 1989 conversation with Nan Laird in *Statistical Science* gives a tantalizing taste of what she might have told:

> I think the period between the 1920s and 1940s was really seminal in statistics and I saw all the protagonists from a worm's eye point of view. It's now been 50 years. I am far enough away to be able to see the pattern without having to take sides . . ..

Gosset was an extraordinary man. I think he was really the big influence in statistics . . .. Most extraordinary person. He asked the questions, there's no question about that. He asked the questions and Pearson or Fisher put them into statistical language and then Neyman came to work with the mathematics. But I think most of it stems from Gosset. I had enormous respect for him, he was a great man.

Ten years later, when I reread this interview, I became intrigued by her assessment of Student's influence, and I investigated it in a 1999 paper based on Gosset's correspondence with Fisher and Egon Pearson. It was fascinating to follow the gradual development of Fisher's normal theory tests and of the Neyman-Pearson theory, and Student's impact was indeed seminal.

Because of her interest in the history of probability, the Berkeley statistics department in 1970 asked David to give a course in this subject. The course, which met for two hours on Fridays, was given by her regularly for a number of years. It was one way to satisfy a statistics requirement and it soon became very popular, with a steadily increasing enrollment that eventually rose to five hundred students. There were two reasons for this popularity. One was that David was a lively and entertaining lecturer; the other, which I am afraid was an even more important reason, was that she demanded very little of the students. She assigned no homework and there were no exams. The only requirement was the final, an essay written at home on any topic of some relevance. Toward the end of my term as chair, I began to hear rumors that a brisk market had developed in essays recycled from previous years. As a result, we decided soon after to discontinue the course.

David had a forceful personality and you could count on her telling you what was on her mind. Her style can be illustrated by an incident that, more than thirty years later, I still vividly remember. As I was standing in our department's coffee room, she came up from behind and hit me so hard on the shoulder that I nearly dropped to my knees. "Dear boy," she said (that's what she always called me), "all you need is a straw between your teeth to be the perfect hayseed." I did not live up to her sartorial standards for a department chair.

31. Students: From Colin Blyth (b. 1922) to Javier Rojo (b. 1951)

The papers and books produced by members of the Berkeley department, as well as the Berkeley symposia, all contributed to its reputation as an international center of statistics. However, perhaps no factor played a greater role in this regard than the almost five hundred Ph.D. students from all over the world who have graduated from the department since Neyman's arrival in 1938.

Personally, I found working with Ph.D. students very rewarding. Between the first, Colin Blyth, who obtained his degree in 1950, and the last, Javier Rojo, who completed his in 1986, I supervised close to fifty students, although not all of them took their official degrees at Berkeley. They greatly enriched my research, and several of them became lifelong friends.

I usually first met these students when they took a course from me, particularly the main first-year graduate course in theoretical statistics. In the early years, this course was usually taught by Neyman, who based it largely on his own work. When he took a leave in 1946, he assigned it to me and, having just completed my own graduate studies, I closely followed his script. But when asked to teach it again in 1948, I modernized it by incorporating some of Wald's decision theory and the invariance considerations I had learned from Charles Stein. One of the students that second time was Colin Blyth, and what he did in connection with this course profoundly affected my life and career. A letter he wrote many years later describes what happened.

I attended your course 260A in testing in the fall of 1948 and wrote up careful notes. (After each lecture I went home and wrote up the rough notes I'd taken in class, putting them into readable form, and settling to my own satisfaction any details omitted or points I hadn't been clear about in class.) Some time in the spring of 1949, you saw these notes (I don't remember how this happened, and can think of no reason that it might have) and suggested mimeographing them for other students. I preferred to attend your course again in the summer of 1949 and put them in a form more suitable for distribution, and this we did. I wrote them up, you read them carefully and made numerous suggestions, and after a final revision they went to the typist.

The notes were mimeographed and sold at cost, first by the Statistical Laboratory and later by the university's bookstore. The next year they were followed by a second set of notes by Colin, prepared in the same way and based on the other part of my course, which dealt with the theory of estimation. As our students graduated and took up positions at other universities, they recommended the notes or used them in their courses. As a result, orders started arriving from other places. In the absence of any other systematic treatment of this still fairly novel material, the notes gradually became something of an underground text.

The reception of the testing notes suggested that they satisfied a need that a fleshed-out book could fill better. Consequently, I began to develop a full treatment of hypothesis testing, for which the notes served as a skeleton. However, it took me a decade to complete the project. I wrote and rewrote, trying to find better ways to explain, to reach greater clarity, and to include more applications. And even after the manuscript was essentially in final form, I found it hard to let go. Publication is so final, and the next issue of the *Annals* might bring some new results that should be included.

The push to call a halt to this stalling came from an unexpected source. Neyman had not been sympathetic to this project. After I taught the theory course for the second time, he realized that I had included much material that was not part of his presentation. He became quite upset and told me that he would not let me teach the course again (and in fact this embargo lasted until nearly ten years later, when David Blackwell succeeded Neyman as department chair). But now he said rather gruffly that I had dawdled over the book long enough and that the time had come for me to get off the dime. And so in 1959, *Testing Statistical Hypotheses* was finally published by Wiley.[12]

It would have been natural to follow this publication by also converting the Blyth estimation notes into a book. But such a project did not appeal to me at the time and had to wait for more than twenty years, until in 1983 I finally published the companion volume, *Theory of Point Estimation.*

While he was working on the notes, Colin one day told me that he had found the solution to an open problem that I had mentioned in class. It was the fact (stated more precisely in Section 13) that the average $\bar{X}$ of a number

[12] The book had many adventures after publication, which are recounted in *Statistical Science* 12 (1997).

of normally distributed measurements is admissible. Blyth's result not only closed an important gap in the theory, but his method of proof became one of the basic ways of attacking such problems and is often referred to as Blyth's method.

This work formed the core of Blyth's thesis, with which he obtained his Ph.D. in the spring of 1950, thus becoming my first Ph.D. student. He went on to a distinguished career, first at the University of Illinois and later at Queen's University in Kingston, Ontario.

However, he had other interests and talents besides statistics. In 1994, he published a book, *Gaelic Names of Pipe Tunes,* which, according to one review, "achieved very well its purpose of making the Gaelic heritage of piping more accessible for pipers." It was the result of spending, as Blyth once wrote, "hundreds of hours playing the pipes in marching bands, and marching or hiking to English and Gaelic and German hiking songs." To publish it, he set up his own publishing company, Iolair, which, he tells me, is Gaelic for "golden eagle."

After many years of little contact, we started corresponding again when, in the early 1990s, Colin worked on a translation of Heinrich Hoffmann's 1844 German children's book, *Struwelpeter*. He produced not only an enjoyable verse translation but provided more hopeful endings to the stories, which in their original versions ended in gruesome consequences of misbehavior.

Struwelpeter was highly successful, and Colin followed it with a translation of *Max and Moritz,* the most popular book by the German poet and humorist Wilhelm Busch. Although many friends argued strongly against this course, he again made a radical change in the ending. Both these books were published by Iolair.

Colin and I remained in contact and my wife and I had a most enjoyable stay with him and his wife, Valerie, when we were invited to give some lectures at Queen's University.

After Blyth's successful degree, supervision of Ph.D. students became a regular part of my teaching. The nature of the supervision varied greatly according to the ability of the student. At one extreme, there were students who found their own problems, worked on them independently, and then one day presented me with a draft of a thesis, which in some cases contained very original and important results. In such cases, the term *supervisor* gives an entirely wrong picture. At the other end were students who from week to week had to be given a small piece to work out, so that supervision came close to dictation. The great majority of theses fell somewhere between these extremes.

The students also greatly varied in their country of origin. Most were American, but many came from Asia, particularly India, Taiwan, and Korea; others came from Europe: Norway, France, and Germany; and still others came from Israel.

In most cases, the students worked on problems suggested by me, which typically were part of my own research program. But many, once they had completed their degrees, went in entirely different directions. In particular, although neither I nor most of my Berkeley colleagues supported the Bayesian approach or even paid much attention to it, quite a number of my students later became Bayesians.

On a personal basis, the relationships with my students varied greatly from being purely formal to becoming quite close. Twice I was asked to walk a bride to the altar, standing in for their (Asian) fathers, who were unable to come to the U.S. Some of my students became lifelong friends and occasionally, later, collaborators. I wrote joint papers with Wei-Yin Loh and Fritz Scholz, and for many years collaborated with Peter Bickel, who, after obtaining his degree, became a member of our faculty.

A close relationship also developed with my last student, Javier Rojo. In 1986, he wrote a thesis on L-unbiasedness, a general decision-theoretic concept I had introduced more than thirty years earlier, and which reduced to the classical concepts of unbiasedness in standard testing and estimation problems. In his thesis, Javier undertook a thorough investigation of this concept.

After completing his degree, Rojo joined the mathematics department of the University of Texas at El Paso (UTEP), but continued working with me during extended visits (often with his family) in each summer from 1988 to 1992. Some of this work resulted in a joint paper, "Invariant Directional Orderings" (1992), which contributed to the understanding of a topic that

had long interested me and on which I had published before: the ordering of random variables and their distributions. It is concerned with the question of what we mean by saying that a random variable Y is larger than another variable X, for example that women live longer than men. In 1992, on the occasion of my seventy-fifth birthday, Javier put together a very nice volume of reminiscences by many of my former students.

Although other attractive job possibilities opened up, Javier found it difficult to leave El Paso, where both his and his wife's families lived in closely knit, large, extended families. Finally, in 2001 he accepted a very attractive offer of a professorship at Rice University in Houston.

Soon after his move to Rice, Javier approached me with a very ambitious plan: a symposium organized jointly by him and Victor Perez-Abreu, director of Centro de Investigationes Matemáticas (CIMAT). It would follow the model of the Berkeley Symposia, but be devoted primarily to the role of optimality, be held every two years, and carry my name. I thought it was a bit too much and demurred but eventually gave in, partly because I did not believe that they would really be able to pull it off. But I underestimated the energy and resourcefulness of these two organizers. The first symposium took place at CIMAT in Guanajuato (Mexico) on May 23–25, 2002, and was a wonderful occasion. With slightly over eighty participants, it was small enough to provide a certain intimacy; the level of the talks was high, and the social and cultural events marvelous. The proceedings of the symposium appeared in 2004 and provide more detail.

As originally planned, the second symposium took place in 2004 at Rice University, and matched the expectations raised by the first. The proceedings appeared in 2006. A third symposium took place in 2007 at Rice.

The friendships with Colin Blyth, Javier Rojo, and many other of my students have been one of the great pleasures of my life, and has greatly enriched it in many unexpected and wonderful ways.

7
The Berkeley Statistics Department II: The Second Generation

The preceding chapter discussed Neyman's struggle that ended with the establishment of the statistics department in 1955, and the subsequent development of the department up to 1976. It provided an account of the faculty members hired by Neyman—what might be called the first generation. This chapter sketches the careers of the four members of the second generation to whom I was closest.

The account of the department given in these two chapters suffers from a serious omission. It makes no mention of the department's role with regard to probability theory. From the start, Neyman had realized the need for instruction in advanced probability for his students. Since the mathematics department was offering no course in the subject, in his third year in Berkeley he added a year-long graduate course in advanced probability theory to the statistics offerings. For a number of years, the course was taught on a hit-or-miss basis, by a visitor, a member of the mathematics department, or by whomever Neyman could get a hold of for this task. Finally in 1948, ten years after his arrival in Berkeley, he was able to appoint an outstanding probabilist to his faculty. This was Michael Loève (1907–1979), a student of the great French probabilist Paul Lévy.

The gradual (rather slow) development of a substantial probability program to an outstanding probability center within the statistics department and, more generally, of probability theory as an important separate subject in the United States, is a story of its own. Since my contact with it was quite superficial, I have not included an account of it here.

32. Peter J. Bickel (b. 1940)

Since the time I joined Neyman's Statistical Laboratory in 1942, the members of the lab (and later the department) have formed the core of my professional community. In the preceding chapter, I wrote about Neyman and the first generation after him, the group that was hired by him. In addition to myself, it included Blackwell, Fix, Hodges, Le Cam, Scheffé, Scott, and Stein. I shall

now turn to the second generation and begin with Peter Bickel, who over the years became one of my closest friends and a longtime collaborator.

Bickel came to the Berkeley mathematics department after first studying physics at Cal Tech. In reminiscences on the occasion of my seventy-fifth birthday,[1] he described his move to statistics:

> In 1960, as a graduate student in mathematics, I took Joe Hodges's senior statistical inference course. Joe's brilliant problem-oriented teaching lured me into statistics. The following year, I took the graduate inference course from E.L. Lehmann, the system-building partner of Hodges and Lehmann. The generality and power of Erich's point of view and the innumerable examples he covered astonished me.
>
> I asked Erich to pose a thesis problem for me.

Peter obtained his degree in 1963 with a thesis on nonparametric methods in the multivariate case. Recognizing his great talent, the department offered him a position, and he has been a member of the statistics faculty since then.

He quickly became a prolific researcher. His (so far) close to 150 papers cover a broad spectrum of problems. His work on robustness led to his being invited to spend the year 1970–71 in Princeton as one of four principal investigators in what became known as "the Princeton robustness year."

[1] In an unpublished volume edited by J. Rojo.

Some of the results of this work were published in the multiauthored book, *Robust Estimates of Location* (Andrews et al., 1972). Additional material can be found in a paper by Hampel (1997).

A second area of special interest to Bickel was adaptive estimation, which was the topic of his Wald Lectures in 1981 and eventually led to a book, jointly authored with his collaborators Klaassen, Ritov, and Wellner, *Efficient and Adaptive Estimation for Semiparametric Models* (1993).

A problem that occupied Bickel throughout much of his research was to provide more detailed approximations through higher order expansions. Some of his most important results in this area were obtained in joint work with van Zwet. Other topics on which he worked were the distribution of order statistics, inference in restricted parameter spaces, minimax procedures in various settings, properties of the bootstrap, and more recently hidden Markov chains. In the later stage of his career he has also become interested in some applied problems, particularly in the areas of biology, traffic, and transportation.

Bickel has enjoyed collaborating with others, and has written joint papers with more than forty coauthors. Some of his principal collaborators were Yahav, Freedman, Ritov, van Zwet, and myself. Of his joint work with me, I shall only mention a series of five papers that we jointly wrote between 1973 and 1979 on a concept we called descriptive statistics for nonparametric models. The idea is most easily explained by the example of measures of location. For a symmetric distribution it is natural to specify its location by its center of symmetry, and the problem of how best to estimate this center has been studied extensively. For example, the Princeton Robustness study referred to previously considered the properties of sixty-eight different estimators. However, when the distribution is not symmetric, many different measures of location might be used to specify the center, such as the mean, the median, or a symmetrically trimmed mean. Peter and I investigated the conditions such measures should satisfy, and compared the efficiency with which they could be estimated. In a similar manner, we treated measures of scale and two other examples. Further cases were later taken up by others.

Another important form of collaborative research has been Peter's supervision of Ph.D. students. So far, the impressive number of fifty-two students have taken their degree with him, and the total number of his academic descendants is over two hundred.

In addition to his research, Peter has been also very active in administration, both within the department and nationally. After serving as vice chair of the department during my term as chair, he served as chair from 1976 to 1979, and from 1980 to 1986 was dean of physical sciences. For the next ten years, he returned to administrative work within the department, first as director of the Statistical Laboratory, and then for a second term as chair. In 1998, he was appointed to a three-year term as chair of the Committee on Applied and Theoretical Sciences and Applications of the National Research Council (NRC), and in 2000 he took on the even broader responsibility of chairing the NRC's Board on Mathematical Sciences and Applications, a surprising appointment for a statistician.

In recognition of his work, Peter has received many honors, including election to the National Academy of Sciences and the Royal Netherlands Academy of Arts and Sciences, an honorary degree from the Hebrew University of Jerusalem, and a MacArthur Foundation Fellowship. For his sixty-fifth birthday, his student Jianqing Fan organized a conference in Princeton that was attended by more than 150 friends, colleagues, and students. In addition to the talks, which have been published in a festschrift, the meeting was highlighted by a surprise: the Dutch government bestowed on Peter the title of Knight Commander of the Order of Orange and Nassau.

33. Kjell Doksum (b. 1940)

Three years after Peter, another student of mine joined our faculty. Kjell Doksum had come to statistics in a rather unusual way. At eighteen, he had left his native Norway for San Diego to learn from a relative how to become a fisherman. However, that career proved to be impossible for him when it turned out that he suffered from violent seasickness. So instead he enrolled at San Diego State College, majoring in mathematics. There, the statistician Chuck Bell got him interested in mathematical statistics. After obtaining his bachelor's

degree in San Diego in 1962 and his master's in 1963, Kjell transferred to Berkeley There, he received his Ph.D. degree two years later, with an outstanding thesis in which he found a very surprising nonparametric optimality property of the Wilcoxon test. He followed this with a year of postdoctoral research in Paris and then joined our faculty as assistant professor in 1966.

Doksum was not my first Norwegian student. He had been preceded by Arnljot Hoyland, who (together with his wife, Liv) became a close friend, and whom I visited a number of times in Trondheim. After Kjell and Arnljot, several other Norwegian students took their degrees at Berkeley, so that for a while the majority of chairs of statistics in Norway were held by professors trained at Berkeley. Kjell kept in close contact with the Norwegian statistical community, spending the years 1970–71 and 1975–76 in Oslo. In recognition of his contributions to Norwegian statistics, he was elected to the Royal Norwegian Society of Sciences and Letters.

After completing his thesis, Kjell continued his work on asymptotic optimality of nonparametric procedures with a number of additional publications. As a result of this work, he became interested in nonparametric Bayes procedures, a field to which he made a number of important contributions, including in particular his papers "Tailfree and Neutral Random Probabilities and Their Posterior Distributions" (1974) and "Constant and Robust Bayes Procedures for Location Based on Partial Information" (1990, joint with Lo).

Kjell also moved into other areas, especially relating to survival analysis and to transformations. Much of his work was carried out in collaboration with several different coauthors. In 1976, he published, jointly with Peter Bickel, a graduate text, *Mathematical Statistics: Basic Ideas and Selected Topics,* which soon became the standard text at its level and was translated into Russian and Chinese. The first volume of a greatly expanded second edition appeared in 2000, and the second volume is in preparation.

Another collaborative effort of Peter and Kjell, in which they were joined by Joe Hodges, was to edit a Festschrift for my sixty-fifth birthday. It was a splendid volume with many outstanding papers close to my interests.

When his wife, Joan Fujimura, a historian of science, accepted a tenure appointment at the University of Wisconsin, Kjell took early retirement and joined the Wisconsin statistics department. We miss him.

34. David R. Brillinger (b. 1937)

The other two members of this second generation on the Berkeley statistics faculty who were close to me are both Canadians. David Brillinger received his B.A. in mathematics from the University of Toronto, and followed this with graduate studies at Princeton. Under the supervision of John Tukey, he obtained his Ph.D. there in 1961. He remained in Princeton for another three years, both as lecturer in the university's mathematics department and as a staff member at Bell Telephone Laboratories. From 1964–69 he was first lecturer,

then reader, at the London School of Economics. Since 1970, he has been my colleague at Berkeley, where he served as department chair from 1979 to 1981.

David's work, published in close to two hundred papers, centers on time series analysis, a subject he studied with John Tukey at Princeton. He not only made contributions to the theory of the subject, but also became an expert in some of its applications. Thus, he devoted his Wald Lectures to (1983), "Some Statistical Methods for Random Process Data from Seismology and Neurophysiology," and his Fisher Lecture (1991), "Nerve Cell Spike Train Data Analysis: A Progression of Technique." He served on the advisory committee for Berkeley's earthquake engineering research center (1993–97), and since 1997 he has been a member of the Pacific Earthquake Engineering Center. From 2003 to 2005, he chaired the advisory committee of the Berkeley Seismographic Laboratory.

Time series is a subject about which I know very little, and as a result I had little contact with David's work. An exception occurred in connection with David's 1975 book on time series. It had been very successful and had been translated into Russian, but after a few years it went out of print. Since I thought highly of the book, I arranged for my publisher, Fred Murphy of Holden Day, to reissue an expanded version in 1981.

For my 1983 Festschrift, as a special favor, David wrote an enjoyable paper close to my interests on a general class of models for which least squares provides useful estimates. Another paper of his which I greatly admire is his memorial article: "John W. Tukey: His Life and Professional Contributions." This forty–page definitive survey of Tukey's life and work was clearly a labor of love. It combines a broad perspective and careful scholarship with David's personal experience as a student and lifelong friend of Tukey.

Brillinger has been much in demand as editor, and the positions he held give an indication of the breadth of his interests and expertise. He was editor of the *International Statistical Review* from 1987 to 1991, and served in various editorial capacities for *Statistical Science,* the *Brazilian Journal of Probability and Statistics,* for *Case Studies in Biometry*, the *Canadian Journal of Statistics,* the *Journal of Theoretical Neurobiology,* the *Journal of Time Series Analysis,* and the magazine *Chance.*

In addition to this editorial work, Brillinger was elected president of the Institute of Mathematical Statistics (1994–95) and of the Statistical Society of Canada (2001–02). In recognition of his work, he received the Gold Medal of the Statistical Society of Canada and honorary doctorates from the University of Western Ontario and the University of Waterloo. In 1993 he was elected to the American Academy of Arts and Sciences. He became a foreign member in 2004 of the Norwegian Academy of Science and Letters, and in 2006 of the Brazilian Academy of Sciences.

35. David Freedman (b. 1938)

David Freedman, who succeeded Brillinger as department chair, has achieved great success not only in research but also as consultant and as principal author of a text that revolutionized the teaching of elementary statistics. Like Brillinger, Freedman was born in Canada and obtained his Ph.D. at Princeton. However, his thesis supervisor was not Tukey but the probabilist Will Feller. After a fellowship year at Imperial College (London), Freedman joined our faculty in 1961.

Freedman's research extends into many areas, of which I shall mention only a few. One of his early contributions was an investigation of the asymptotic behavior of Bayes estimates. Among other results, he provided a counterexample to the commonly held belief that as the sample size gets large the evidence overpowers the initially held beliefs and the Bayes estimate becomes independent of the prior distribution. He continued his work in this area, with most of the later papers being joint with Persi Diaconis.

A new challenging area of research arose from Efron's publication in 1979 of the bootstrap approach (discussed in Section 40). Freedman became interested in this new method, and made a number of important contributions to its theory. Besides this and much other work in mathematical statistics, Freedman's research also encompassed a second, quite different and more applied area. During the last twenty-five years, he has devoted much of his energy to a critique of statistical work based on observational (rather than experimental) studies in the social and health sciences. Some of the resulting papers are focused on a single case. For example, "Econometrics and the Law" (joint with Daggett) is concerned with the arguments in an antitrust case brought by tomato growers in which Freedman had appeared as an expert witness for the defense. He criticized the method used to establish damages:

> An econometric analysis may seem quite attractive. However, on closer examination the econometric analysis may turn out to be no more than a series of unsupported assumptions, even if they are expressed in formidable equations.

Another example is his paper, "As Others See Us: A Case Study in Path Analysis." It is a critique of a book by Keith Hope that dealt with the effects of education on class mobility. Freedman's assessment is similar to that in the first example cited:

> One problem noticeable to a statistician is that investigators do not pay attention to the stochastic assumptions behind the models. It does not seem possible to derive these assumptions from current theory, nor are they easily validated empirically on a case-by-case basis.

Freedman concludes the paper by stating:

> My opinion is that investigators need to think more about the underlying process, and look more closely at the data, without the distorting prism of conventional (and largely irrelevant) stochastic models. Estimating nonexistent parameters cannot be very fruitful. And it must be equally a waste of time to test theories on the basis of

statistical hypotheses that are rooted neither in prior theory nor in fact, even if the algorithms are recited in every statistics text without caveat.

Others of Freedman's papers are more general and include several examples, but the conclusions are the same. The 1997 paper, "From Association to Causation via Regression" ends with this admonition:

Can quantitative social scientists infer causality by applying statistical techniques to correlation matrices?. . . As I read the record, correlation methods have not delivered the goods. We need to work on measurement, design, theory. Fancier statistics are not likely to help much.

In a paper with the provocative title, "Statistical Models and Shoe Leather," Freedman discusses not only his concern about the misuse of statistical methods but also examples of successful research, in particular his favorite success story, Snow's discovery of the source of the cholera epidemic of 1853–54. For this purpose, besides assembling a varied collection of detailed information, Snow identified the source of the water supply for the houses of all 1422 cholera victims. Freedman concludes:

The force of the argument results from the clarity of the prior reasoning, the bringing together of many different lines of evidence, and the amount of shoe leather Snow was willing to use to get his data.

Shoe leather! That is Freedman's alternative to the methodology he was criticizing: better data, more substantive knowledge and input, and multiple studies under varying conditions as had been used, for example, in establishing smoking as a major cause of lung cancer and other diseases.

David also practiced what he preached, by providing statistical advice as consultant or expert witness in more than one hundred cases. In many of his appearances as expert witness, he testified for the defense of firms or agencies against claims of employment discrimination or wrongful termination by showing that the statistical models used to justify the claims were based on unwarranted assumptions.

An example of this work is his expert testimony for the U.S. Bureau of the Census. The State of New York had sued to force the Bureau to adjust its 1980 population figures for an undercount. The proposed adjustment was a regression model. In the resulting trial, a number of statisticians testified for each side, with Freedman testifying for the defense.

He gave an account of the proceedings and issues in a paper, "Regression Models for Adjusting the 1980 Census" (jointly written with Navidi), which appeared, with discussion, as the opening paper of volume 1 (1986) of *Statistical Science*. In it, the authors list seven assumptions that underlie the model on which New York based its claim, and state that

New York's experts did not make these assumptions explicit, nor did they give any empirical foundation for them . . . . Granting assumptions (1–7), New York did have a good way of adjusting the Census. However, no evidence was presented to show these assumptions were true, and all seemed suspect.

A university department is, within given boundaries, essentially a self-governing body that depends for its well-being on the willingness of its members to take on the necessary administrative duties. As was the case for most of us, David Freedman did his share of this work, as graduate adviser, vice chair, and for five years (1981–86) chair of the department.

But perhaps his most significant contribution to the department was his development, starting in 1968, of a new introductory (lower-division) course to replace the cookbook course that Scheffé had characterized as being suitable for students who would use statistics but had no need to understand it. The revised course emphasized statistical thinking rather than routine application of formulas that had little meaning for the students, and it minimized the use of mathematical symbols. Centered on interesting examples, it tried to pique the students' curiosity and to show the valuable role statistics could play in real-life situations.

After teaching the course for ten years to large numbers of students, David published (jointly with his colleagues Bob Pisani and Roger Purves) a text, *Statistics,* which was, and still is, phenomenally successful. It is now in its a fourth (2007) edition.

In 2005, Freedman published another book, *Statistical Models—Theory and Practice*. "The contents of the book," the author states in the preface, "can fairly be described as what you have to know in order to start reading empirical papers in the social and health sciences. The emphasis throughout is on the connection—or lack of connection—between the models and the phenomena."

The book explains the standard methodologies of regression and path models, and illustrates their use on many real examples of both appropriate and inappropriate applications.

The high standards Freedman advocates for statistical work he also requires in other areas, for example the qualifications for a Ph.D. Remembering my own unimpressive thesis, my attitude is more lenient, and related differences of opinion have occasionally arisen in other personnel decisions. Despite these disagreements, our relations always have been friendly. We have invited each other to meals, and on various occasions have given each other support. I wrote comments for the back covers of some of his books, for example, and he wrote a strong letter recommending the reissue of one of mine.

Freedman's work has been honored in various ways. Early in his career, he received a coveted Sloan Fellowship; in 1991, he was elected to the American Academy of Arts and Sciences; and in 2003, he received the prestigious John J. Carty Award for the Advancement of Sciences.

8
The Stanford Statistics Department

The Stanford statistics department was founded in 1948, ten years after Neyman started a statistics program in Berkeley but seven years before that program became an independent department. Since its beginning, the Stanford department has been a friendly rival—we often compete for the same students and the same faculty—but also an invaluable source of strength for our Berkeley group. The rivalry is accentuated by the fact that for many years now our departments have been ranked as the top two statistics departments in the country, sometimes in one order, sometimes the other, and sometimes tied.

The proximity of the two institutions—they are only a little over an hour's drive apart—has led to much interaction. This is illustrated by the fact that eight of the subjects of this book are, or for many years were, members of the Stanford department: Stein, Bowker, Chernoff, Moses, Efron, Olkin, Anderson, and Diaconis.

One regular joint program of the two departments has been the Berkeley–Stanford Colloquium (by some at Stanford called the Stanford–Berkeley Colloquium), which has now been in existence for over fifty years. It meets regularly once a semester, alternately at the two institutions, with the guests providing the speaker. The colloquium talk is preceded by refreshments and followed by a reception. There are also other occasions at which members of the two groups get together, such as celebrations of round-number birthdays and other important milestones.

One result of this continuing contact is much collaborative work. The series of Diaconis–Freedman papers mentioned in Section 35 is one example. Joint papers that I wrote with Chernoff, Diaconis, and very recently Arrow provide another. Of great importance to me has been my five-year collaboration with Joe Romano on the third edition of my testing book.

I have a special tie with Stanford, since in 1951–52 it gave me refuge when I needed it (see Section 19) and even offered me a permanent position. This chapter is concerned with three Stanford colleagues who were important to me in various ways and have not been discussed elsewhere: Abe Girshick, Lincoln Moses, and Ted Anderson.

36. Meyer Abraham (Abe) Girshick (1908–1955)

A key figure in the development of the Stanford department was Abe Girshick. As Al Bowker, the founding chair of the department, states[1] about his early conversations with Stanford president Wallace Sterling:

> In some ways the turning point was the availability of Abe Girshick to join the department. He was then at RAND Corporation. Girshick had a remarkable mind with a deep interest in theory, but firmly grounded in applications from his government experience at the Department of Agriculture and wartime work at SRG [Statistical Research Group].

And in his obituary (joint with Blackwell) of Girshick, he continues:

> His intellectual leadership in both the statistics department and projects, and enthusiastic interest in scholarly work, were major factors in the growth of statistics at Stanford. Most of the work produced by the statistics department represents his ideas or spirit.

Abe Girshick was born in Russia and came to the United States at age 15. In 1934, he took up graduate studies at Columbia, where he worked with

[1] Olkin (1987).

Hotelling. After leaving Columbia in 1937, he spent the next ten years in various government positions at the Department of Agriculture, the Census Bureau, and at the RAND Corporation. In 1948, he joined Al Bowker at Stanford, and together they led the new department of statistics there.

Much of Girshick's early work was in multivariate analysis. (A list of his publications is provided in Blackwell's and Bowker's 1955 obituary.) Outstanding is his 1941 study (with O'Brien and Hunt) of body measurements of 147,000 American children to help manufacturers develop improved sizing of children's clothing.

His interests changed as a result of his one-year service during World War II with the Statistical Research Group at Columbia University. There he met Wald and was greatly impressed by Wald's work on sequential analysis and decision theory. Some of Girshick's papers resulting from this new interest were close to my own concerns. This was particularly the case with the fundamental paper (joint with Arrow and Blackwell), "Bayes and Minimax Solutions of Sequential Decision Problems" (1949), and the 1951 paper (joint with Savage), "Bayes and Minimax Estimates for Quadratic Loss Functions."

Girshick also became interested in the idea of invariance. In my writing, I had emphasized the importance of this principle for testing and estimation. Girshick, in his 1954 book with Blackwell, *Theory of Games and Statistical Decisions,* provided its first decision theoretic treatment.

I saw much of Abe during my year at Stanford, and two events from that period stand out in my memory. At social gatherings he frequently told Jewish stories, which everyone greatly enjoyed and of which he seemed to have an endless supply. Once he was asked how he could come up with so many wonderful tales. "Oh," he said cheerfully, "that's easy: I get them from Ausubel's *Treasury of Jewish Humor*."

The other event occurred on the last day of my year at Stanford. As I was making my goodbyes, Abe, who was the president of the Institute of Mathematical Statistics, took me aside. It was not official yet, he told me, but Ted Anderson was retiring as editor of the *Annals* and the institute was planning to ask me to succeed him. The story of my editorship is told in Chapter 5, but this was the big moment. America had truly become for me the land of opportunity.

It was only three years later that Abe Girshick quite unexpectedly died after a short illness. It is sad that this gifted man, who had so much vitality and enthusiasm, died at the early age of forty-six.

37. Lincoln Moses (1921–2006)

The connection of Lincoln Moses with Stanford preceded by more than ten years the founding of the Stanford statistics department by Bowker and Girshick. It began in 1939, when he was accepted at Stanford as a junior after two years at a community college. Despite a strong interest in science and mathematics, he decided to major in social science because, "I thought

the world doesn't need more science, it needs more social science."[2] His decision to become a statistician was the result of a course in advanced psychological statistics he took from Quinn McNemar, who, however, told him, "there was no way to do it [i.e., become a statistician], really. I would become a mathematician, or an economist, or a psychologist, and then work in statistics." This reflects the fact that at that time statistics did not exist as a profession, a situation that began to change a few years later, largely as a result of World War II.

After war service and two years in the federal government, Moses returned to Stanford in 1947 as a graduate student in mathematics, but he transferred to statistics when it became a separate department the following year. He obtained his Ph.D. in 1950 with a thesis in sequential analysis, under the supervision of Herman Rubin and Abe Girshick. His first academic appointment was as assistant professor of education at Teacher's College, Columbia University, where he remained for three years. But then a position opened up at Stanford. It was an assistant professorship split between the department of statistics and the medical school. Although it involved a substantial cut in pay, Moses accepted the offer, since he was interested in applying statistics to medical research and because he was not happy with the working conditions at Teacher's College.

[2] This and later quotes in this section are taken from Brown and Hollander (1999).

"At that time," he wrote later, "it was very unusual, although not unknown, for a medical school to have a statistician." In fact, the medical profession had been slow to accept a statistical view of its work. But once Moses was available, he was found to be so useful that he soon was overwhelmed with consulting work. As a result, he was gradually able to build up a small biostatistics group within the medical school and with close relations to the statistics department.

Moses's career involved a substantial amount of administrative work. From 1964 to 1968, he served as executive head of the statistics department, and from 1969 to 1975 as dean of the graduate division. For two-and-a-half years (1978–80), he took leave from Stanford to serve as the first head of the Energy Information Administration, in charge of statistics for the U.S. Department of Energy. He later joked that he had expected this position to require only minimal statistical expertise, that knowledge of the mean and standard deviation would suffice. What turned out, he claimed, was that the standard deviation really had not been needed—the mean alone was enough.

This reminds me of another Moses story. In the early 1980s, we served together on the visiting committee for the Princeton Statistics Department.[3] We were staying at the same hotel, and the first morning we had breakfast together. Lincoln ordered a soft-boiled egg but the waitress apologized. They weren't serving boiled eggs this morning, she said, since their egg-cooking machine was out of order. After she left, Lincoln remarked, "We have one of those machines at home; we call it a P-O-T."

At the ensuing committee meeting, we were faced with a more serious problem than boiled eggs. The administration, discouraged by dissension in the faculty and low enrollments, was proposing to abolish the Department of Statistics. By presenting prospects for future improvements in the most favorable light, we obtained a stay of execution, but at the next meeting of the committee, three years later, we were informed that the decision would be implemented. Since then, Princeton has had no statistics department and no coherent program in the subject. When in the 1990s my wife and I spent two years in Princeton, we had to drive to Rutgers if we wanted to participate in a statistics seminar.

Moses's early research was in nonparametric methods and included a chapter in the 1953 text by Walker and Lev, *Statistical Inference,* written while he was Helen Walker's colleague at Teacher's College. This twenty-five–page chapter not only covered the most important nonparametric tests, but also contained a novelty: a graphical procedure for obtaining nonparametric confidence intervals for the difference of two location parameters based on the Wilcoxon two-sample test, and the corresponding intervals (attributed to Tukey) for the paired comparisons case.

A very different contribution was Moses's work, much of it joint with Mosteller, stemming from concerns regarding the anesthetic halothane. This

[3] Such committees provide university administrations with outside evaluations of their departments.

major study involved many statistical innovations and was eventually published as a book (Bunker et al., The National Halothane Study, 1969). Its surprising finding: that halothane, which was highly suspect at the beginning of the study, was actually as safe as, or possibly even safer than, the standard anesthetics with which it was being compared. Lincoln Moses contributed several chapters to the book.

As an offshoot of this work, Moses wrote two joint papers with Mosteller. One, "Institutional Differences in Post-Operative Death Rates" (1968), strongly influenced the way the government ranks hospitals. The other, "Safety of Anesthetics" (1972), was written for SAGTU (Statistics: Guide to the Unknown), a collection of essays intended to show a general audience the usefulness and importance of statistics. This particular paper was given to all prospective authors of the volume as a guide to the kind of presentation for which the editors were striving.

Moses continued collaborating with Mosteller on various papers and projects. One noteworthy effort of theirs was to edit and publish a monograph, *Planning and Analysis of Observational Studies* (1983), which its author, Bill Cochran, had nearly but not quite completed before his death. It has joined two other books by Cochran, *Experimental Designs* (1950, jointly written with Gertrude Cox) and *Sampling Techniques* (1953), in that author's distinguished series of expositions.[4]

The Cochran book and the earlier halothane study were only two of many book projects in which Moses has been involved. More recently, the AIDS epidemic has been a principal concern of his, which resulted in his coediting three volumes: *AIDS: Sexual Behavior and Intravenous Drug Use* (1989) and *AIDS: The Second Decade* (1990), both with Turner and Miller, and *Preventing HIV Transmission* (1995), with Normand and Vlahov.

Moses also wrote two elementary texts, *Elementary Decision Theory,* with Herman Chernoff (1959), which was translated into Russian, Japanese, and Spanish, and *Think and Explain with Statistics* (1986), of which he was the sole author and which unfortunately very soon went out of print.

The totality of these books make clear the three main strands of which Moses's distinguished career was composed: statistical issues in public health, and in public policy, and statistical education.

38. Theodore (Ted) W. Anderson (b. 1918)

Compared with Girshick and Moses, Ted Anderson was a latecomer to Stanford, which he joined only in 1967. After obtaining his Ph.D. at Princeton in 1945 with a thesis on multivariate analysis, and a year at the

[4] William G. Cochran (1909–1980) was one of the most influential applied statisticians of his generation. An account of his work and influence is provided in "W.G. Cochran's Impact on Statistics" (Rao and Sedransk, 1984).

Cowles Commission for Research in economics, he took up a faculty position at Columbia, where he remained until his move to Stanford twenty-one years later.

His Columbia appointment came about through his meeting Wald at the Cowles Commission. Since Ted had evinced an interest in economics, Wald offered him a position in his new department at Columbia, with the expectation that they would collaborate on econometric problems. But by the time Ted arrived at Columbia, Wald's interests had shifted and he was focusing instead on his development of decision theory. On the other hand, Ted retained an interest in econometrics throughout his career.

I first met Ted on a visit to Columbia in 1948, and saw much of him during the fall semester of 1950, which I spent at Columbia. This was the year he was appointed editor of the *Annals* and I was one of his associate editors. When at his recommendation I succeeded him three years later, the transition of one editor to another required much collaboration, particularly concerning manuscripts handled by the retiring editor but appearing in issues edited by his successor. My correspondence with Ted about these and other editorial matters fill a whole folder in my files.

During his Columbia years, Ted and I would see each other once or twice a year at committee meetings and meetings of the Council of the Institute of Mathematical Statistics, but our contact became much closer when he moved to Stanford in 1967 (with a joint appointment in statistics and economics), and we thus became neighbors. We discovered that we both subscribed to the San Francisco Opera and in fact to the same series, and we then made a habit of meeting (with our wives) for dinner before the opera. On the other hand, although we never interacted much scientifically since our areas of interest were very different, we did collaborate on two memorial articles, one in the introduction to Wald's *Selected Papers* (1955), the other on P.L. Hsu in the *Annals of Statistics* (1979).

Our careers ran in curiously parallel tracks. We were about the same age (he was half a year younger), and he obtained his degree a year before I did. So we got started at about the same time. In 1950, Ted was appointed editor of the *Annals;* three years later, at the end of his term, I became his successor. We published our first (and I believe most successful) books at about the same time. His *An Introduction to Multivariate Statistical Analysis* came out in 1958 (2nd Ed. 1984). I followed with *Testing Statistical Hypotheses* in 1959 (2nd Ed. 1986). His third edition appeared in 2004; mine came out in 2005. Ted was elected to the National Academy of Sciences in 1976, I two years later, and it was he who called to tell me of my election.

Anderson's scientific work covered many different areas in statistics and econometrics. Particularly influential were his investigations in multivariate analysis, the analysis of time series, and structural equations estimation, and his books on the first two of these subjects. Two of Anderson's contributions that have been very influential and are close to my own work are the Anderson-Darling test for goodness of fit and his 1955 discovery that for unimodal symmetric densities the probability of a symmetric convex set decreases as the center of the distribution moves away from the center of the set. A collection of his more than one hundred papers up to 1985 was published in two volumes edited and introduced by George Styan (1990). The second volume also includes comments on different aspects of Anderson's research by experts in the various areas. Earlier (in 1983), on the occasion of his sixty-fifth birthday, he received a festschrift edited by Karlin, Amemiya, and Goodman, to which I was one of the contributors.

Ted, although retired, is still active at Stanford, writing, lecturing, traveling—and going to the opera.

9
Nonparametrics and Robustness

The classical theories of testing and estimation are based on the assumption that the underlying distributions are normal or belong to some other parametric family. This chapter considers the development of new methodologies appropriate to models in which the distributions are not so restricted. Following Wolfowitz (1942), such models are called nonparametric.

For nonparametric models, tests based on ranks (for example the Wilcoxon or rank correlation tests) were introduced since the levels of these tests are distribution-free.[1] It should, however, be noted that they are not assumption-free since they still assume that the observations are independent. They are as vulnerable to deviations from that assumption as their parametric counterparts.

A nonparametric theory of point estimation was initiated by Hoeffding (1948). He viewed the problem as that of estimating functionals $\theta(F)$ defined over large classes of distributions *F*, and developed a theory of unbiased estimators of such functionals—the so-called U-statistics. This formulation (and the earlier introduction by von Mises of differentiable statistical functionals) paved the way for Efron's very general concept of the bootstrap (1979), with its estimation of functionals $\theta(F)$ by the plug-in estimators $\theta(F_n)$, and the approximation of the latter through resampling. The bootstrap methodology turned out to be widely applicable to previously unmanageable estimation and testing problems, both parametric and nonparametric.

An approach that is intermediate to the parametric and nonparametric formulation was initiated by Peter Huber (1964). He suggested as a frequently more appropriate assumption that the distribution is approximately normal (or belongs to a neighborhood of some other parametric family), and accordingly developed a theory of robust inference. Here, robustness meant insensitivity to small deviations from an ideal parametric model. His theory was developed further by Frank Hampel, who introduced measures of the degree of robustness of

[1] So are those of Fisher's earlier permutation tests. These tests are in fact distribution-free adaptations of parametric tests and in this sense are still associated with parametric models.

a procedure, most importantly the influence function. This new approach led to a wealth of new procedures as well as important insights into earlier ones.

39. Edwin J.G. Pitman (1897–1993)

The development of nonparametric testing, as was mentioned in Section 10, may be considered to have begun in 1936 with the publication of the paper by Hotelling and Pabst on the rank-correlation test. This was followed by the proposal of a number of other rank tests, for example Friedman's 1937 test for randomized blocks. However, this new nonparametric approach did not really take off until the publication in 1945 of Wilcoxon's rank tests for paired (one-sample) and unpaired (two-sample) comparisons.

The first self-contained exposition of nonparametric inference was provided by the lecture notes of Pitman's 1947 and 1948 courses at Columbia and North Carolina. In particular, in these notes he proposed the efficiency measure called asymptotic relative efficiency (ARE), or Pitman efficiency, which was to play a central role in assessing the value of nonparametric techniques.

Pitman's notes, although not published, achieved wide distribution and exerted great influence. Pitman (1982) describes the history of these notes.

He had been invited to give nonparametric courses at Columbia in 1947 and at Chapel Hill in 1948, and, he reports:

> After the course was finished, with the help of the students, I produced a set of Notes. The Chapel Hill Notes on nonparametric inference became well known and much in demand. They were widely circulated and were frequently referred to in the literature. . . .
>
> It was not entirely my fault that the Notes were not published in a more permanent and more accessible form. Shortly before I left the United States, I was visited by a representative of an American publisher, who asked if I had any manuscripts. I said yes, and told him about the nonparametric notes, but he was not interested. They would make only a small book,[2] and his firm was interested only in big books. Could I expand the manuscript? No, not much. No deal. Twenty years later, a publisher wanted to print the Notes, but I refused. I said they had done their work, and were now out of date.

Edwin James George Pitman was born in Melbourne (Australia), where he also received his education. After a number of brief appointments in New Zealand and Australia, he was appointed professor of mathematics at the University of Tasmania in 1926, and he remained there until his retirement in 1962.

Pitman came to statistics in a way that was typical of the times. When in 1925 he applied for the professorship of mathematics at the University of Tasmania, he was asked whether he had any knowledge of statistics and would be prepared to teach a course in the subject. He replied, "I cannot claim to have any special knowledge of the theory of statistics, but, if appointed, I would be prepared to lecture on this subject in 1927." He later commented on this response: "I think the word *special* could have been deleted with accuracy, but I was being careful not to exaggerate."

Pitman used the two-year grace period he had requested to study both probability and statistics, and soon found himself not only teaching statistics but also in demand as a statistical consultant. Eventually (beginning in 1936), he became an important contributor both to the theory of statistics and to probability theory.

Between 1936 and 1938, he published a series of three seminal papers in which he developed the theory of permutation tests (introduced earlier by Fisher) as tests that do not assume the form of the distribution to be known. Some of his other papers dealt with sufficient statistics, the Cramér-Rao inequality, and characteristic functions. In 1979, he published a small, elegant book—really a collection of papers—on various mathematical and conceptual aspects of statistical theory, and then of course there were the Columbia and Chapel Hill lecture notes.

The list of Pitman's publications is relatively short (twenty-one papers and the book), due to the heavy load of his teaching (for many years twelve lectures a week on many branches of mathematics) and administration work. However, they have been very influential. In recognition for his contributions,

---

[2] They ran to seventy-five double-spaced, typed pages.

the Statistical Society of Australia in 1978 established the Pitman medal "for high distinction in statistics." The first recipient was Pitman himself.

I met Pitman only once, when he visited Berkeley for the Fourth Berkeley Symposium. However, his ideas played a significant role in my own work. In addition, Berkeley has a special link with him. His son, the probabilist Jim Pitman, is a member of our department.

40. Hodges–Lehmann II: Nonparametrics

As discussed in Section 14, my joint work with Joe Hodges at first dealt with problems in parametric inference and decision theory. However, in the 1950s we became interested in the new, developing methodology of nonparametric inference. Our first paper in this area had its origin in a very surprising result obtained by Pitman concerning the Wilcoxon tests.

These tests enjoyed great popularity due both to their simplicity and their freedom from the assumption of normality. At the same time, however, users worried about the resulting loss of power since the two-sample test, for example, utilized not the detailed values of the observations but only their relative order. Pitman's efficiency was a good way to measure the seriousness of this loss. As an example, Pitman computed the efficiency of the Wilcoxon to the t-test when the observations actually are normal, the situation for which the t-test is optimal. He found this efficiency to be $3/\pi$, about .955. Thus, to everyone's surprise, the efficiency loss in this case is quite small. The Wilcoxon test requires only 5% additional observations to match the power of the t-test.

Since the principal advantage of the Wilcoxon test is its independence of the assumption of normality, Joe and I wondered what its efficiency to t would be for nonnormal distributions. We carried out the calculation for a number of distributions and in each case found the efficiency to be quite high, in some cases much greater than 1 (i.e., Wilcoxon much more efficient than t), but in no case much less than 1.

When we started to look into the problem, we realized we had taken it for granted that the efficiency could be arbitrarily close to 0, but now we were no longer so sure and decided to look directly for the minimum possible efficiency. A fairly easy argument showed that the lowest possible efficiency of the Wilcoxon to the t-test is .864.

The surprising conclusion, therefore, was that on the whole the power of the Wilcoxon test, rather than being vastly inferior to that of the t-test, was in fact, if anything, superior to it. We conjectured, but were not able to prove, an even more one-sided result. A rank test alternative to the Wilcoxon test that was first proposed by Fisher and Yates in 1938 is the so-called normal scores test. We surmised that its Pitman efficiency relative to the t-test is 1 when the underlying distribution is normal, and greater than 1 for all other distributions. The conjecture was proved two years later by Chernoff and Savage. Those results helped to legitimize statistical procedures using only the rank order of the observations.

Our next paper in this area was concerned with nonparametric methods rather than theory. Rank tests for the comparison of two or more treatments had been suggested by Friedman (1937), Wilcoxon (1946), and others for randomized block designs. Since these tests were based on separate rankings within each block, observations from different treatments were compared only with other observations in the same block. We found that such procedures have rather low efficiencies, and proposed a modification that could be expected to be more efficient.

We suggested removing the block effect by subtracting from all observations in a given block their mean or median for that block, thus making it reasonable to compare observations from different blocks. By ranking the totality of these aligned observations, one obtains what we called aligned ranks. Tests can then be based on the sums (over all blocks) of the aligned ranks of the different treatments. The paper discussed both the exact and the asymptotic distribution of the resulting test statistics, and provided heuristic arguments suggesting that the Pitman efficiency of these aligned rank procedures should be as high as those of the Wilcoxon tests. This conjecture was confirmed by Mehra and Sarangi (1967).

Of our series of nonparametric papers, the one that attracted the most attention was a 1963 paper on "Estimates of Location Based on Rank Tests." In it, we proposed estimates of a location parameter that would share the good efficiency properties of the Wilcoxon tests. For this purpose, we developed a general method of generating estimates from rank tests of location parameters (later called R-estimators) whose asymptotic efficiency was the same as the tests from which they were derived. For the particular case of the one-sample Wilcoxon test of H: $\theta = 0$ based on a sample $X_1, \ldots, X_n$ of i.i.d. variables from a distribution symmetric about θ, the R-estimator turned out to be the median of the averages $(X_i + X_j)/2$ $(i < j)$. In the literature, this has become known as the Hodges-Lehmann estimator.

I shall mention only one other paper from our nonparametric period, which, although dealing primarily with parametric applications, grew out of our interest in Pitman efficiency. In this 1970 paper, we considered the case in which the Pitman efficiency is 1, and so does not tell us which of the two tests being compared is superior and by how much.

The Pitman efficiency is the limit of ratio of the sample sizes required for the two tests to achieve the same power as the sample sizes tend to infinity. When that limit is 1, it often turns out that the difference of the sample sizes tends to a limit, which we called the deficiency of the inferior test to the other. (For example, if the sample sizes are n and $n + 3$, respectively, their ratio tends to 1 and their difference to 3.) The calculation of deficiencies is much more delicate than that of efficiencies, and we carried it out for only a few simple examples. In particular, we determined the deficiency of the t-test relative to the normal test that is appropriate when the variance is known. This turned out to be between 1 and 3, depending on the level of the test when that level is between .1 and .01. Not knowing the variance thus entails the trivial loss of about two observations.

Hodges and Lehmann 25 years later

In addition to our joint work, Joe and I also published a number of nonparametric papers either alone or with other coauthors. After Joe stopped doing research to go into administration, I collaborated with Peter Bickel in the late 1970s on the series of papers mentioned in Section 32. Finally, as reported in Section 29, I wrote a book on the subject of nonparametric inference, which was published in 1975 and has recently been reissued by Springer.

41. Wassily Hoeffding (1914–1991)

The Hodges-Lehmann estimator discussed in the preceding section estimated the center θ of a distribution symmetric about θ. Here the model was really semiparametric rather than nonparametric, since the distribution is restricted to be symmetric about a parameter θ. A fully nonparametric treatment of estimation was initiated by Wassily Hoeffding in 1948.

Hoeffding was born in Finland to Danish parents, who settled in Berlin when Wassily was 10. In 1933, he entered the *Handelshochschule* with the intention of studying economics, but he found the subject too vague. At the same time he became interested in chance phenomena and came across a book on the subject, *Die Analyse des Zufalls (The Analysis of Chance)*, by H.E. Timerding, that fascinated him. As a result, in 1934 he switched to the University of Berlin to study mathematics. By that time, von Mises, the leading authority in the field of probability and other areas of applied

mathematics, had already left Berlin as a result of the Nazi takeover, and probability and statistics were poorly represented. However, a course in mathematical statistics was being offered and was based on von Mises' remarkable text of 1931, *Wahrscheinlichkeitsrechnung und ihre Anwendung in der Statistik und Theoretischen Physik*.

In 1940, Hoeffding obtained his Ph.D. with a thesis on correlation, and he remained in Germany with two part-time assistant jobs until the end of the war. In 1946, he moved to New York, where he attended lectures by Wald and Wolfowitz and also by Neyman, who was visiting there at the time. The following year, he accepted an offer from Hotelling as research associate in the Statistics Department at Chapel Hill. He remained there for the rest of his life, interrupting his stay by many travels and visiting appointments despite suffering from diabetes and other health problems.

The work Hoeffding produced during his career was distinguished by great depth and originality and spanned a wide range of topics, including tests of independence, sequential analysis, and the theory of large deviations. However, I shall here consider only his contributions to nonparametrics.

Hoeffding's best known and most influential work is his 1948 paper on U-statistics. The starting point of this investigating was the problem of estimating certain functionals $\theta(F)$ defined over a large nonparametric class D of distributions F, and in particular to determine their best unbiased estimators. Hoeffding solved this problem and called the optimal estimators U-statistics (U for unbiasedness). The principal results of his paper concern the asymptotic distributions of these statistics (and some of their generalizations).

Through a decomposition of U-statistics, he was able to characterize the situations in which their limit distribution is normal. The great success of this theory is due partly to its elegance, but primarily to the wealth of its applications. A book on the subject is Lee (1990).

As an illustration, consider a two-sample situation with distributions F and G, and the functional

$$\theta(F, G) = P(X < Y),$$

where X and Y are distributed according to F and G, respectively. If $X_1, \ldots, X_m$ and $Y_1, \ldots, Y_n$ are samples from F and G, the best unbiased estimator of θ is W/mn, where W is the number of pairs (X_i, Y_j) satisfying $X_i < Y_j$. W is the Mann-Whitney form of the Wilcoxon test, and in 1951 I was able to use Hoeffding's theory to obtain the asymptotic power of the Wilcoxon test.

A second paper of Hoeffding's with far-reaching results concerned permutation tests (1952). These tests were introduced by Fisher as distribution-free randomization versions of normal-theory tests such as the t-test. Comparing the two tests in a particular example in his book on the design of experiments, Fisher found that the permutation test provided "a result very nearly equivalent to that obtained using the t-test." Without his stating so, he seemed to suggest that the two tests could be expected more generally to give similar results. In 1952, Hoeffding showed that, at least asymptotically, this is indeed the case.

More specifically, the two tests can be seen to differ only in the critical value for the t-statistic, this value being a constant for the t-test and random for its permutation version. Hoeffding showed that these two values tend to the same limit, and that asymptotically the two tests have the same power. These results justify Fisher's suggestion that the usual t-test could be viewed as an approximation to its distribution-free permutation version.

The last nonparametric paper of Hoeffding's that I shall mention dealt with the topic of optimum nonparametric tests (1951). A theory of optimum permutation tests had been developed by Stein and me in 1949. Hoeffding now considered optimum rank tests, more specifically locally most powerful rank tests, which turned out to be based on linear rank statistics.

My personal contact with Wassily was rather limited. In fact, the only times I recall meeting him were on the occasions of the second to fifth Symposia, at each of which he presented a paper. Since he was reserved—partly perhaps as a result of bad eyesight and hearing—I did not get to know him well as a person. However, we strongly interacted in our work.

Hoeffding's early work on correlation provided an important tool for my 1966 paper, "Some Concepts of Dependence." Also, as mentioned earlier, my work on the Wilcoxon test utilized his results on U-statistics.

Conversely, both Wassily's papers on permutation tests and optimal rank tests were closely related to an earlier paper by Charles Stein and me on optimum permutation tests. In addition, he devoted a section of his 1968 paper, "Some Recent Developments in Nonparametric Statistics," to my attempts at developing a nonparametric version of the analysis of variance.

Hoeffding's work was recognized by his election to the American Academy of Arts and Sciences and to the National Academy. In 1967, he gave the Wald lectures, on "Recent Results in Parametric Large-Sample Theory," and in 1969 he served as president of the Institute of Mathematical Statistics (IMS). A Festschrift in his honor, edited by Chakravarti and with an opening address by Neyman, was published in 1980. A beautiful record of his achievements is the volume of his collected works (1994), edited by N.I. Fisher and P.K. Sen and containing three articles reviewing the principal aspects of his work. A memoir of his life is provided in Fisher and van Zwet (2005).

42. Bradley Efron (b. 1938)

A problem that confronted many nonparametric procedures was the difficulty of calculating their small-sample performance. A highly effective and broadly applicable solution for this problem was proposed in 1979 by Bradley Efron.

I first met Brad Efron in 1960, when, after graduating in mathematics at Cal Tech, he considered coming to Berkeley for graduate work in statistics. He describes this episode and its outcome in Holmes et al. (2003):

> I talked to Berkeley and had a very nice interview with two men named Jerzy and Erich, who were very kind to me, but somehow I wound up at Stanford.

Except for occasional leaves, Brad has been at Stanford since then, as faculty member and in various administrative positions. He chaired the statistics department from 1976 to 1979, 1991 to 1994, and 1996 to 1997, and the Stanford Advisory Board in the two years 1993–94 and 1996–97. From 1987 to 1990, he served as associate dean of the humanities and sciences. This is a lot of administration for someone who at the same time was extremely active in research.

Efron's statistical work spans a wide arc. It includes the treatment of very specific problems in a number of fields such as Shakespeare scholarship, astronomy, and medicine. At the other end of the spectrum are issues of statistical philosophy and the role of computers in statistics.

However, the core of his research is concerned with theoretical and methodological topics, prominent among them exponential families, the empirical Bayes approach and Stein estimation, and most importantly the bootstrap, perhaps the most widely used methodological innovation since Fisher's work on analysis of variance and covariance.

While Fisher's methods were based on the assumption of normality, the bootstrap is particularly useful in (although not restricted to) nonparametric settings. I shall illustrate the idea of the bootstrap with an example. Let $X_1, \ldots, X_n$ be i.i.d. according to an unknown distribution F and let $T = T(X_1, \ldots, X_n)$ be some statistic of interest, perhaps the estimator of some functional of F. We want to estimate the distribution of T,

$$(*) \qquad P_F\,[T(X_1, \ldots, X_n)] < c$$

where the subscript F indicates the distribution of the X's.

A simple and often reasonable estimator of the probability (*) is the so-called plug-in estimator. It replaces F by the sample distribution $\hat{F}_n$, which assigns probability $1/n$ to each of the observed values $x_1, \ldots, x_n$ of $X_1, \ldots, X_n$. The resulting estimator of the probability (*) is then

$$(**) \qquad P_{\hat{F}n}\,[\mathrm{T}\,(X_1^*, \ldots, X_n^*) < c,$$

where the subscript $\hat{F}_n$ denotes the fact that (**) is the probability that T, evaluated for a sample of $\hat{F}_n$, does not exceed c, and where $X_1^*, \ldots, X_n^*$ denote a sample from $\hat{F}_n$.

The formula (**) for the estimator of the distribution of T is easy to write down, but is prohibitive to calculate except for small n. To see this, recall that each of the X_i^* is capable of taking on the n values $x_1, \ldots, x_n$, so that the total number of values of $T(X_1^*, \ldots, X_n^*)$ that has to be considered is n^n. To calculate (**), one has to count how many of these n^n values are $< c$. This is not practicable. A standard device for evaluating (at least approximately) probabilities that are too difficult to calculate exactly is simulation. To calculate the probability of an event, one generates a sample from the underlying distribution and notes the frequency with which the event occurs in the sample. If the sample is sufficiently large, this frequency will, with high probability, provide a good approximation to the original probability.

In the present instance, this approximation to the probability (**) constitutes the second step of the bootstrap process. A number B of samples $(X_{i1}^*, \ldots, X_{in}^*)$, the "bootstrap samples" are drawn from $\hat{F}_n$, and the frequency with which

$$T(X_{i1}^*, \ldots, X_{in}^*) < c$$

provides the desired approximation to the estimator (**).

The two-step procedure illustrated by this example is very flexible and applicable, with suitable modifications, to many different situations such as the bias and variance of an estimator, to the calculation of confidence intervals, and so on.

The bootstrap was first proposed, and named, by Efron in a 1979 paper in the *Annals*. He followed this by several papers in 1981 and a small monograph in 1982. Several additional papers appeared throughout the next decade, culminating in Efron's 1993 book (with Tibshirani), *An Introduction to the Bootstrap*. The idea was taken up by others and has resulted in a flood of papers and several books, treating theoretical as well as applied aspects of the method.

Not surprisingly in view of his accomplishments, Efron has received many honors. They include a MacArthur Fellowship in 1983, election to the National Academy in 1985, the Rietz, Wald, and Fisher lectureships, and honorary degrees from Chicago, Madrid and Oslo. He served as president of the IMS in 1987–88 and of the American Statistical Association (ASA) in 2004. In 2007 he received the Presidential Medal of Science.

43. Peter J. Huber (b. 1934)

Peter Huber was born in Wohlen, Switzerland, and his unusual abilities showed up early. Since mathematics, physics, and astronomy were so easy for him, he realized in high school that he needed different intellectual stimulation. As he wrote in a recent letter: "By chance I discovered that some clergyman had donated his *Assyriological* books to the cantonal library, and delving into that was much more fascinating than doing crossword puzzles." Early cuneiform astronomical writings remained an interest for him, and resulted in occasional publications, throughout his life.

After completing high school and a semester at the University of Zürich, Huber studied mathematics and physics at the Eidgenössische Technische Hochschule (ETH), the Swiss Federal Institute of Technology, and in 1961 obtained his Ph.D. in topology. The next two years he spent at Berkeley in our department. How this came about is related to my own story.

When in 1959 I spent a sabbatical semester in Zürich, one of my contacts was Walter Saxer, a mathematician at the ETH specializing in insurance mathematics and hence with an interest in probability and statistics. We saw each other socially, and on one such occasion he told me that the ETH had decided to establish a chair in mathematical statistics and would like to offer me this position.

Since I had spent five years in Zürich, first in high school and then at the university, and since I loved the city, it was a tempting thought. On the other hand, I had found a home in Berkeley after much wandering and had many friends there. I loved Berkeley too, and leaving it would be difficult.

There was also another factor. In my interview with the president of the ETH, I had asked him how large a statistics group he envisioned if the program turned out to be as successful as he hoped. He replied that in a few years he might add one junior faculty member. The contrast was stark. In Berkeley I was a member of a group of about twenty colleagues with similar interests. In Zürich, on the other hand, I would be rather isolated, and would alone have to carry the burden of administration and examinations. Belonging to a community was of great importance to me. Thus, in the end I decided to remain in Berkeley.

Not long after my return to Berkeley, I received a letter from Saxer saying that the ETH was thinking of one of its own students for the position. Peter

Huber had just obtained his degree in topology and had some informal background in statistics. He would come to Berkeley on a Swiss fellowship to study the subject more systematically, and one would then see.

Peter stayed in Berkeley for two years, the second on a Miller Fellowship from the University of California. During the second year, he received an offer from the ETH of a professorship in statistics. So he had to decide if he really wanted to make his career in that field.

This was a soul-searching time for him. We had many discussions, but probably more influential were talks he had with John Tukey (on visits to Princeton), who himself had moved from topology to statistics. In the end, statistics won out, and during his two years in Berkeley Huber wrote the seminal paper (1964) that initiated his robustness theory. After visiting for a year at Cornell, he took up his position as professor of mathematical statistics at the ETH in 1964 and remained there—with leaves spent at Cornell, Princeton, Yale, and Harvard—until 1978. He then moved to Harvard (1978–88), MIT (1988–1992), and finally to the University of Bayreuth, where he remained until his retirement in 1999.

Huber's 1964 paper, "Robust Estimation of a Location Parameter," was concerned with the estimation of a location parameter θ on the basis of a sample from a distribution $F(x-\theta)$. This problem had been considered in the literature under three assumptions: that F is (i) normal; (ii) completely unknown with mean θ; (iii) symmetric about θ but otherwise unknown. Huber suggested that a more reasonable assumption often is that (iv) F is approximately normal, that is, lies in some appropriate neighborhood of the normal distribution. The aim of the paper was to determine estimators that perform well over such neighborhoods.

Two classical principles of estimation are least squares and minimum absolute error, which in the present case reduce to minimizing

$$\Sigma\,(x_i-\theta)^2 \text{ and } \Sigma\,|x_i-\theta|\,,$$

respectively. Huber introduced the more general class of estimators minimizing

$$\Sigma\,\rho\,(x_i-\theta)$$

for any given function ρ. These estimators, which also generalize maximum likelihood estimators, he called M-estimators. He proved asymptotic normality of these estimators for convex ρ, and obtained the minimax estimator within the class of M-estimators.

He then treated the special case in which

$$\rho\,(t) = \begin{matrix} t^2/2 \text{ for } |t| < K \\ K|t| - K^2/2 \text{ for } |t| > K, \end{matrix}$$

so that it is quadratic for small $|t|$ and linear in the tails. For the resulting M-estimator, he proved that it is minimax in a neighborhood of the normal distribution, that is, the class of all distributions of the form

$$F = (1 - \theta)\,\Phi + \theta\, H$$

where Φ is the standard normal distribution and H any distribution that is symmetric about 0.

This startlingly original paper, which contains much else, was reprinted in Kotz and Johnson volume II (1992), with a substantial introduction by Frank Hampel. Huber followed up this work with extensions to more general estimation problems, for example in his 1973 paper on robust regression. As a side issue, this paper brings an important new result on classical least squares estimation: a necessary and sufficient condition (now known as Huber's condition) for the asymptotic normality of the least squares estimators of all linear functions of the regression coefficients.

In other papers, Huber considered the problem of robust hypothesis testing. A beautiful result in this area generalizes the Neyman-Pearson lemma (mentioned in Section 7) to the testing of one neighborhood against another (1965). The minimax procedure for testing a neighborhood of P_0 against one of P_1 turns out to be a censored version of the likelihood ratio test for testing P_0 against P_1.

A systematic account of robustness theory (including Hampel's infinitesimal approach, to be considered in the next section) was provided in Huber's 1981 book, *Robust Statistics,* which gave the first comprehensive treatment of this new field that he had initiated.

I shall mention only two other of Huber's papers. In 1985, he published a very influential discussion paper on projection pursuit, a body of methods for finding interesting low-dimensional projections of high-dimensional data. The paper gives a unified rigorous treatment of what up to then was "a sea of isolated, seemingly disjoint ideas" (Diaconis, 1985). In his discussion of the paper, Tukey refers to the process as "Huberizing a field."

The other paper is nontechnical. A contribution to the Festschrift for Tukey (Brillinger et al., 1997), it is entitled, "Speculations on the Path of Statistics." It provides a review of the nature of the field of statistics, its past, present, and likely future. It is the kind of paper only someone with a very broad view of the field as a whole such as Tukey or Huber could have written.

Huber's great accomplishments and influence were acknowledged in a festschrift, "Robust Statistics, Data Analysis, and Computer Intensive Methods" (Rieder, 1996), on the occasion of his sixtieth birthday. The volume, in addition to papers by friends and colleagues in areas "that Peter Huber himself had markedly shaped," also contains a list of his publications.

44. Frank Hampel (b. 1941)

Huber's work was continued, and developed in new directions, by Frank Hampel, who in 1968 obtained his Ph.D. in statistics at Berkeley with a thesis on robust estimation. After completing his degree, he took up a position at

the University of Zürich, thus becoming a close neighbor of Huber, who was at the ETH. In 1974, Hampel moved to the ETH, where he joined Huber as associate professor. Five years later, after Huber left for Harvard, Hampel took over the responsibility for the statistics group.

About his relationship with Huber, Hampel writes in the Festschrift for Huber:

> Since my arrival at the University of Zurich in 1968, and until his departure from ETH to Harvard about ten years later, we had a wonderful scientific relationship, and we managed to keep up our friendship ever since. Our scientific relationship was not of the usual type; we never wrote a joint paper together, but rather we exchanged our ideas and results while pursuing our own lines of research which were often closely parallel, and certainly I was greatly stimulated and motivated in this atmosphere of deep mutual understanding and pursuit of common scientific aims.

In a recent letter to me, Hampel describes the origin of his interest in robust inference:

> In very early 1965, my then professor in Göttingen, Konrad Jacobs, gave me the freshly printed 1964 paper of Huber with the remark that it seemed to be a "hot topic," and asked me whether I would be interested in doing further research in this direction.

Hampel says that he was "immediately convinced" and started writing on this topic. But instead of continuing in Göttingen, he went to Berkeley on a one-year exchange scholarship and then decided to stay a second year. By that time, he writes, he already had an idea, but the solution turned out to be "incredibly complicated and not suitable for any publication." But, he continues,

> I had already a new idea (qualitative robustness) and managed to stay a third year. While writing up my theorems on qualitative robustness, I got the idea of the influence curve. . . .
>
> After you had accepted me as a doctoral student, I busily wrote up my results and brought them to the typist (in pieces), and every week or so I collected the pieces and brought them to you (and Peter Bickel). To my surprise, you never uttered any criticism or other remark, and after a number of weeks the thesis was complete.

Thus this thesis was formally written under my supervision, but in fact I had essentially no input. My "contribution" consisted of my immediate realization of the importance and maturity of this work, that it was quite beyond the usual kind of thesis, and that my task was to encourage, smooth the process, and otherwise stay out of the way.

Hampel's thesis is highly technical and rich in concepts and results. To give at least a flavor, I shall consider only one aspect: the assessment of the degree of robustness of an estimator. Two key measures that he introduces for this purpose are the breakdown point and the influence function.

The breakdown point of an estimator (foreshadowed by Hodges [1967]), in one of its finite-sample versions, is the smallest proportion of the n observations that can cause the estimator to take on arbitrarily large positive or negative values. Thus, the breakdown point of the sample mean is $1/n$, since even a single sufficiently large observation, with the other observations fixed, can make the mean arbitrarily large.

As a second example, consider the symmetrically trimmed mean, which deletes the largest and smallest observation and then averages the remaining ones. Here a single observation can no longer do unlimited damage since—if it is sufficiently large—it will be deleted. On the other hand, if there are two extremely large observations, only one of them will be deleted and the other can make the estimator arbitrarily large. So the breakdown point is $2/n$.

The breakdown point is a rather simple (but global) measure of robustness and does not play a great role in Hampel's thesis. (It was later studied systematically, and its usefulness emphasized by Donoho and Huber [1983]). More central to Hampel's approach is the influence function. In fact, Hampel gave his 1986 book, *Robust Statistics,* the subtitle *The Approach Based on Influence Functions*. Huber (1981) calls it "perhaps the most useful heuristic tool of robust statistics."

To define the influence function, consider the estimation of a functional $\theta(F)$ and the associated plug-in estimator $\theta(\hat{F}_n) = T(X_1, \ldots, X_n)$. The influence function measures the effect on $\theta(F)$, and hence on $\theta(\hat{F}_n)$, of a small contamination at a point x, that is, the behavior of $\theta(F^*)$ with F^* given by

$$F^* = (1 - \varepsilon) F + \varepsilon\, \delta_x,$$

where δ_x is the distribution that assigns probability 1 to the point x. Thus, F^* is the distribution of an observation which with probability $1 - \varepsilon$ comes from F but with small probability ε takes on the value x.

The influence function at x is the rate of change of $\theta(F^*)$, as a function of ε at $\varepsilon = 0$, that is, its derivative at $\varepsilon = 0$ (if this derivative exists). It thus measures the influence on $\theta(F)$ of a small proportion of observations at x. The influence function depends on the contaminating value x, the functional θ, and the distribution F. It is often denoted by $IF(x, \theta, F)$. For the purpose of robustness, one wants the influence function to be bounded, and its maximum—called the gross error sensitivity—is then a measure of the resulting robustness.

The influence function, like the breakdown point, was originally defined in terms of the functional θ. A "finite sample version," directly in terms of the estimator, is also available but will not be discussed here.

The influence function is useful not only as a measure of robustness but also for calculating the asymptotic variance of $\theta(\hat{F}_n)$, which under suitable conditions equals the integral (with respect to F) of the square of the influence function. These conditions tend to be difficult to check, but once the value has been obtained it can be checked in other ways.

Robustness was a major focus of Hampel's early work, including a systematic exposition in his 1986 book (with Ronchetti, Rousseeuw, and Stahel). However, he has also worked in other areas such as the effect of long-range dependence (robustness against violation of the independence assumption) and particularly foundational issues. He also has done much work in applied statistics (see, e.g., Hampel [1987]). Completely different interests, also with some publications, have been ornithology and more recently the study of orchids. Introductions to his work on some of these topics can be found in Hampel (1996, 1998).

With their robustness theory, Huber and Hampel provided a new point of view, created some beautiful theory, and generated a wealth of methods complementing the classical parametric methodology. By focusing on neighborhoods of parametric models, they forged a compromise between parametric and nonparametric approaches. This work received a strong impetus from the "Princeton robustness year" (1970–71), which brought together Bickel, Hampel, Huber, and John Tukey, who had had a major impact on robust estimation (see Section 32). They were joined by a number of other workers in the area for a year-long seminar on the topic, the results of which were published in a volume, *Robust Estimates of Location* (Andrews et al., 1972). The importance and reach of the robust approach is indicated by books such as Huber (1981); Hampel et al. (1986); Staudte and Sheather (1990); Rieder (1994); and Jureckovà and Sen (1996), as well as more specialized monographs.

10
Foundations I: The Frequentist Approach

A key feature of twentieth-century science is the clear understanding of the role played by mathematical models of real phenomena. One of the first to fully articulate this was the applied mathematician Richard von Mises, who constructed such models for a number of disciplines. One of these was his 1919 model for frequentist probability. An alternative subjective concept of probability was axiomatized slightly later by Bruno de Finetti and Frank Ramsey. An axiomatization of probability in purely mathematical terms without regard to its interpretation was provided by Kolmogorov in 1933. It has the advantage of being applicable to both the frequentist and the subjective concepts of probability and, unlike those interpretations, is accepted fairly generally and is noncontroversial.

The frequentist concept of probability that von Mises axiomatized interprets probability as a model of the empirical phenomenon of stable frequency in a long series of repeated independent random events. This interpretation goes back to, among others, Bernoulli, Ellis, Cournot, and Venn. After von Mises, it was championed by Neyman as a foundation for statistical inference. However, Neyman noted that the long-run stability of a frequency held even for a series of quite different random events as long as they were independent. This greatly increased the usefulness of the frequentist approach for statistics.

A second basic issue for Neyman was how to interpret the result of a statistical investigation. Fisher thought he had solved the century-old problem of induction with his concepts of likelihood and fiducial probability. Neyman protested that Fisher's idea of inductive inference was meaningless and instead advocated a behavioral philosophy: that the aim of statistics was to provide a guide to the best action, and to accomplish this by minimizing the probability of errors.

Adopting Neyman's approach and utilizing concepts of the theory of games developed by von Neumann and Morgenstern, Wald established a new framework for statistics in his 1950 book, *Statistical Decision Functions*. Wald's book provided the basic concepts and results for his decision theory but was very abstract and contained only a few examples of its application. The implementation of the theory in many areas of statistics was carried out by the next generations of statisticians, particularly by Jack Kiefer, in whose work the minimax principle played a central role, and by Larry Brown, much of whose work was concerned with admissibility problems.

45. Richard von Mises (1883–1953)

Richard von Mises was an outstanding applied mathematician and probabilist. In addition, he made contributions to philosophy and to the literature on the poet Rainer Maria Rilke.

Von Mises grew up in Vienna and, after graduating from high school with high distinction in mathematics and Latin, from 1901 to 1906 he studied mathematics, physics, and mechanical engineering at the Vienna Technical University. In 1908, he wrote a dissertation on the theory of water wheels, and the following year was appointed associate professor of applied mathematics at the University of Strassburg, where he remained until the outbreak of the First World War.

At the beginning of the war, von Mises joined the Flying Corps of the Austro-Hungarian army (he already had a pilot's license) but was soon transferred to act as technical advisor, organizer, and instructor. His lectures on the theory of flight became the basis for his book, *Fluglehre,* first published in 1918 and subsequently going through many editions.

After the war ended, von Mises could not return to Strassburg, which had become Strasbourg and part of France. After short faculty appointments in Frankfurt and Dresden, in 1920 he became founding director of the Institute of Applied Mathematics in Berlin. The following year, he founded the *Zeitschrift für Angewandte Mathematik und Mechanik,* "through which he exerted a profound and beneficent influence on applied mathematics in general, in Central Europe in particular."[1]

When the Nazis came to power in 1933, von Mises left Germany to accept the position of professor and director of the Mathematical Institute in Istanbul, Turkey, and there played a major role in making Istanbul an important center of applied mathematics. In 1939, with another war approaching, he decided to leave Istanbul for a lectureship at Harvard, where he soon became Gordon McKay Professor of Aerodynamics and Applied Mathematics. During his Harvard years, von Mises' interest in probability and statistics was relegated to the sidelines and his work was concerned mainly with hydro- and aerodynamics. At the end of the academic year 1952–53, he went into mandatory retirement, and he died a few weeks later.

All of von Mises' work was infused by his view that the task of applied mathematics is to build mathematical models of some aspects of the real world, and he may have been the first to clearly treat probability theory in this way. In 1919, he published an ambitious attempt to build a model for the basic physical phenomenon underlying frequentist probability: the stability of the long-run frequency of an outcome in a long sequence of independent repeated random events—for example, the frequency of heads in a long sequence of tosses with a coin.

The principal constituents of his model were infinite sequences of trials, of which he assumed that the frequency of a given outcome tends to a limit. For the outcomes to be random, he required that the same limit would obtain given the observations up to this point. Later, investigators found the model too cumbersome and unconvincing. Another drawback was its narrowness, since it applied only to situations that allowed a large number of repetitions.

Concerning its statistical applications to probabilities such as the level and power of tests, and confidence coefficients, it was pointed out by Neyman that this narrowness could be somewhat alleviated. Although he continued to interpret these probabilities as long-run frequencies, he noted that they did not have to refer to repetitions of the same event. In discussing the coverage probability of confidence intervals in his basic 1937 paper on the subject, he wrote:

> It is not necessary . . . that the problem of estimation should be the same in all cases. For instance, during a period of time the statistician may deal with a thousand problems of estimation and in each the parameter θ to be estimated and the probability

---

[1] Quoted from Goldstein's biographical note in von Mises' *Selected Papers* (1963–64).

law [of the observations] may be different. . . . [However, if the confidence intervals] correspond to the same value α,. . . the probability of their resulting in a correct statement will be the same, α. Hence, the frequency of correct statements will approach α.

Neyman broadens the frequentist concept of probability still farther in his 1977 paper, "Frequentist Probability and Frequentist Statistics," where he permits not only the situation to change from case to case but also the value of α. Discussing a sequence of hypothesis tests with levels $\alpha_1, \alpha_2, \ldots$, he states,

The relative frequency of first kind errors will be close to the arithmetic mean of [the] numbers $\alpha_1, \alpha_2, \ldots, \alpha_n$ adopted by particular research workers.

That this broader interpretation of frequentist probability makes it much more useful in applications has been emphasized by Berger (1985).

Von Mises' axiomatic foundation was superseded by an axiom system proposed by Kolmogorov (1933) that did not specify the nature of probability. Instead, it treated probability as an undefined concept satisfying certain axioms. Nevertheless, von Mises' modeling effort exerted great influence, particularly on Kolmogorov, who cited this influence on his own formulation. He later took von Mises' ideas as a starting point when he made a renewed attempt to get a grip on the crucial and difficult concept of randomness.[2]

A very different fundamental contribution was provided in von Mises's 1947 paper, "On the Asymptotic Distribution of Differentiable Statistical Functions." (Actually, he published an earlier version of this work in 1936 in the *Annales de l'Institut Henri Poincaré,* but at that time no notice of it was taken in the English or American literature.) The paper presents a far-reaching extension of the Central Limit Theorem (CLT). This theorem, under mild conditions, asserts asymptotic normality for sums of independent (and some dependent) random variables. Von Mises' extension explains why so many nonlinear functions of i.i.d. random variables (e.g., the sample median) also are asymptotically normal. To discuss this extension requires some background.

The distribution of a random variable X can be represented by its cumulative distribution function (cdf)

$$F(x) = P(X \leq x).$$

If $X_1, \ldots, X_n$ is a sample from F, the natural estimate of the probability $F(x)$ is the proportion of X's that are $\leq x$, that is, the sample cdf $\hat{F}_n(x)$ defined in Section 42.

Consider now a real-valued function h defined for all distributions F (subject to some minor exceptions depending on the problem), for example the parameters $\theta(F)$ discussed in Section 41. If F is unknown, the natural estimate of $h(F)$ is the plug-in estimate $h(\hat{F}_n)$ (considered for a special case

[2] For recent accounts of the history of these foundational issues, see von Plato (1994) and Howie (2002).

in Section 42). This differs slightly but is asymptotically equivalent to the U-statistics in the case considered in Section 41.

If h is a feature of the distribution, for example, a moment, then $h(\hat{F}_n)$ is that feature of F_n and this is not a constant but a random variable. A simple example of such an h is the expectation

$$h(F) = E_F(X).$$

Since $\hat{F}_n$ assigns probability $1/n$ to each of the values $X_1, \ldots, X_n$, its expectation is

$$h(\hat{F}_n) = (X_1 + \ldots + X_n)/n.$$

Similarly, if $h(F)$ is the median of F, $h(\hat{F}_n)$ is the sample median.

The next step, for which von Mises credits the Italian mathematician Vito Volterra, consists of making a Taylor expansion of $h(\hat{F}_n)$ around the true distribution F_0. Von Mises then shows that the asymptotic distribution of $\sqrt{n}[h(\hat{F}_n) - h(F_0)]$ is determined by the first nonvanishing term of this expansion. If the first (linear term) is nonzero, the asymptotic distribution is normal. Von Mises also provides a detailed analysis of the nonnormal distributions that arise when the second term of the expansion is the first nonvanishing term. This class includes the distributions of many goodness-of-fit statistics.[3]

Von Mises made seminal contributions not only to probability and statistics but also to many other areas of pure and particularly applied mathematics. In recognition of the importance of his work, the American Mathematical Society in 1963 published two volumes of his selected papers. The first volume contains papers on geometry, mechanics (including work on plasticity, hydro- and aerodynamics), and analysis. Most of the second volume is devoted to probability theory and statistics, but it ends with a section titled "General." This latter section is largely concerned with von Mises' scientific philosophy. However, the last paper is of a very different nature. It is the introduction to a volume of letters of the poet Rainer Maria Rilke. This paper is only one of eight entries concerning Rilke listed in von Mises' bibliography at the end of Volume 2 of his selected papers. An explanatory paragraph states the following:

> Throughout his life, von Mises devoted much time and thought to German literature and in particular to the study of the life and work of the poet Rainer Maria Rilke (1875–1926). Von Mises is considered an authority on the "young Rilke." He also assembled the largest privately owned collection of the poet's manuscripts and works, and of books and papers about Rilke. The collection is now at the Houghton Library of Harvard University.

---

[3] An elementary exposition of the von Mises theorem and some of its principal applications is given in Lehmann (1999), Chapter 6.

Von Mises was a person of exceptionally broad interests and accomplishments. I very much regret that I never met this remarkable man whose work I greatly admire and whom I consider a major influence.

46. The Fisher–Neyman Controversy

R.A. Fisher and Jerzy Neyman, the two principal architects of twentieth-century statistics, argued about many topics, including the analysis of Latin squares, the Behrens–Fisher problem, fiducial inference, and the concept of power of a test. However, more basic was their disagreement concerning the nature of statistics, which is captured by the contrast between Fisher's "inductive inference" and Neyman's "inductive behavior."

The first signs of the controversy appeared in a mild form in 1934, when Fisher presented a paper at a meeting of the Royal Statistical Society entitled, "The Logic of Inductive Inference." In it, he stated,

> The inferences of the classical theory of probability are all deductive in character. . . . The fact that the concept of probability is adequate for the specification of the nature and extent of uncertainty in these deductive arguments is no guarantee of its adequacy for reasoning of a genuinely inductive kind. . . . However, a mathematical quantity of a different kind, which I have termed mathematical likelihood, appears to take its place as a measure of rational belief when we are reasoning from the sample to the population.

Fisher and Neyman

In his discussion of the paper, Neyman raises questions concerning this statement. He argues that the properties of the likelihood are probabilistic ones, and that "in fact we are calculating the maximum likelihood estimates not because we believe in some magic properties of this function, but because there are mathematical proofs of the important properties, easy to explain in terms of other conceptions of the theory of probability, such as the variance, etc." He then proposes that the choice of statistical procedure should be based on "the conception of frequency of error."

This idea goes back to his 1933 paper with Pearson on hypothesis testing, in which they suggested that:

> Without hoping to know whether each separate hypothesis is true or false, we may search for rules to govern our behavior with regard to them, in following which we insure that, in the long run of experience we shall not too often be wrong.

And in subsequent passages the authors point out that a test constitutes such a "rule of behavior," namely by telling us when to reject the hypothesis and when to accept it.

Neyman developed his behavioristic approach further in a 1938 paper (in French), in which he introduced the term *inductive behavior,* or rather its French counterpart *comportement inductif.* To explain this concept, he distinguishes between "knowing" and "believing" (here and below my translation). But, he claims,

> what frequently happens is neither of these two but rather an "assertion." . . . It is a voluntary act preceded by certain experiences and some deductive reasoning. . . . As a result, it seems to me that the term "inductive reasoning" does not correspond to what is happening, which begins with some assumptions concerning the variables whose values are observable and ends up with an assertion.

As an example of this argument, Neyman considers the estimation of the degree λ of radioactivity of some radioactive substance. Suppose the result of the investigation is a confidence interval

$$(*) \qquad 8.04 < \lambda < 11.96.$$

"In examining this conclusion," he states, "one sees that the sole reason for the physicist to decide that λ lies between these limits, is that the long run frequency of the cases in which the [random] confidence intervals $(\underline{\lambda}, \bar{\lambda})$ cover the value λ, will approach [the confidence coefficient] $\alpha = .95$."

He points out that the conclusion (*) is thus based on a deductive argument.

Neyman's attack an inductive reasoning and his alternative behavioral interpretation would likely have remained a philosophical argument of little interest to the statistical profession, if it had not led to an important innovation, in fact an entirely new framework for statistics, Wald's statistical decision theory. I shall discuss this theory in the next section, but note here that Wald clearly considers himself as Neyman's follower. In his 1950 book on the subject, at the end of Chapter 1 Wald discusses some of the "ideas and results preceding the present developments," and there states that the decision character of the test and estimation procedures has been emphasized by Neyman, who termed the adoption of a particular . . . procedure "inductive behavior."

Wald's decision theory was received by the statistical community with great enthusiasm. It not only unified the previously quite separate theories of testing and estimation, but also included many other possibilities that had not yet been explored. It was a magnificent conception that gave the field a new identity. But for Fisher it was an abomination—an abstract theory with few examples, far removed from statistical practice and embracing Neyman's behavioristic approach, which Fisher considered completely inappropriate for work in science.

Earlier, Fisher had been welcomed in America as the great originator of a new, and immensely useful, statistical methodology. Now he was sidelined and supplanted by a new champion. He was dismayed at the direction the field was taking and voiced his strong disapproval in a 1955 paper, "Statistical Methods and Scientific Induction," in which he also provided a clear statement of his own position:

Logicians, in introducing the terms "inductive reasoning" and "inductive inference," evidently imply that they are speaking of processes of the mind falling to some extent outside those of which a full account can be given in terms of the traditional deductive reasoning of formal logic. Deductive reasoning in particular supplies no essential new knowledge, but merely reveals or unfolds the implications of the axiomatic basis adopted. . . . It is the function of inductive reasoning to be used, in conjunction with observational data, to add new elements to our theoretical knowledge. That such a process existed, and was possible to normal minds, has been understood for centuries; it is only with the recent development of statistical science that an analytic account can now be given, about as satisfying and complete, at least, as that given traditionally of the deductive processes.

He then proceeds to his indictment of Neyman:

When, therefore, Neyman denies the existence of inductive reasoning, he is merely expressing a verbal preference. For him, "reasoning" means what "deductive reasoning" means to others. He does not tell us what in his vocabulary stands for inductive reasoning, for he does not clearly understand what it is.

Fisher carries his criticism further, without mentioning Neyman by name, in his 1957 book, *Statistical Methods and Scientific Inference,* where he writes:

To one brought up in the free intellectual atmosphere of an earlier time, there is something rather horrifying in the ideological movement represented by the doctrine that reasoning, properly speaking, cannot be applied to empirical data to lead to inferences valid in the real world.

In the same year, in a paper, " 'Inductive Behavior' as a Basic Concept of Philosophy of Science," Neyman explained his strong disagreement with Fisher's claims:

Fisher introduces two new measures of our "mental confidence or diffidence." Thus, if a scientist inquires why should he reject or accept hypotheses in accordance with the calculated value of P, . . ., the unequivocal answer is: because these values of P are the ultimate measures of beliefs especially designed for the scientist to adjust his attitudes to. . . . It must be obvious that, with the above essential contents of the inductive reasoning approach, its use as a basic principle underlying research is unsatisfactory. The beliefs of particular scientists are a very personal matter and it is useless to attempt to norm them by any dogmatic formula.

Neyman returned to the issue in a 1961 paper in which he reviews his dispute with Fisher, and states:

After a conscientious effort to find the exact meaning of this term [inductive reasoning], I came to the conclusion that, at least in the sense of Fisher, the term is empty, except perhaps for a dogmatic use of certain measures of "rational belief" such as the likelihood function and the fiducial probability.

At the center of the dispute are Fisher's interpretation of likelihood as "a rational measure of belief" and as an example of inductive reasoning, and Neyman's opposing concept of "inductive behavior." Both of these ideas have proven enormously useful and have exerted great influence.

That neither of these great originators could appreciate the contribution of the other is to a large extent due to their very different ways of thinking. Fisher relied heavily on his intuition and had little interest in formal proofs. This is illustrated by his geometric derivations of small-sample distributions, which many readers—not sharing his intuition—found difficult to follow. Neyman, on the other hand, insisted on the utmost clarity and detailed understanding. Any argument that did not satisfy this criterion was unacceptable to him.

This dichotomy extended to the way they viewed the world. For example, Fisher's daughter Joan Fisher Box (1978), in the biography she wrote of her father, states:

Having formed a largely intuitive judgment of any man, usually but not always sound, he was fully committed. A similar loyalty bound him to his country, his church and his profession. He was a patriot, a political conservative, a member of the Church of England.

While Fisher was a loyal member of his church,[4] Neyman, who was brought up as a Roman Catholic, soon became deeply suspicious of the church and an unbeliever. Believing something that could not be proved to be true was not for him.

As a result of this difference in outlook, neither Fisher nor Neyman was able (or willing) to see any merits in the other's point of view. This is a pity because their two approaches are not as incompatible as they proclaimed.

Despite Neyman's denial, the outcome of nearly any scientific investigation has a cognitive aspect: it either confirms one's expectations or it changes them. On the other hand, the end of an investigation is always followed by an

[4] He even wrote a paper, "Science and Christianity" (1955), with the subtitle "Faith Is Not Credulity," on the compatibility of science with Christian beliefs.

action, if only whether to continue the investigation, to publish the results obtained so far, and so on. And although Fisher derides any consideration of consequences or losses, his choice of an estimator is based on the size of the variance, which is exactly such a measure. (For further discussion of these issues, see, for example, Bernardo and Smith [1994], Section 2.7.1, entitled: "Reporting Beliefs as a Decision Problem.")

Generally, this Fisher–Neyman controversy attracted little attention. This is partly due to the fact that it was concerned with interpretation rather than methodology. In addition, it was overshadowed by the much more consequential Bayes–frequentist debate, which will be discussed in Sections 50 to 53.

47. Wald's Decision Theory

The life and career of Abraham Wald were the subject of Section 16. At the center of his work was his decision theory, which provided a new foundation for the field of statistics. Shortly before his untimely death in December 1950, Wald had the satisfaction of seeing the publication of his book, *Statistical Decision Functions,* the definitive account of the subject. This section describes the main ideas of Wald's approach, both because it is so central to Wald's work and because of its crucial role for the field of statistics. Although for the sake of simplification I shall omit some of the complications of Wald's general formulation, this sketch reflects the principal concepts and results of decision theory.

As in the classical work of Fisher and Neyman–Pearson, the starting point is a set X of observations. While Wald's assumptions are more general, we can for the sake of simplicity think of X as n real valued observations $X_1, \ldots, X_n$. Continuing in the classical mode, we shall assume that X follows some probability distribution P_θ depending on an unknown parameter $\theta = (\theta_1, \ldots, \theta_s)$. For example, X might be the number of successes in n binomial trials with success probability p. The distribution of X is then the binomial distribution depending on the parameter p. Or X might be a set of n independent measurements $X_1, \ldots, X_n$, with each of the X's having a normal distribution with mean μ and variance σ^2, thus depending on the parameter $\theta = (\mu, \sigma^2)$.

At this point, classical statistics splits into three branches: point estimation, which tries to pinpoint the unknown parameter θ; confidence sets, which provides a set in which θ can be stated to lie with a certain guaranteed probability; and hypothesis testing, where a hypothesis about θ is either accepted or rejected.

Wald's crucial step is to replace these three possibilities by a set D of abstract, completely unspecified decisions d. This includes point estimation, in which the decisions are the possible values of the parameter θ; confidence intervals (or more generally sets), with D the set of intervals in which θ can be asserted to lie; and hypothesis testing, in which D consists of just two possible decisions d, acceptance or rejection of the hypothesis.

It is surprising that at this level of generality anything useful can be said. But it was Wald's genius to see that it is still possible to make constructive proposals and obtain important insights.

Within the above framework, it is the statistician's aim to provide a decision procedure, that is a rule δ, which to each possible observation x assigns a decision $d = \delta(x)$. It is the task of the theory to determine how such a rule should be chosen.

For this purpose, it is necessary to introduce one last ingredient: a measure of performance of a decision rule that will enable us to compare the desirability of different decision rules. Wald's measure is based on a weight function $W(\theta, d)$ (most later writers prefer the term *loss function*), which expresses the loss suffered by making decision d when θ is the true value of the parameter θ. The loss is zero when d is the correct decision and positive for an incorrect decision. The performance of a decision rule δ is then measured by the loss it entails on the average, that is by the expected value of $W(\theta,\delta(X))$, which is a function of θ and is called the risk function of the decision rule δ.

The risk function generalizes the way point estimates are evaluated in classical statistics, typically by their expected squared error, an idea that goes back to Gauss.

Since typically there exists no procedure that minimizes the risk uniformly, that is, simultaneously for all values of θ, Wald proposed two types of compromise procedures. The first of these minimizes the average risk, averaged with regard to a probability distribution over θ; he calls this an a priori distribution and the resulting minimizing procedure a Bayes solution.

This language is appropriate because this is exactly how one would proceed as a Bayesian, that is, if one believed that θ was a random variable with that particular distribution. Such a Bayesian approach (due to Bayes and Laplace) was commonly used during the nineteenth century, with the prior distribution rather arbitrarily chosen to be "noninformative." In the binomial case, for example, p would have been assumed to be uniformly distributed on (0, 1). Both Fisher and Neyman argued strongly against this approach, and were concerned with building an alternative theory that would be free of this arbitrary and unrealistic assumption. (Bayesian inference later had a revival with different choices and interpretations, which will be discussed in the following sections.)

Wald explains his own position in the first chapter of his book, *Statistical Decision Functions* (1950, p. 16):

> In many statistical problems the existence of an a priori distribution cannot be postulated, and, in those cases where the existence of a prior distribution can be assumed, it is usually unknown to the experimenter and therefore the Bayes solution cannot be determined. The main reason for discussing Bayes solutions here is that they enter into some of the basic results in Chapter 3.

We shall consider these results in a moment.

For the case that an a priori distribution does not exist or is unknown, Wald proposes that "a minimax solution seems, in general, to be a reasonable solution of the decision problem." Here a procedure δ is minimax if it minimizes the maximum (rather than the average) of the risk.

Bayes solutions and minimax procedures are the subject of the two principal results of Wald's theory. The first of these states that under certain assumptions the class of all Bayes procedures is a complete class.[5] They are therefore the only ones worth considering. Given any procedure that is not Bayes, there exists a Bayes procedure that is at least as good no matter what the true θ.[6]

In the wake of Wald's book, these complete classes were worked out for a number of cases, but the results were disappointing: the classes were too big to be of much use in practice.

However, Wald's complete class theorem made a fundamental contribution in quite a different context, namely to the debate regarding the Bayesian point of view. It showed that the Bayesians were right in insisting that statisticians should act as if θ were a random variable with some prior distribution, and thus led to an important new type of question: if a procedure was proposed on some other grounds, one now had to ask whether it was a Bayes solution and if so to which prior it corresponded. The investigator was then in a position to examine whether these weights or probabilities seemed reasonable for the situation at hand.

What the complete class theorem of course does not do, and what from a Bayesian point of view is a primary task, is to determine which prior to use. Wald's second principal theorem offers one possible solution to this problem. This second theorem establishes the existence of a minimax procedure and characterizes it as the Bayes solution corresponding to a "least favorable distribution," that is, the distribution for which the average risk (the Bayes risk) is the largest possible.

The above is a considerably simplified account of Wald's theory. Unfortunately, the book (which also includes sequential experimentation) is difficult to read. It bristles with assumptions, many of them hard to verify, and offers few examples or other help to the reader. Wald worked hard to get the details right, but they are not the important part. What matters is that Wald's general formulation gave statistics a new identity. Instead of being a fragmented collection of different approaches, it now became the set of models and problems delineated by Wald's framework. Although in the intervening half century additional considerations have emerged, decision theory continues to hold its place as a framework for both Bayesian and non-Bayesian statistical theory.[7] On the other hand, the expectation that decision theory would become the dominant mode of statistical investigations was not

---

[5] For a definition, see Section 16.

[6] A technical note: Under somewhat weaker assumptions, limits of Bayes solutions must also be included in the complete class.

[7] In this connection, see Brown (2000).

fulfilled. Its very generality and abstraction worked against it, and most research continues to be carried out within the traditional forms: hypothesis testing (including multiple tests), point estimation, or estimation by confidence intervals.

48. Jack Carl Kiefer (1924–1981)

In his book on decision theory, Wald had erected an imposing structure, but at the time of his death this building was still empty. Practically, no examples of his minimax procedures and complete classes had yet been worked out.

The person mainly responsible for fleshing out the theory and showing its usefulness for specific situations was Jack Kiefer, a student not of Wald but of his closest colleague, Jack Wolfowitz.

During my semester at Columbia in 1950, Kiefer was a graduate student and I was invited to attend his oral examination. What greatly impressed me about this event was the calm and self-assured way Kiefer stood up to Wolfowitz's aggressive and bullying questioning.

When Wolfowitz left Columbia for Cornell (after Wald's death in 1951), Kiefer went with him, and he remained on the faculty of the Cornell mathematics department for the next twenty-eight years. During that time

I followed his work with great interest but saw little of him except occasionally at meetings (including the fourth, fifth, and sixth Berkeley Symposia). I much appreciated it when in 1978 he sent me a copy of the statement he had written on my behalf when he sponsored my election to the National Academy. (He had been elected three years earlier.)

In 1979, Kiefer accepted an offer from the Berkeley statistics department and became a close colleague and friend. Sadly, after little more than two years, he died on August 10, 1981, of heart failure, five days after Neyman's death. Jack's death (in the shower after a vigorous swim) came as a tremendous shock. When a colleague called to tell me that Jack had died, I replied, "You mean Neyman," since I had seen Jack the day before in perfectly good health.

His death was a very great loss for me personally as well as for the department. As I wrote in an obituary for the university's *In Memoriam* volume for 1985,

> During his short time, he had established himself as a central figure in the Department of Statistics. He had for example served as its Vice Chair [and was expected a year later to become its Chair], and he had become a regular, highly successful instructor in a large lower-division course. At the time of his death he was supervising six Ph.D. students.

That he was successful in large lower-division courses and enjoyed teaching such courses should not have come as a surprise. Successful lecturing to a group of two hundred or three hundred lower-division students requires a performance. And Jack was a performer who at one time had considered going into the theater or becoming a pianist.

Jack had many interests—not only theater and music, but also politics (in 1968 he ran unsuccessfully as a Liberal Party candidate for the New York State Assembly) and the science and collection of mushrooms. Julie and I never joined him on his mushroom-hunting excursions, but once or twice were invited to share in a feast of morels he had found that day.

It is fortunate for our field that of the many paths open to him Jack chose statistics. He went on to become one of the deepest and mathematically most powerful statisticians of his generation.

Kiefer, perhaps more than anyone else, fleshed out Wald's decision theory by applying it to a great variety of situations. His most extensive and influential such application was to the new area of optimal experimental design, which he essentially created in the more than forty papers that he (often jointly with Wolfowitz and other collaborators) devoted to the subject.

One of the most remarkable of these papers is the first, with the punning title, "On the Nonrandomized Optimality and Randomized Nonoptimality of Symmetrical Designs" (1958). In this paper, Kiefer establishes a general decision theoretic framework for the problem of choosing a design. He then shows (in a generalization of earlier results of Wald and Ehrenfeld) that many standard designs have various optimum properties among the class of nonrandomized designs. Here, by a randomized design he means that the design is chosen according to a fixed probability distribution from a given class of possible designs. He follows these optimality results by proving that, as the title indicates, surprisingly these results no longer hold when randomized designs are allowed.

The optimality criteria treated in this first paper (some of them in the literature, others new) were somewhat arbitrary, but Kiefer and Wolfowitz two years later were able to show that D – optimality was in fact equivalent to a minimax criterion (called G -optimality). Although the paper (1960) is quite short and the proof fairly easy, it must have given the authors great satisfaction.

During a sabbatical year (1958–59) in England, Kiefer presented a paper, "Optimum Experimental Designs," to the Royal Statistical Society. It was mainly a survey of the work done in this area so far but also included some new results. His presentation was followed by the comments of nine discussants. To his surprise and dismay, the reaction was nearly uniformly negative. The tone was set by Tocher, who proposed the traditional vote of thanks and stated:

> I think it is now recognized among practical statisticians that statistical decision theory cannot be a complete theory of inference . . . that a new formulation is probably needed. This attempt to found design theory on similar lines reinforces that viewpoint.

The meeting was chaired by George Barnard, who stated:

> Some indication of my major philosophical differences with Dr. Kiefer is given on p. 273 where the procedures of Box and Wilson are said to be "often not even well defined rules of operation." There is a suggestion here that this is a defect; but it should be pointed out that in the field of practical human activity rules of operation which are not well-defined may be preferable to the rules which are.

Kiefer had become the victim of a clash between two cultures. The American decision theoretic point of view focused on the desirability of clearly stated objectives, precise formulations, and the derivation of optimal procedures. The British statisticians instead emphasized intuition, practicality, and the unknown multiple uses to which a procedure might be put.

The discussion upset and angered Kiefer, but fortunately it did not discourage him. For the next twenty years, he continued his investigations of both general aspects and particular designs. However, he also applied the decision theoretic approach to other areas such as sequential analysis, nonparametric inference, and multivariate hypothesis testing.

One example is the group of his papers concerned with the minimaxity and admissibility of Hotelling's T^2 and other multivariate tests. As mentioned in Section 13, this is a problem in which the Hunt–Stein theorem does not apply and that therefore has to be considered on its own merits. Giri and Kiefer were successful in treating local and asymptotic minimaxity. In addition, Giri, Kiefer, and Stein tackled the much more difficult form of this problem when the alternatives are restricted to an invariant shell. However, they were able to solve this problem only for the simplest case (dimension 2, sample size 3).

Another example is provided by Kiefer's work on nonparametric testing and estimation, particularly of the Kolmogorov-Smirnov type. This includes both asymptotic minimax results and the limiting distributions of the k-sample multivariate analogues of the Kolmogorov-Smirnov tests for goodness of fit and for the equality of several distributions.

Jack's great scientific accomplishments were recognized by his giving the Wald lectures "On Optimum Experimental Designs" in 1962 and his service as president of the Institute of Mathematical Statistics (IMS) in 1967. He also was elected to both the American and National Academies. After his early death in 1981, his memory was honored by conferences in Berkeley and at Cornell. The second volume of the *Proceedings of the Berkeley Conference in Honor of Jerzy Neyman and Jack Kiefer* substitutes for the festschrift Jack would undoubtedly have received had he lived longer.

The June 1984 issue of the *Annals of Statistics* was dedicated to his memory. It contains a list of his publications and writings and articles on his life and work by his students Jerome Sacks and Lawrence Brown, and a survey of his work on experimental design by Henry Wynn. These articles, and the bibliography, were reprinted in what constitutes his most enduring memorial: the three volumes of Jack Kiefer's *Collected Works*.

49. Lawrence D. Brown (b. 1940)

The description of Kiefer's decision theoretic work in the preceding section may give the impression of a deliberate program to provide more substance to Wald's theory. However, this would be misleading. Kiefer investigated

problems because they interested him, and decision theory—particularly the minimax approach—seemed the best way to formulate them. That this in turn served to develop and enrich decision theory was, I believe, a consequence rather than a motive. This substantive development of Wald's theory was continued in the same spirit by Kiefer's student Larry Brown. But while the minimax principle was the main focus for Kiefer, with admissibility playing a smaller role, the converse was true for Brown.

Lawrence (Larry) Brown, while majoring at Cal Tech in mathematics and physics, took one statistics course and, he says,[8]

> the subject immediately appealed to me. I suppose that my interest in statistics was rooted in a desire to use formal mathematics in a pragmatic way.

For his graduate studies, Brown went to Cornell to work with Kiefer. However, he took his main decision theory course from Peter Huber, who was spending the year 1963–64 at Cornell after two years in Berkeley.

After completing his Ph.D. in 1964 with a thesis written under Kiefer, Brown went to London for a year to work with David Cox, and then accepted a tenure-track position as assistant professor in the Berkeley statistics department. There his closest contact was with Lucien Le Cam. In DasGupta (2005), Larry mentions that he also had a nice relationship with me but that he did not get to see much of me because of my schedule.

I typically taught and held office hours from 8 to 11 o'clock in the morning, but apparently a myth developed among the students that I would come to the office at 3 a.m. As Larry explains in a letter to me: "It's not hard to understand how such a story could have arisen and survived. After all, to most grad students and even to us young faculty 8 in the morning was practically the middle of the night."

Unfortunately, Larry remained with us only for a year. He was happy in Berkeley and we were happy with him, but it was the time of the Vietnam War and it turned out that Larry's Los Angeles draft board considered mathematics as a deferrable subject but not statistics. It therefore became essential for him to be in a mathematics rather than a statistics department. So Larry contacted Jack Kiefer, who arranged a position for him at Cornell, where statistics was in the mathematics department.

We were really unlucky. This was the second time that we lost an outstanding member of our faculty for political reasons: first Charles Stein, now Larry Brown. Both were irreplaceable.

Larry remained at Cornell for nearly thirty years, a stay that was broken up by five years at Rutgers. In 1994, he left Cornell to accept a position as professor of statistics at the Wharton School of the University of Pennsylvania, where he still is teaching today.

As mentioned earlier, much of Brown's work was concerned with questions of admissibility. Of this group of his papers, the most original and influen-

[8] Quoted from DasGupta (2005).

tial was his 1971 paper, "Admissible Estimators, Recurrent Diffusions, and Insoluble Boundary Problems." It grew out of Stein's result (discussed in Section 13) that when estimating a number of independent normal means, an improvement over the standard estimator is possible when the number of means is three or more, but not when it is one or two. As Brown points out, a fundamental difference between the cases "three or more" and "one or two" also occurs in a completely different field, the theory of recurrence in diffusion. Brown discovered a close connection between the statistical question of admissibility and the probabilistic question of recurrence.

This work is too technical to present here, but to get at least a flavor of the meaning of recurrence, consider random walks, a discrete analogue of diffusion. A simple example is a walk on the line that starts at the origin and takes steps of length 1, either to the left or right with constant probabilities $p = q = \frac{1}{2}$. Then it can be shown that with probability 1 the walk will sooner or later return to the origin (i.e., be recurrent). This result continues to hold for a random walk in two dimensions, but is no longer true in dimensions of three or higher. To find a close connection between this kind of result and Stein estimation was a major achievement.

In addition to this 1971 paper, Brown's work included admissibility investigations more generally for inferences about location and scale parameters, in sequential problems, for Poisson processes, and in some nonparametric situations. Of his contributions to many other areas, I shall mention only two. One is his 1986 book, *Fundamentals of Statistical Exponential Families (with Applications in Statistical Decision Theory),* which has become the definitive exposition of this subject.

The other is a recent series of papers (with Cai and DasGupta) that uncovered the surprising fact that the standard confidence intervals for a binomial probability p do not have the nominal coverage probability even for fairly large n and for values of p far from 0 or 1. The authors found an explanation for this phenomenon in the two-term Edgeworth expansion of the coverage probability. They also used this expansion to compare a number of alternative intervals, some of which turned out to be considerably more satisfactory. In the latest of these papers (2003), it is shown that similar results hold for some other exponential families. This work has important implications for statistical practice.

In addition to his research papers, Larry has on several occasions written on today's role of decision theory. Examples are "Minimaxity More or Less" (1993) and "Minimax Theory" (1998) (Encyclopedia of Biostatistics); and "An Essay on Statistical Decision Theory" (2000) and "Decision Theory, Classical" (2001) (International Encyclopedia of Social and Behavioral Sciences).

He has given the Wald Lectures (1985), served as president of the IMS (1992–93) and as coeditor of the *Annals of Statistics* (1995–97). He received an honorary degree from Purdue University and was elected to the National Academy of Sciences, and in 2002 he received the Wilks Award of the American Statistical Association.

11
Foundations II: Bayesianism and Data Analysis

The frequency approach of Neyman and Wald (which built on a formulation of Fisher [1922]) assumed a statistical model that was only partially known. The unknown aspect was specified by certain parameters θ, which were unknown constants. A different approach, later called Bayesian, was developed by Savage (1954) following earlier work of Ramsey and de Finetti. It was based on the assumption, justified by axioms of rational behavior, that θ was a random quantity with a known distribution. The probabilities defining this distribution were interpreted as being subjective, representing the investigator's degree of belief in their possible values. The outcome of the statistical analysis was to be an action, in accordance with Neyman's behavioristic approach. This foundation, unlike that of Neyman and Wald, led to a unique optimal procedure—the Bayes solution.

Implementation of this program, which required the elicitation of the subjective prior distribution of θ, proved to be quite difficult in practice. As a result, gradually a modified approach was developed by Berger, Bernardo, and others that retained the Bayesian paradigm but replaced the subjective prior by a more convenient (although harder to interpret) reference distribution. A different modification, called empirical Bayes, was initiated by Robbins.

While the Bayesian approach added a strong assumption, that of a specified prior distribution, to the model, a movement by Tukey went in the opposite direction: he argued that much statistical activity should take place without the use of any models. His exploratory data analysis advocates a first completely open-minded and unstructured look at the data to see what they might tell us. More generally, Tukey stressed the primacy of the data, and his views had a strong effect on the way statisticians perceived their task and the seriousness with which they took their models.

I had little involvement with these foundational debates. However, to commemorate the fiftieth anniversary of the Neyman-Pearson theory, I did write a paper (1985) in which I argued that this theory continued to play an important role by its position intermediate between that of the more structured Bayesian formulation and the looser practice of data analysis. The paper showed how these three different approaches influence each other, and how each had its part to play.

50. Leonard J. Savage (1917–1971)

A serious shortcoming of von Mises' frequency concept of probability is its inapplicability to the probability of unique events, for example the probability that there is life on Mars. There exists, however, another concept of probability that does not suffer from this limitation. It considers probability as measuring the confidence that a particular individual has in the truth of a particular proposition.

These two different concepts of probability lead to different approaches to statistical inference, called respectively frequentist and Bayesian (the latter for reasons that are explained below). Which of these approaches should be preferred was subject of a lively debate throughout the nineteenth century, with the Bayesian version preferred by most authors. The Bayesian approach, however, was violently opposed as unscientific by both Fisher and Neyman in the 1920s and 1930s, and as a result fell into disuse. The person bringing it to life again was Leonard J. Savage, who wrote under that name but preferred to be called Jimmie.

Jimmie Savage and I were born on the same day, November 20, 1917. He received his B.S. degree in 1938 in mathematics from the University of Michigan and was awarded the Rackham Fellowship, a prize given to the most promising student in the department who was planning to go on to

graduate work. He remained at the University of Michigan as a graduate student and obtained his Ph.D. in 1941 with a thesis in geometry. There followed a postdoctoral year at the Princeton Institute for Advanced Studies, where he benefited from his contact with John von Neumann.

By 1942, Jimmie writes in an autobiographical sketch,[1] "it became intolerable not to be doing something about the war." After a year of teaching "calculus and spherical trigonometry to pretty unwilling students," he came to the attention of Warren Weaver, who, as chief of the Applied Mathematics Panel of the National Defense Research Council (NDRC), was largely responsible for the administration of war-related mathematical and statistical activities. This led in 1944 to Savage's joining the Statistical Research Group (SRG)[2] at Columbia under the direction of Harold Hotelling and W. Allen Wallis. Savage had no background in statistics, but, as he writes, "it would have been impossible at that time not to have learned something about statistics, for I was stationed at the Statistical Research Group at Columbia . . ., which was one of the greatest hotbeds statistics has ever had." Savage, a fast learner, quickly made himself useful, and was an important contributor to two of the books the SRG published after the war.

When his service with the SRG ended, Savage moved to the University of Chicago, where he worked first in the Institute of Radiobiology and Biophysics, then in the Department of Mathematics, and finally, beginning in 1949, in the Department of Statistics, which he chaired from 1957 to 1960. He left Chicago in 1960 for personal reasons for the University of Michigan, and from there in 1964 went to Yale, where he died seven years later at the age of fifty-four.

Savage's interests were broad and he was a superb mathematician. He published significant papers in economics, pure mathematics, probability theory, and statistics. I shall here mention only two papers that I found particularly interesting.

The first of these is a 1956 joint paper with Bahadur on "The Nonexistence of Certain Statistical Procedures in Nonparametric Problems." It resolved an important open question concerning the testing and estimation of the mean of an entirely unknown distribution. The paper showed that no useful procedure exists in this situation regardless of how large a sample is taken or even with a sequential procedure. The same conclusion is shown to hold for other parameters that can be changed by an arbitrarily large amount through a very small change in the tail of the distribution.

The second paper, "On rereading R.A. Fisher" (1976), is a wonderful survey of Fisher's ideas and results. It is a written version of the Fisher Lecture that Savage gave in 1970. At the time of Savage's death, it was not quite complete, and we must be grateful to John Pratt, who carefully

[1] Quoted in a tribute in Ericson (1981).

[2] For more about the SRG, see Section 20.

edited it and prepared it for publication. The paper is full of insights and surprising discoveries. The following two passages give at least a flavor of this superb piece.

Of Fisher's temperament, Savage writes:

> Fisher burnt even more than the rest of us, it seems to me, to be original, right, important, famous, and respected. And in enormous measure, he achieved all of that, though never enough to bring him peace. . . . As in the works of other mathematicians, research for the fun of it is abundant and beautiful in Fisher's writings, though he usually apologizes for it.

In the section, "Just What Did Fisher Do in Statistics?" Savage writes:

> It would be more economical to list the few statistical topics in which he displayed no interest than those in which he did. . . . It stands to reason that he would not have investigated noncentral distributions, because their raison d'être is the power function, a concept on which Fisher turned his back. So much the worse for reason: Fisher was the first to give formulas for the important noncentral distributions, chi-squared, *t*, and singly noncentral *F*.

However, Savage's most influential publication was not one of his papers but his 1954 book, *The Foundations of Statistics*, in which he examined statistics as the science of making decisions under uncertainty. More specifically, he treated the problem of what action to take in the presence of uncertainty as to which of a number of states (e.g., possible causes of some medical symptoms) is the true one. Drawing on work of Ramsey and de Finetti, as well as von Neumann and Morgenstern, Savage formulated a set of plausible axioms for rational behavior. The principle of these axioms requires that a person faced with a choice of actions can establish an order of preference among them, in particular to be able for any two possible actions to determine which one he or she would prefer.

Savage then deduces (by a purely mathematical argument) that a rational person who obeys these axioms has a prior distribution corresponding to numerical degrees of belief in the various possible states and a loss function, and acts so as to minimize the expected loss. This degree of belief is the personal (or subjective) probability the person attaches to the state in question. Once these prior probabilities (i.e., before any observations are taken) are determined, the statistical analysis proceeds by updating them in the light of the observations, and thereby converting them into posterior probabilities. This is done by means of Bayes' rule (due to Thomas Bayes, 1701–1761),[3] and is the reason the adherents to this approach are called Bayesians.

As a result of Savage's book, and his advocacy of the Bayesian approach in later papers, a Bayesian movement developed that competed with the established frequentist approach to statistics. The number of Bayesians

[3] For a biography of Bayes, see Bellhouse (2004).

steadily grew, leading to the organization of Bayesian meetings (and the publication of their proceedings), and eventually to the establishment of institutions such as a section of the American Statistical Association on Bayesian Statistical Science, the International Society for Bayesian Analysis, and the *Bayesian Journal*. At the same time, variations and modifications of Savage's original formulation arose within this emerging Bayesian community, particularly regarding the specification of the prior probabilities. Some of these developments are sketched in the next two sections.

Savage's importance is that of a great catalyst. He not only brought the ideas of Ramsey and de Finetti to the attention of the English-speaking statistical community when the time was ripe for them, but also combined them with other ingredients into a worldview that was persuasive to many. His book launched a movement that had a serious impact on both statistical theory and practice.

Owing to his early death, Savage did not receive many formal honors. He was awarded a Guggenheim Fellowship in 1951–52, served as president of the Institute of Mathematical Statistics (IMS) in 1958, and was awarded an honorary degree by the University of Rochester in 1963, but perhaps his greatest mark of distinction came posthumously. In 1981, ten years after Jimmie's death, *The Writings of Leonard Jimmie Savage—A Memorial Selection* (Ericson, 1981) was published jointly by the ASA and IMS. The volume of more than seven hundred pages contains not only most of Savage's papers, but also a complete bibliography as well as tributes by W. Allen Wallis, Fred Mosteller, William and Esther Sleator, and Francis Anscombe, together with an essay, "L.J. Savage—His Work in Probability and Statistics," by Dennis Lindley.

My own direct interaction with Savage was slight. We saw each other at some of the Berkeley symposia and at statistical meetings, but I did not agree with his point of view and, since I dislike controversy, avoided serious discussions with him. What I could not, however, avoid in the long run was thinking about the issues he had raised. In that sense he exerted a strong influence on me and many statisticians of my generation.

51. Dennis Lindley (b. 1923)

After Savage's death, the principal spokesperson for the subjective Bayesian movement became the British statistician Dennis Lindley. Born and raised in London, Lindley studied mathematics at Trinity College, Cambridge. His studies were interrupted by wartime service in the Ministry of Supply. Of this work, Lindley says[4]:

[4] In Smith (1995).

> Much practical work was done, but generally speaking, in our section, under the direction of George Barnard,[5] we were just learning statistics. We read all the "big papers" and slowly began to understand what the subject was about.

The "big papers," he explains, were "mainly the Neyman-Pearson material because that was the most mathematical. Then there were papers on probability, by Cramér and Doob, for example."

So, like so many statisticians of his and my generation, Lindley slithered into statistics as a result of World War II. After a brief period at the National Physics Laboratory (NPL), he went back to Cambridge for a year's further study, and then once more to the NPL. Then in 1948 he accepted an offer from John Wishart of a faculty position at Cambridge.

At Cambridge, Lindley's aim was to make statistics "a respectable branch of science" by establishing a system of axioms from which the theories of Fisher and Neyman-Pearson could be derived. As a result of meeting W. Allen Wallis, he was invited to spend 1954 in Chicago with Savage, who was engaged in a similar endeavor. Of his encounter with Savage, Lindley says (in his conversation quoted above):

[5] For more about this fascinating and influential statistician see De Groot (1988), and Lindley (1990b).

His approach to the axiomatization was far better than mine, but he had the same idea. Neither of us would have known at the time what was meant by saying we were Bayesians. What we were doing was justifying the classical techniques. If you read the preface to the second edition of Savage's book, he says something about what a fool he was. We were both fools because we failed completely to recognize the consequences of what we were doing.

After his year in Chicago, Lindley returned to Cambridge, where he later became director of the Statistical Laboratory. However, in 1960 he was told that Cambridge for the first time was going to establish a chair of statistics but that he would not be appointed to that position.[6] As a result, he moved to Aberystwyth in Wales, "the first of the new wave of statistics chairs that was created." In Aberystwyth, he organized a new department, but he left in 1967 to accept the chair of statistics at University College, London. In 1977 (at age fifty-four), he took early retirement, and since then he has been a freelance statistician and world traveler.

Lindley has written more than one hundred papers, mostly on various aspects of the Bayesian approach. In 1965, he published a two-volume account of Bayesian statistics, in which he fleshed out the consequences of Savage's approach for statistical inference. Unlike Savage's book, Lindley's version was written as a text and as such was very influential (and was translated into Japanese). It was followed by two shorter books, *Making Decisions* (1971b) and *Bayesian Statistics: A Review* (1971a), and more recently a less technical book, *Understanding Uncertainty* (2006).

Lindley's enthusiasm for Bayesianism is boundless and leaves no room for doubt. In a comment on a paper by Efron, "Why Isn't Everyone a Bayesian?" (1986), he writes that, "Every statistician would be a Bayesian if he took the trouble to reads the literature thoroughly and was honest enough to admit that he might be wrong." In Smith (1995), he is asked whether he has ever thought about the fact that inferential debates might be detrimental to the wider image and impact of statistics, to which he replies: "Yes, it is detrimental, but truth is more important than image in my view. We have got to get it right and I think we will. We will all be Bayesians in 2020, and then we can unite the profession."

Most of us will agree that truth is more important than image, but I don't believe it has to be presented quite as confrontationally as Lindley does by replying to the question of how the Bayesian view could be encouraged: "Attend funerals" (*Statistical Science* 10, p. 313).

In the late 1970s and early 1980s, Lindley frequently visited Berkeley, and despite our disagreement on foundations, we were on friendly terms and I saw more of him than I had of Savage. The Berkeley invitations came not from the statistics department, which generally was very unsympathetic to the Bayesian approach, but from the Department of Industrial Engineering and Operations Research, more specifically from Richard Barlow, an enthusiastic Bayesian.

[6] The Cambridge chair went not to a statistician but to the probabilist David Kendall.

As in the case of Savage, I did not engage in debate with Lindley, with one exception. The occasion was Lindley's 1988 Wald Lectures, with the title "The Present Position in Bayesian Statistics," which were published in the 1990 volume of *Statistical Science,* with discussion. In the preface to his paper, Lindley writes:

> There is no generally accepted name for non-Bayesian statistics. Since Bayes had little to contribute to Bayesian statistics, it is not inappropriate to refer to Berkeley statistics, since the two ecclesiastics disagreed during their lifetimes, and because the University of California campus named after the latter has perhaps the best department broadly holding to that view.

I was invited to contribute to the discussion of the paper, and I provided some comments on points on which I differed with Lindley.

Among the honors Lindley has received for his important contributions are not only the Wald Lectures but also the Royal Statistical Society's Guy Medals in Silver and Gold, and a festschrift on the occasion of his seventieth birthday, edited by Freeman and Smith (1994). The volume of twenty-two papers opens with a biographical essay by Peter Armitage, and concludes with a bibliography of 118 entries covering the years up to 1993.

52. James O. Berger (b. 1950)

In contrast to Lindley, who has never wavered in his belief in the inevitability and universal applicability of the subjective Bayesian formulation, some Bayesians of the next generation found that an objective, less personal, Bayesian approach tended to be more practicable. As a result, a split developed between those who subscribed to Lindley's idealistic and uncompromising position and others who saw a role for an objective Bayesian approach that goes back to Laplace in the nineteenth century. Laplace championed the idea of a noninformative prior representing a state of ignorance. In the twentieth century, more sophisticated versions of noninformative priors were developed by the geophysicist Harold Jeffreys (1939) and the physicist Edwin Jaynes (1983). A leading proponent of an objective Bayesian movement has been Jim Berger.

James O. Berger was born in 1950 in Minneapolis, and obtained his B.A., M.A., and Ph.D. in mathematics from Cornell University in 1971, 1973, and 1974, respectively. He dates his decision to become a statistician to a graduate course in inference he took from Jack Wolfowitz. As he recalls,[7] "That got me to start thinking about statistics as a career. Wolfowitz was an entertaining lecturer and we heard all sorts of funny things about Bayesians and other undesirables."

---

[7] In Wolpert (2004).

Berger wrote his Ph.D. thesis in (frequentist) decision theory under the supervision of Larry Brown and then was appointed to a faculty position at Purdue, where he remained for twenty-three years. In 1997, he moved to the Institute of Statistics and Decision Sciences at Duke University. In addition, he spearheaded the effort to create the Statistical and Applied Mathematical Sciences Institute (SAMSI) in Research Triangle Park and became its founding director.

Having started as a frequentist, Berger describes how he became a Bayesian in the preface to his 1980 book, *Statistical Decision Theory*. He states:

> The original goal I had in writing this book was to find some middle ground [i.e., between the frequentist and Bayesian approaches]. . . . This original goal seemed indicated by my philosophical position at the time, which can be described as basically neutral. I felt that no one approach to decision theory (or statistics) was clearly superior to the other, and so planned a rather low-key and impartial presentation of the competing ideas. In the course of writing the book, however, I turned into a rabid Bayesian. There was no single cause for this conversion; just a gradual realization that things seemed ultimately to make sense only when looked at from the Bayesian viewpoint.

Of Berger's postconversion Bayesian work, I shall mention three strands, all part of his desire to cast the Bayesian net as wide as possible.

In the first place, as mentioned at the beginning of the section, he relinquishes Lindley's insistence that Bayesian analysis must be based on subjective priors. In fact, he states in Wolpert (2004):

> By necessity most priors used today are objective rather than subjective; subjective elicitation is just too hard to be done in even a limited way for more than a few unknowns in a problem, so the vast majority of unknowns must be handled via objective Bayesian methods.

Objective priors representing a state of complete ignorance were favored by Laplace. However, this concept turned out to be more difficult to implement than might have been expected. A series of papers by Berger and Bernardo (and others) in the 1980s and 1990s, initiated by Bernardo (1979), developed a more general concept of "reference priors" as conventional baselines. (For a discussion of this approach, see, for example, Bernardo and Smith [1994], Section 5.4.) Objective Bayesian analysis continues to be a very active area of research.

A second strand of Berger's Bayesian enterprise is a "robust Bayesian viewpoint," which he describes (in a 1984 paper with that title) as that "essentially one should strive for Bayesian behavior which is satisfactory for all prior distributions which remain plausible after the prior elicitation process has been terminated."

The last aspect of Berger's work I want to mention is his effort to bridge the separation of the Bayesian and frequentist approaches. In his conversation with Wolpert, he states, "In the long run, I think that reconciliation is inevitable as it becomes better understood that good Bayesian and good frequentist viewpoints are simply two illuminations on what I think are the central core truths of statistics." (The same issue of *Statistical Science* contains a paper by Bayarri and Berger entitled, "The Interplay of Bayesian and Frequentist Analysis.")

Berger's Bayesian work has been very influential and has been acknowledged by many honors. In 1985, he received the Committee of Presidents of Statistical Societies (COPSS) Award. He was elected (as a foreign member) to the Spanish Real Academia de Ciencias in 2002, and to the (U.S.) National Academy of Sciences the following year. In 1995–96, Berger served as president of the IMS, and from 1998 to 2000 as editor (joint with Künsch) of the *Annals of Statistics*. He also served as president of the International Society for Bayesian Analysis.

One of Jim's major works was the previously mentioned 1980 book, *Statistical Decision Theory,* and I was pleased with the inscription in the copy he sent me of the second (1985) edition (now with the title enlarged by the addition of "and Bayesian Analysis").[8] The inscription reads: "To Erich with best wishes (and a feeling that we are a lot closer in basic outlooks than our books might reveal)."

[8] Between these two editions, Berger also published (with Wolpert) a very informative and influential book, *The Likelihood Principle* (1984).

This raises the question: What is my outlook? Foundational issues have not been an active interest of mine, so I find it easiest to describe my attitude with a number of (rather superficial) comments:

1. As a student of Neyman, my starting position was that of a strict frequentist: probability meant long-run frequency, and any idea of probability as state of mind was to be dismissed out of hand.
2. Later, I realized that in our personal lives we do have beliefs or feelings that make some outcomes seem more likely to us than others and which influence our actions. In particular, we take many risks in the belief that their probability is very small.

However, it seems to me that the strength of these beliefs tends to be rather fuzzy, and not sufficiently well defined and stable to assign a definite numerical value to it. If, with considerable effort, such a value is elicited, it is about as trustworthy as a confession extracted through torture.

3. On the other hand, there are many repetitive situations, for example in education, industry, and medicine, where substantial past experience does provide sensible prior distributions. In such situations, frequentists and Bayesians share a common view.
4. The most important link between the two approaches is the crucial result of Wald that, roughly speaking, any sensible statistical procedure is a Bayes procedure corresponding to some (proper or possibly improper) prior distribution. This result suggests to the frequentist two useful Bayesian strategies:
   i. Bayes solutions as a way of constructing procedures with good frequentist properties. This of course leaves unsettled the choice of prior suitable for this purpose. The development of reference priors could be viewed as one possible approach to this problem.
   ii. To determine for any proposed procedure whether it is a Bayes solution and if so, to what prior it corresponds. Answering this question is likely to produce useful insights.

Thus, over the years my frequentist position has been somewhat contaminated by Bayesian ideas and, as Jim Berger has indicated, we may not be as far apart as our writings suggest.

53. Herbert Robbins (1915–2001)

As mentioned in Section 3, I first met Herb Robbins at Courant's house in 1940, on my arrival in New York from England. At that time, he was a pure mathematician working with Courant on their book, *What Is Mathematics?* But later, by a curious chain of events, he became a mathematical statistician. While an officer in the navy during the war, he happened to overhear a conversation between two naval officers regarding the number of bombs required

for their impact to cover most of a target. He found a simple mathematical (probabilistic) formulation of the problem that he was able to solve, and he published the results of this investigation in two papers in the 1944 and 1945 volumes of the *Annals of Mathematical Statistics*. The papers came to the attention of Harold Hotelling, who in 1946 was moving to the University of North Carolina, and he offered Robbins a faculty position in his new department. Robbins demurred, pointing out that he knew nothing about statistics, but Hotelling reassured him that he would only be required to teach measure theory and probability theory.

And what had presumably been Hotelling's speculation proved successful. In the stimulating statistical atmosphere of the new department, Robbins soon became interested in the unfamiliar subject and by 1951 began making highly imaginative and original discoveries. Of Robbins's many innovations, I shall mention only three. Particularly characteristic of his work is a 1952 paper entitled, "Some Aspects of the Sequential Design of Experiments."

It is concerned with two populations Π_1 and Π_2 with unknown, different means μ_1 and μ_2. We draw a sample $X_1, X_2, \ldots, X_n$ and at each stage have the choice of drawing from Π_1 or Π_2. The aim is to draw in such a way that the expected value of $X_1 + \ldots + X_n$ is as large as possible. A simple example would be that of two slot machines with different average payoffs, where the X's are the amounts paid out by the machines (in this case most often 0) on the successive turns. After having played for a while and having observed the results, which machine should we play on the next turn? A natural answer is to play the machine that has done better up to this point, that is, which has had the bigger average payoff. We shall denote this rule for playing by R.

Unfortunately, the use of Rule R could lead us into trouble. Suppose, for example, that we have one observation on each machine, and that by chance the better machine comes up empty while the worse one pays out a positive amount. Then we would select the worse machine for the next turn and, regardless of the outcome, its average payoff would be positive, while that of the better machine would still be zero. For the next turn, Rule R would therefore again tell us to play what is in fact the worse machine (although of course we don't know this), and so on. We would continue to play the worse machine, never giving the better one another chance. Similar difficulties can arise at any stage.

To avoid this problem, Robbins suggests modifying Rule R in a way of which the following Rule R′ is an example.

Rule R′: Follow Rule R except: on the 10th, on the 100th, on the $1{,}000^{th}$, . . . turn, play machine 1; on the 20th, the 200th, the $2{,}000^{th}$, . . . turn, play machine 2—regardless of how the two machines have performed up to this point.

What Rule R′ ensures is that eventually each machine gets an opportunity to show what it can do, regardless of the chance outcomes up to a particular point. On the other hand, the exceptions to Rule R are sufficiently rare, so as not to load up the total payoff with too many plays from the inferior machine. In fact, Robbins shows that with rules such as R′, the payoff will eventually (i.e., for a sufficiently large number of plays) be arbitrarily close to what it would have been had only the better machine been used.

These considerations generalize to more than two populations and have applications to clinical trials for the comparison of two or more treatments. Various related problems were taken up by Robbins in later investigations. With this work, he initiated the consideration of sequential allocation. A second area that he founded (together with his student Sutton Monro) was that of stochastic approximation. However, this is rather technical and I shall now turn to his most influential contribution: a new approach that was startlingly surprising from a theoretical point of view and that at the same time provided a highly useful methodology. It was written four years before Stein's paper on the estimation of several means (discussed in Section 13), with which it shares some features. However, its conclusions—though similar in nature—are much weaker than those obtained later by Stein.

The paper considered a sequence of situations $\Pi_1, \ldots, \Pi_s$, each involving its own data, say $X_1, \ldots, X_s$, which are assumed to be independent, and its own parameters $\theta_1, \ldots, \theta_s$. The performance of a decision procedure for the whole set of s situations is measured by the average of the performance measures for the s individual situations. Robbins considered two versions of this problem. The first (1951), which he called a compound decision problem, treats the θ's as unknown constants. (A special case of this problem was described in Section 13 as the setting for Stein estimation.)

The second formulation of 1956 assumes that the θ's are themselves random quantities governed by some distribution Λ. If Λ were known, this would be a Bayesian situation and the best rule would be the associated Bayes procedure. However, Robbins considers the case that Λ is unknown.

In both cases, Robbins shows that the preferred procedure is not, as one would expect, to make the decision regarding θ_i on the basis of X_i alone, but that certain improvements are possible by letting the other (seemingly irrelevant) observations influence the decision in a suitable way. To see why this might be so, we shall consider the second of the two formulations, which assumes that the θ's follow some unknown distribution Λ.

Robbins points out that it is then possible to estimate Λ, by using the full set of data from all *s* situations. If the estimated distribution is $\hat{\Lambda}$, he proposes to use the Bayes procedure corresponding to $\hat{\Lambda}$ and in his 1956 paper calls it empirical Bayes. For sufficiently large *s,* this procedure will do nearly as well as the Bayes procedure itself. Since the decision regarding θ_i is now based on $\hat{\Lambda}$, and $\hat{\Lambda}$ depends on the full set of data $(X_1, \ldots, X_s)$, it is seen that with this procedure the decision on θ_i involves not only X_i but also the other *X*'s. Robbins developed the empirical Bayes approach further in succeeding papers, and it was taken up by many other authors.[9]

The success of the empirical Bayes approach rests on the assumption of a probability distribution for the θ's. That Robbins showed similar kinds of improvements to be possible in the compound decision problem even without this assumption seemed very surprising. Yet, in that case, results even stranger and more startling were obtained by Stein in 1955, leading to the Stein estimation procedures discussed in Section 13. (Roughly speaking, Stein showed that his procedure provides an improvement in all cases, while Robbins obtained an improvement only in most cases.) The understanding of Stein's procedures was greatly enhanced when, in a series of papers in the 1970s, Efron and Morris (1973a,b, following Lindley, 1971a) showed how to interpret them as empirical Bayes procedures.

Empirical Bayes provides an important approach that is intermediate between frequentist and Bayesian methods.

Having first met Robbins briefly in 1940, I did not see him again for a number of years. However, unexpectedly, during my Princeton semester in 1950 he invited me to give a series of three lectures at the University of North Carolina in Chapel Hill. He had the reputation of being difficult, but I found him and his wife most welcoming and hospitable. Only toward the end of my stay did I receive a Robbins barb. He opened the third and last of my lectures by saying: "Well, Professor Lehmann has told us nothing new in his first two lectures; let's see whether he has anything new to say today."

---

[9] A book-length treatment of the subject is provided by Maritz and Lwin (1989).

I cannot resist telling another Robbins story, although I did not witness it myself. At one point in his career, he was considering an offer from another university. The idea was that he would assemble a statistics group with several new appointments. Negotiations had progressed well, and a meeting with several deans was organized to discuss some outstanding problems. "But what would we do with all these people if they became unproductive," one of the deans asked. "Oh," replied Robbins cheerfully, "we could always make them deans."

After seven enormously productive years in Chapel Hill, Robbins moved to Columbia in 1953 to take over the chairmanship of the Department of Mathematical Statistics. In 1958, I saw much of him when he spent a leave in Berkeley, where he gave courses on recent developments in statistics and on applications of stochastic processes. In 1974, he came to Berkeley to speak on the occasion of Neyman's eightieth birthday.

After that, we had little contact until my wife and I moved for a two-year period to Princeton in 1995. Since Princeton had no statistics program, we often attended the statistics seminar at nearby Rutgers University. Rutgers had a strong statistics department, in which Robbins held a post-retirement position. Although in his eighties, he still taught with enthusiasm. He was a superb lecturer, and I remember an interesting talk he gave on the Secretary Problem. It is concerned with the choice of a secretary (he framed it as the choice of a wife) where you successively interview candidates as they become available. After each interview, you have to make an irrevocable decision to choose or reject this candidate (no second chance). The problem, to which Robbins had made several contributions, is when to stop the process. This talk may have been the last occasion on which I saw him. He died a few years later.

Robbins's brilliance and the influence of his contributions were recognized by many honors, including the Rietz, Neyman, and Wald lectures, and membership in the National Academy of Sciences and the American Academy of Arts and Sciences. The Institute of Mathematical Statistics, of which he had served as president in 1965–66, dedicated the April 2003 issue of the *Annals of Statistics* to his memory. This issue also contains four essays that give a good overview of his work:

1. Herbert Robbins and Sequential Analysis (Siegmund)
2. Robbins, Empirical Bayes, and Microarrays (Efron)
3. Compound Decision Theory and Empirical Bayes Methods (Zhang)
4. Stochastic Approximation (Lai)

They are followed by a list of his writings.

54. John W. Tukey (1915–2000)

John Tukey is a towering figure of twentieth-century statistics who made important contributions to nearly all aspects of the discipline, both theoretical and applied. His collected works, although still incomplete, comprise

eight substantial volumes dealing with time series, data analysis, graphics, analysis of variance, and multiple comparisons. A detailed account of Tukey's life and achievements is provided in the December 2002 issue of the *Annals of Statistics* (pp. 1535–1680), which also contains a bibliography and which is dedicated to Tukey's memory. The issue opens with an article by David Brillinger on Tukey's life, prefaced by a statement of the Princeton physicist John Wheeler:

> I believe that the whole country—scientifically, industrially, financially—is better off because of him and bears evidence of his influence.

John Wilder Tukey, born in New Bedford, Massachusetts, was a prodigy who by the age of three had taught himself to read. He was schooled at home but did take some courses at New Bedford High School, where both his parents were teachers. Before entering Brown University in 1933, Tukey had already studied calculus and chemistry by reading at the public library. As a result, he was able to take graduate courses in mathematics at Brown as a sophomore. However, his major was chemistry, a field in which he graduated after three years.

From Brown, Tukey moved to Princeton for graduate study in chemistry, but after a year he changed to mathematics. He obtained his Ph.D. in 1939 with an outstanding thesis in topology, which was published as volume 2 of the *Annals of Mathematics Studies*. After completing his degree, he was appointed to the faculty of the Princeton mathematics department.

In 1941, with war approaching, Tukey joined Princeton University's Fire Control Research Office and there came under the influence of Charlie Winsor. As he writes in the foreword to Volume VI of his collected works:

> There I met Charles P. Winsor, who taught me much about statistics not known then in books or other literature. It was Charlie, and the experience of working on real data, that converted me to statistics. By the end of late 1945, I was a statistician rather than a topologist.

After the war, Tukey divided his position between Princeton University and Bell Laboratories, where he was a member of the technical staff, becoming assistant director of research, communication principles, in 1958 and associate director of research, information science, in 1961. At the university, Tukey's home was the section of mathematical statistics in the mathematics department. He advanced to professor of mathematics in 1950, and in 1966—when the section became an independent Department of Statistics—served as its first chair. In 1970, he was succeeded in this position by Geoff Watson, and he retired in 1985 at the mandatory age of seventy.

In addition to his jobs at Princeton and Bell Labs, Tukey did a great deal of consulting and much high-level work for the government. The latter includes his service on the President's Science Advisory Committee from 1960 to 1965, and again in 1971–72. A list of these activities is provided in the Tukey festschrift edited by Brillinger, Fernholz, and Morgenthaler (1997).

This festschrift is only one of his many honors, which include his election not only to the National and the American Academy, but also to the American Philosophical Society. Most prestigious of all, in 1973 he received the National Medal of Science, "for his studies in mathematical and theoretical statistics . . . and for his outstanding contributions to the applications of statistics to the physical, social, and engineering sciences." (A more complete list of his honors can be found in the festschrift.)

I do not remember when I first met John Tukey, but recall that I found early encounters with him both frustrating and uncomfortable. It was frustrating when he talked about what he was working on. I was, of course, interested. However, his conversation was sprinkled with new technical terms that he delighted in creating (a partial list of these inventions can be found in Brillinger, 2002), and unless one interrupted him constantly to ask for their meaning he was unintelligible, at least to me. The situation got much better in 1951, when I spent a semester at Princeton and gradually was able to learn his language. This was also the period when we started playing Ping-Pong, a game in which we were evenly matched and which we later played often on his frequent visits to Stanford's linear accelerator.

What also made me uncomfortable in my early contacts with John was his attitude toward my own work. He made a distinction between mathematical and theoretical statistics, and while the difference was not very clear to me, it was clear that the first was bad and the second good, and that my work fell into the first category. In particular, he thought optimization, the search for the best procedure, was a mistaken goal, while this was exactly the focus of my early work and of my lecture notes on testing and estimation.

In a 1961 paper, "Statistical and Quantitative Methodology," Tukey discusses these issues in some detail. He seems to feel that the basic difference is one of attitude, of intent. A section entitled, "Mathematical and Scientific Statistics" (a term he used as an alternative to theoretical statistics) opens with this statement:

> Mathematical statistics was once the knight in armor to save us from the dragon of ill-used descriptive statistics. This it did. Today it is the home of many respected colleagues, whose motivations are basically mathematical rather than scientific. Far less is heard of scientific statistics (which I like to call theoretical statistics), where the motivations are basically scientific. Yet the latter field is the more important.

This is considerably more tolerant than the impression he gave in our early conversations.

Tukey takes up the difference between the two approaches in a later section of the paper titled, "Mathematicians and Mathematics":

> The danger of mathematics to the outside world in general, and to science in particular, is simple. Pure mathematics must take its assumptions most seriously, wringing from them all possible consequences, questioning not at all. Pure mathematics must value its results in its own terms, with far less attention to the relation of the assumptions to the real world than to the aesthetic nature of the results. . . . Yet [this] is just what science and technology must not do. . . . Science and technology . . . must avail itself of the aid of mathematics, yet dare not accept its attitudes.

Later, John's criticism of me abated since my work, especially on nonparametrics, became more methodological. In addition, our personal relations became much more cordial, particularly after he and his wife, Elizabeth, spent several weeks in Berkeley as guests of our department while I was chairing it. This visit came about as a result of Fred Mosteller's appointment as a research professor in our department for the year 1974–75.

Tukey had been one of Fred's closest collaborators for many years, and Fred thought it would be useful if we could arrange for Tukey to visit Berkeley. Fortunately, a perfect vehicle existed for this purpose, the Hitchcock Lectures, which bring distinguished persons to the campus for a period of three to four weeks, during which time they give a number of lectures. The first Hitchcock lecturer in statistics was R.A. Fisher in 1936, who had been invited when he was being considered for a position. The visit had not been a success, and two years later the position went to Neyman. We now had much better luck with the talks by Tukey, who lectured on his new work on data analysis. The department enjoyed his visit and the Tukeys seemed to be having a good time.

My last extended contact with John was during 1995–1997, when my wife and I spent two years in Princeton at the Educational Testing Service (ETS). John visited ETS once a week for a consulting session that was open to all, and then stayed for the rest of the day. From time to time, he also invited me for lunch at his club. Unfortunately, Elizabeth Tukey was suffering from terminal cancer. We saw her only once during our stay, in late 1997 when she and John joined us for lunch, shortly before her death. Life without her was hard for John and he died two years later, at age eighty-five.

In the same year, 2000, my colleague Lucien Le Cam also died. The two were about as far apart in their interests and attitudes about statistics as is possible. Le Cam constructed his great asymptotic theory at the greatest possible level of abstraction and generality, writing statistical theory in the mathematical style of Bourbaki. In contrast, Tukey stressed exploratory data analysis without any probability or mathematics. Between them they seemed to define the great sweep of the field. To honor these so extraordinarily different great statisticians, my coauthor Joe Romano and I dedicated the third edition of my testing book to their memory.

55. Tukey's Robust Statistics and Exploratory Data Analysis

This section considers just two areas of Tukey's many contributions that are close to my own interests (a third such area is discussed in Section 57): robust statistics and data analysis. As is pointed out in the introduction to a book dealing with these two subjects, *Understanding Robust and Exploratory Data Analysis* (Hoaglin, Mosteller and Tukey, 1983), they have a common purpose:

> The classical statistical techniques are designed to be the best possible when stringent assumptions apply. However, experience and further research have forced us to recognize that classical techniques can behave badly when the practical situation departs from the ideal described by such assumptions. The more recently developed robust and exploratory methods are broadening the effectiveness of statistical analyses.

Robustness was first investigated by E.S. Pearson (1931) and later by George Box (1953), who coined the term. The issue then had been robustness (i.e., insensitivity to assumptions) of the level of a test. The corresponding problem for point estimation was first taken up by Tukey (1960), who considered the robustness of the efficiency of estimators. The new viewpoint he brought to the problem has several aspects:

1. The formulation of the issue in terms of efficiency.
2. The emphasis on robustness against small deviations from the assumed model.
3. Illustration of the approach by considering mixture distributions of the form $F(x - \theta)$ with

$$F(x) = (1 - \varepsilon)\, \Phi(x) + \varepsilon\, \Phi\,(x/3)$$

(i.e., contamination, with small probability ε, of a normal distribution with variance, by gross errors with variance 9.)

4. The comparison in this contamination model of the efficiency of the mean with that of trimmed means resulted in a startling finding. That, for example, a 6% trimmed mean is at least 96% efficient for all ε while the efficiency of the mean decreases rapidly as ε increases, from 1 at $\varepsilon = 0$ to 70% at $\varepsilon = .1$.

By showing the great advantage of robust procedures, the paper was influential and provided motivation for Huber's robustness work.

Tukey's interest in robustness led Geoff Watson, his successor as chair of the Princeton statistics department, to invite Peter Huber, Frank Hampel, and Peter Bickel to join Tukey for a year-long seminar on the subject in 1970–71. The project, in which a number of other statisticians also participated and in which Tukey played a central role, resulted in a book, *Robust Estimates of Location,* by Andrews, Bickel, Hampel, Huber, Rogers, and Tukey, which compared sixty-eight estimates of location, some well known, others developed during the study. Much other work developed during the seminar that has not been published is outlined in Hampel (1997). Tukey's role can be imagined from a comment by Huber (2002):

> In robustness as in every other area he touched, John Tukey produced hundreds of original ideas, some brilliant, fundamental and lasting, some ephemeral.

This characterization applies very strongly also to the area of Tukey's statistical work that perhaps affected the field of statistics most profoundly—data analysis. This work is contained in his book, *Exploratory Data Analysis* (1977), the papers collected in volumes 3 and 4 of Tukey's *Collected Works*, a book with Mosteller, *Data Analysis and Regression* (1977), and two books edited by Hoaglin, Mosteller, and Tukey: *Understanding Robust and Exploratory Data Analysis* (1983), and *Exploring Data Tables, Trends, and Shapes* (1985).

In an early (1962) key paper, "The Future of Data Analysis," Tukey describes data analysis as including, "among other things: procedures for analyzing data, techniques for interpreting the results of such procedures, ways of planning the gathering of data to make its analysis easier, more precise or more accurate, and all the machinery and results of (mathematical) statistics which apply to analyzing data.

Of this paper, Huber (1997) writes:

> Very few people will have realized at that time (I certainly was not among them) that Tukey, while ostensibly speaking about his personal predilections, was in fact redefining statistics.

It was Tukey's great achievement to emphasize the primacy of the data and, in an unrelenting campaign, to provide the outlook, and a multitude of tools, for a more realistic approach. To accommodate the sweep of his definition of the subject, he distinguished between two aspects of data analysis: exploratory and confirmatory.

In a paper of 1980, "Methodological Comments Focused on Opportunities," he explains the difference by comparing it with a criminal investigation:

> In the paradigm of quantitative detection work, exploration involves finding as many clues as you can, whether or not they point to the right criminal. And confirmation corresponds to the trial, whose aim . . . is to decide whether the desired degree of proof has been attained.
>
> Exploration, then, corresponds to: what appears to be going on?; confirmation to: do we have firm evidence that such and such is happening (has happened)?
>
> Exploration has been rather neglected; confirmation has been rather sanctified. Neither action is justifiable.

Because of this neglect, Tukey spent much effort on exploratory data analysis, which resulted in his 1977 book on the subject (with a preliminary version appearing in 1970–71). In the process, he introduced many new techniques, among them stem and leaf displays, hanging rootograms, and boxplots, to mention only a few.

The influence of Tukey's data analysis has been enormous. As Huber said, through it he redefined statistics.

12
Statistics Comes of Age

As a discipline matures and reaches a critical mass, it begins a process of taking stock. This process is served by three types of works, which will be discussed in this chapter: (1) books that may be intended primarily as reference or as text and that lay out the present state of the field; (2) encyclopedias that provide a comprehensive view of the totality of its aspects; and (3) histories that trace the development of the subject.

Three book-length accounts of the state of statistics after the Fisher/Neyman-Pearson revolution were published in the period 1943 to 1946. At one end was *Mathematical Statistics* (1943) by Sam Wilks (which was briefly discussed in Section 21), and at the other end Harald Cramér's *Mathematical Methods of Statistics* (1946). The period was spanned by the two volumes of Kendall's *Advanced Theory of Statistics,* which appeared in 1943 and 1946, respectively.

Of these three works, by far the most successful (at least in the United States) was Cramér's. Wilks' book was a preliminary version that even its author considered not to be definitive. Kendall's suffered from the fact that, as Wald's review in volume 42 (1947) of *Journal of the American Statistical Association* (JASA) states, "the standards maintained [with respect to clarity, precision, and rigor] are not quite so high, in the opinion of this reviewer, as would seem desirable in a book on the advanced theory of statistics." Thus, Cramér's lucid, rigorous, and mathematically self-contained treatment became the standard reference.

The first statistical encyclopedia was the two-volume *International Encyclopedia of Statistics* (1978), edited by Kruskal and Tanur. It was in the main not an original work but, as the editors state, "draws together, expands and brings up to date the statistics articles of the *International Encyclopedia of the Social Sciences* (IESS), edited by David Sills and published in 1968."

Because of its origin, this two-volume work was too limited to adequately serve the purpose of a comprehensive encyclopedia of the whole field of statistics But such an *Encyclopedia of Statistical Sciences* was produced by Kotz and Johnson during the years 1982 to 1988. It consisted of nine volume, to which were added later a supplementary and three update volumes.

The coverage of this work was extraordinarily broad; it could be said to define the field of statistics in its broadest sense.

The third type of work, a history of statistics, had a forerunner in the two-volume collection, *Studies in the History of Statistics and Probability* (1970 and 1977), edited respectively by E.S. Pearson and M. Kendall, and by M. Kendall and R. Plackett. They were reprints of papers published previously, particularly in *Biometrika,* which since 1954 had been publishing a series of articles under that title. Pearson, Kendall, and Plackett were all statisticians with a strong interest in the history of the field.

The first integrated account of the history of statistics (from about 1700 to 1900) was Stephen Stigler's 1986 book, *The History of Statistics,* with the subtitle, *The Measurement of Uncertainty Before 1900*. It was followed by a two-volume work (1990, 1998) by the Danish statistician Anders Hald, which covered a more extensive period (roughly from 1650 to 1930). Together, Hald's two volumes are more than three times as long as Stigler's history. They are more encyclopedic in character than Stigler's book, which tells a more compact and unified story.

A lively and more popular account of this history is provided in *The Empire of Chance—How Probability Changed Science and Everyday Life,* by Gigerenzer et al. (1989). It is more selective and stresses somewhat different topics. As the authors explain: "The empire of chance is too vast for us to map in its entirety. We aim at a comprehensive, but not an exhaustive tour of its domain."

A striking feature of these three types of works—texts or reference books, encyclopedias, and histories—is that in all three categories two or more independent efforts arose more or less simultaneously. The books by Wilks, Kendall, and Cramér, coming from the U.S., England, and Sweden, respectively, were published within a three-year period. The histories by Stigler, the first volume of Hald, and the book by Gigerenzer and his coauthors appeared between 1986 and 1990. And even the Kotz–Johnson encyclopedia had had a forerunner four years earlier.

This near simultaneity shows that the time was ripe for such stock-taking.

56. Harald Cramér (1893–1985)

The Swedish number theorist, actuary, probabilist, and statistician Harald Cramér obtained his Ph.D. in 1917 with a thesis in analytic number theory (the subject of Edmund Landau's life work, with whom Cramér published an early joint paper), under the guidance of the Swedish mathematician Gösta Mittag-Leffler. However, he had a falling out with his very powerful thesis advisor and Mittag-Leffler warned Cramér "that he would see to it that Cramér could not make a mathematical career in Scandinavia."[1]

---

[1] Quoted from Grenander (1995).

As a result, Cramér switched to insurance mathematics and became an actuary. He worked on collective risk theory and this in turn led him to an interest in stochastic processes and, more generally, probability theory and statistics. He made major contributions to all these fields.

One of his most famous results concerns a conjecture stated in a seminal paper of 1934 by the great French probabilist Paul Lévy. Lévy expressed his belief that if the sum of two independent random variables, say X and Y, is normally distributed, then X and Y must also have normal distributions. To his chagrin, Lévy was unable to prove this result; two years later Cramér succeeded in doing so.

Cramér was not only an outstanding research mathematician, but also a wonderful expositor. Particularly influential were his two books, *Random Variables and Probability Distributions* (1937) and *Mathematical Methods of Statistics* (1946). The latter was written during World War II when Sweden was very isolated, and concerning it Cramér expressed the hope that it would be his "entrance card into the new world after the war."

This hope was fulfilled. The book (more complete and definitive than Wilks' *Mathematical Statistics* [1943], discussed in Section 21, which Cramér did not know because of Sweden's isolation) quickly established itself as the standard introduction to the theory of statistical inference developed by Fisher and Neyman-Pearson. Two of its outstanding features were mathematical rigor and readability.

In order for the book to be self-contained, the first 140 pages of the 540–page text were titled "Mathematical Introduction," mainly an exposition of measure theory and the Lebesgue integral. This was followed by 180 pages titled "Random Variables and Probability Distributions," which provided the necessary probabilistic tools. This second part began with a discussion of probability theory as a mathematical model and a set of axioms similar to the 1933 axioms of Kolmogorov for this theory. Finally, Part 3 dealt with statistical inference, both testing and estimation. It included the Neyman-Pearson theory of hypothesis testing, point estimation, and a careful exposition of confidence sets and their interpretation.

In the process of writing, Cramér also developed some new results. In particular, the book introduced what became known as the Cramér-Rao lower bound.[2] (Cramér did not know that this bound had already been obtained by Fréchet [1943], Darmois [1945], and Rao [1945].)

A more important innovation was the book's treatment of maximum likelihood estimation. A property required of any reasonable estimate is consistency, that it is nearly certain to get arbitrarily close to the true value being estimated as the number of observations gets large. Consistency of the maximum likelihood estimate (MLE) was claimed (but not proved) by Fisher, and attempts at proofs by various later authors were unsuccessful.

Cramér found a very ingenious and fruitful way of finessing the problem. The MLE typically is obtained by setting the derivative of the likelihood equal to 0, i.e., by solving the likelihood equation. The MLE is one solution of this equation, but there may be others. Under fairly weak conditions, Cramér proved a result that was slightly weaker than Fisher's claim, namely that there exists a consistent solution of the likelihood equation. This turned out to be the correct result. Examples were later found in which the MLE is not the consistent solution.

Mathematical Methods of Statistics was such a model of clarity and its exposition so persuasive that today, nearly sixty years later, the book is still in print.

The year following the publication of this text marks the beginning of Cramér's long connection with Berkeley. For some time, Neyman and Evans had been considering the idea of organizing an institute of actuarial science in the mathematics department. Since they found no suitable American candidate, Neyman suggested Cramér, whom he had met at various European conferences in the 1930s. At Neyman's invitation, Cramér gave a course on stochastic processes in the 1947 Berkeley summer session. During this stay, Neyman appears to have approached him about the possibility of a permanent move to Berkeley as head of a unit of actuarial science within the mathematics department similar to Neyman's own laboratory. On August 4 of that

[2] Unfortunately, Cramér used this inequality to give an erroneous proof of the asymptotic efficiency of the consistent root of the likelihood equation by failing to distinguish between the limit of the variance and the variance of the limit distribution of an estimate.

year, Neyman followed this up with a letter to Cramér (who had just returned to Stockholm), expressing his appreciation of Cramér's lectures and asking: "Will you kindly let me know whether or not you would consider coming to Berkeley for good?" He had to wait two months for a reply. "The chief cause for my delay," Cramér finally wrote in early October, "is simply that I find it extremely difficult to make up my mind to give you any definite reply to the question you put." Although Cramér emphasized the difficulties such a move presented for him, Neyman was encouraged, and immediately wrote to the president of the university concerning "the opportunity to secure the services of the world's best specialist in actuarial science."

A year later (in November 1948), Evans was able to inform Cramér that "the President of the University has authorized me to discuss with you the possibility of your coming here as Professor of Mathematics with teaching in the broad field of Mathematics–Statistics–Actuarial Mathematics." In a simultaneous letter, Neyman made it clear that the plan was for "an autonomous unit within the Department of Mathematics, somewhat similar to the Statistical Laboratory, which would work and develop under your guidance." In the meantime, a committee of the mathematics department was working on a possible structure if such a unit were added, and in January 1949 recommended the organization of a mathematical center consisting of three departments: mathematics, statistics, and actuarial science.

Cramér was still hesitating. On January 17, he sent separate letters to Evans and Neyman, explaining his difficulty in coming to a decision and responding to the department's invitation to spend the fall term of 1950 in Berkeley before deciding.

To Evans, describing his situation in Stockholm as one that could hardly be bettered, he wrote:

> I find it extremely difficult to make up my mind what to say. There are so many conflicting emotions involved in the question. . . . I am very glad that you indicated the possibility that I might come again and visit you for a limited time, before making a final decision.

To Neyman he was more open:

> Besides the reasons I give in my letter to Professor Evans, there are also the family reasons. Our children are grown up, but may still want there *[sic]* parents now and then, and should we leave the country permanently, we should like to have them do the same.
>
> You will not be surprised by what I write about my position here, which is certainly a very good one. As a matter of fact, if it were not for the political uncertainty, and the risk that sooner or later, we may lose our freedom,[3] I do not think I should give serious consideration to a proposal to go away permanently. As it is, I do consider it very seriously—but I hesitate.

---

[3] He was referring here to the expansionist policies of the Soviet Union and particularly to the 1947 Communist takeover of Czechoslovakia.

While preparations for a 1950 visit were proceeding, a new event forced the decision. In October 1949, the rectorship of the University of Stockholm had fallen vacant and Cramér was being considered for the position, which corresponds to that of an American university president. Should he be elected, Cramér wrote, he felt bound to accept, and in this case even a Berkeley visit for only one term would no longer be possible. On January 3, 1950, Neyman had to admit defeat:

> Dear Harald, Please accept my heartiest congratulations on your election to the Rectorship of the University of Stockholm. We are all very disappointed that you will not be with us for keeps. . . .

At Neyman's urging, Cramér did pay a short visit to Berkeley in September 1950, after attending the Mathematical Congress in Cambridge, Massachusetts. In addition to two lectures, a conference regarding an actuarial program was arranged for interested faculty members and some representatives of insurance companies, but it did not lead to any specific proposals.

After having served as rector for several years, Cramér was able to take a leave and come to Berkeley for the fall semester of 1953. This time he taught a course on statistical studies of risk, as well as a seminar in probability.

During Cramér's various stays in Berkeley, I saw a lot of him and his wife, Marta, and became very friendly with them. On his 1953 visit, he expressed an interest in seeing his old friend George Polya. It so happened that an uncle of mine in Carmel was on vacation and had put his roomy house at my disposal. Taking advantage of this opportunity, I suggested that the Cramérs and the Polyas spend a weekend in Carmel with me and my family, and this turned out to be a very successful venture.

An incident during Cramér's visit vividly illustrated the different social status of a professor in Europe and in the U.S. Shopping for food at our neighborhood market, I ran into Marta Cramér. She was shocked. Never, never, in Sweden, she explained, would a professor do the shopping himself.

Cramér returned to Berkeley one last time in 1983. Two years earlier, Neyman had died, on August 5, 1981, and our colleague Jack Kiefer five days later. The department organized a Berkeley conference in honor of Jerzy Neyman and Jack Kiefer from June 20 to July 1, 1983. The meeting began with the dedication of our seminar room on the tenth floor of Evans Hall to Neyman. The opening address at this ceremony was given by the ninety–year-old Cramér. Since his wife had died in 1973 and he was no longer able to travel alone, he was accompanied by his son Kim. He was frail and both his hearing and his eyesight were failing. Traveling such a distance must have been quite an ordeal for him. That he agreed to undertake it was a token of his friendship with Neyman and with the Berkeley statistics community.

Cramér received many honors. A mark of great distinction was his appointment, after eight years as rector of the University of Stockholm, as chancellor of the Swedish university system. He was elected to the Academies of Science of all four Scandinavian countries, as well as that of Spain and the American Academy of Arts and Sciences. In 1972, he received the Guy Medal in Gold of the Royal Statistical Society. Among his honorary doctorates were those of Edinburgh, Calcutta, and Paris. In 1994, his *Collected Works* were published in two handsome volumes by Springer, with an account of his life by Gunnar Blum.

57. Samuel Kotz (b. 1930)

Sam Kotz was born and raised in Harbin, China, and after completing high school studied electrical engineering at the Harbin Institute for Technology. In 1949 he emigrated to Israel, and for two years served in the Israeli Air Force, mainly as an instructor of mathematics. He then enrolled at the Hebrew University in Jerusalem, where he obtained his M.A. in mathematics in 1956.

After receiving his master's degree, Kotz took a job with the Israeli Meteorological Service and there developed an interest in statistics. A chance encounter with Jack Wolfowitz resulted in his being offered a scholarship to Cornell, where he got his Ph.D. in 1960 with a thesis on information theory.

In 1962, he accepted a position in Chapel Hill, and there met Norman Johnson, who became his lifelong collaborator.[4] The next stop was the University of Toronto, and then in 1967 Temple University in Philadelphia. Kotz remained at Temple for twelve years and in 1979 moved to the University of Maryland, from which he retired in 1997. Since then, he has been Senior Research Scholar at George Washington University.

Kotz has written a large number of scientific papers and several books, but I shall discuss only three of his projects, all of them important reference works that he originated and coedited with Norman Johnson.

The first, *Distributions in Statistics,* appeared in four volumes between 1969 and 1972 that dealt respectively with discrete distributions, continuous univariate distributions (two volumes), and multivariate distributions. For each distribution covered, this work discussed, among other topics, its history, moments, properties, tables, and approximations. The volumes proved to be extremely successful, and as a result a second, much-enlarged, edition appeared in the 1990s (with some additional authors).

While my connection with this work on distributions was only that of an appreciative user, I was heavily involved with the second of these Kotz–Johnson projects, the *Encyclopedia of Statistical Sciences.* From the start I was very enthusiastic about the idea, and Sam gave me many opportunities to participate. He invited me to write a number of entries: on point estimation, Hodges–Lehmann estimators, the Neyman–Pearson lemma and its applications, unbiasedness, and group families. He also encouraged me to suggest entries and possible authors for them.

One of these suggestions had some unexpected consequences. It seemed to me that an encyclopedia of statistical sciences should have an entry on statistics, and I suggested a number of possible authors for such an article. After some time, Sam wrote back that all the prospects had turned him down and urged me to write the article myself. I thought that I was too mathematical and that my interests and experience weren't sufficiently broad, but I agreed to give it a try.

As I reread this twenty–page article now, twenty years later, it sounds to me much more like Tukey or Mosteller than Lehmann. The paper is divided into sections on data interpretation and data acquisition, and these two sections are subdivided, respectively, into

- statistical methodology, exploration vs. verification, the Bayesian approach, and the Bayesian frequency controversy; and
- measuring single units, assessing population characteristics, data from experiments, serial data, and designing experiments.

My involvement with the encyclopedia did not end with its completion. To mark this event, Sam organized a celebration at the University of Maryland, attended by dignitaries from the university and from John Wiley, which had

[4] For personal accounts of this collaboration, see Nadarajah (2002) and Read (2004).

published the nine volumes. Sam invited me to give the principal talk. It gave me an opportunity to point out the importance of the work, not only as an indispensable reference work but also as providing a definition of the field of statistics in all its many different aspects: its concepts, results, methods, applications to many areas, its most significant contributors, and its institutions.

Another such opportunity arose when (in collaboration with my friend and Stanford colleague Persi Diaconis) I wrote a review of the *Encyclopedia for Mathematical Reviews*. There we again stressed the breadth of its coverage:

> It includes not only theoretical and applied statistics and probability theory and their foundations, but also substantial references to fields such as programming (dynamic, linear and nonlinear), operations research, game theory, information and coding theory, pattern recognition—in fact, any discipline containing a major stochastic element. The *Encyclopedia* is particularly strong also in its coverage of the application of stochastic theory to the substantive fields in which it plays a role, such as agriculture, economics, history, linguistics, psychology, and so on.

In addition to ours, the *Encyclopedia* also received a much-more-detailed review in JASA (1989, volume 84, pp. 830–834). Since no one reviewer could do justice to an encyclopedia covering so many different areas, the review was written by a team of sixteen authors, who wrote: "Our consensus is that the editors have done a magnificent job of transmitting statistical knowledge to the men (and women) who will come after them."

That such a gigantic undertaking was conceived, organized, and carried out successfully by just two coeditors in chief (with a five-member advisory board but with only one associate editor, Campbell Read) seems to me remarkable. An account, "The Making of the Encyclopedia," is provided by Kotz and Johnson (1987).

The vitality of the work is indicated by the recent publication of a second edition comprising sixteen volumes. Although I am listed as a member of the editorial board of this new edition and had no official connection with the first, I was this time completely out of the loop and my contribution was negligible.

Even after this enormous achievement, Kotz and Johnson did not rest on their laurels. In the 1990s they embarked on a new project (although of a smaller scale): the reprinting of seminal papers in statistics, each with a substantial new introduction. It resulted in the three-volume work, *Breakthroughs in Statistics*. I was pleased to be asked to write the introductions to two of my all-time-favorite papers: The 1933 Neyman-Pearson paper in which they formulated their theory of optimal tests, and Student's fundamental 1908 paper, which started the modern small-sample theory of hypothesis testing.

In recognition of his great contributions to statistics, Sam Kotz received three honorary degrees: from Harbin Institute of Technology, the University of Athens, and Bowling Green State University. A festschrift in his honor, *Advances in the Theory and Practice of Statistics,* edited by Johnson and Balakrishnan, was published in 1997.

58. Stephen M. Stigler (b. 1941)

Steve Stigler, one of our Berkeley Ph.D. students, obtained his degree in 1967 with a thesis on linear functions of order statistics, under the supervision of Lucien Le Cam. For the next twelve years, he was a faculty member in the statistics department of the University of Wisconsin. In 1979 he moved to the University of Chicago, where he served as chair of the statistics department from 1986 to 1992, and again since 2005.

Stigler continued working in mathematical statistics, but starting in 1973 developed a new research interest that eventually came to dominate. He explains how this came about (in response to a question of mine) in a recent letter:

> During the year 1973–74, I was working on some order statistics papers and in looking into the library I came across a remarkable paper that Percy Daniell had published in the *American Journal of Mathematics* in 1920, "Observations Weighted According to Error." There he used the calculus of variations to derive the optimum weighting functions, and he found various results I had not seen before a 1955 paper by Jung. Digging further, I encountered relevant works of Simon Newcombe, and Laplace. . . . There were publications that came from that and I guess I had "caught the bug." With a Guggenheim Fellowship (1976–77) and a year at the Center [for Advanced Study in the Behavioral Sciences] (1978–79), I pushed further and began what would be my 1986 book.

I kept up some mathematical work, but the historical work became more central. I don't know that there was a single "cause"; mostly the freedom to follow developing interests. I had been a history minor[5] and taken a course in history of mathematics then from Ken May.

And so came about Stigler's 1986 book, *The History of Statistics (The Measurement of Uncertainty Before 1900)*, the first integrated account of the history of our field. The writing of such a book, of course, involves the obvious tasks: collecting facts, searching in archives, deciphering letters, detecting errors, and so on. But Stigler's book was more than a dry recital of facts. What made it particularly attractive was that it had a plot, a story line that connects the facts and captures the reader's interest. Stigler achieved this by dividing the book into three parts, somewhat similar to the three acts of a play. They present, respectively, a first great success, subsequent complications and failure, and in the last act overcoming these obstacles to reach a triumphant conclusion.

The first part describes the development of a methodology for analyzing observations in astronomy and geodesy, and ends with what Stigler calls the Gauss-Laplace synthesis,

> which brought together two well-developed lines—one the combination of observations through the aggregation of linearized equations of condition, the other the use of mathematical probability to assess uncertainty and make inferences—into a coherent whole.

However, as Stigler points out, these methods "remained confined to the narrow disciplines that spawned them."

The second part of the book is concerned with the effort, principally of Adolphe Quetelet and Wilhelm Lexis, to extend this methodology to the social sciences. Stigler explains why this attempt failed. The details of their work and the reasons for its failure are too complex to recount here but the upshot was "that neither Quetelet [n]or Lexis had much long-lasting influence, and today they are of interest mainly to historians."

After this somewhat discouraging interlude, the third and last part of Stigler's book treats the breakthrough brought about by the development of the concepts of correlation and regression, principally by Galton, Edgeworth, Karl Pearson, and finally Yule.

If the method of least squares and the normal linear model were motivated by the needs of astronomy and geodesy, and the efforts of Quetelet and Lexis by their desire to extend this approach to the social sciences, it was biology (and particularly the study of heredity) that was the starting point for Galton and for a development that ends with Yule's showing how to apply regression combined with the method of least squares to the social sciences.[6]

---

[5] At Carleton College, which recently awarded him an honorary degree.

[6] Yule's seminal 1899 paper on the causes of poverty forms one of the lead examples in Freedman's 2005 book mentioned in Section 35.

It is this progression from the use of least squares and the normal distribution in the physical sciences to the unsuccessful attempts to extend the method to the social sciences, the addition of the new concepts of correlation and regression stemming from work in biology, and finally the combination of these ideas to provide a successful approach in the social sciences, that constitutes the story line for Stigler's book. It holds the reader's attention and provides a compass for the presentation of a great amount of factual information.

Both before and after the publication of his history, Stigler wrote many papers on historical subjects. In revised versions (and with the addition of a previously unpublished paper on Karl Pearson), most of them were collected in his 1999 book, *Statistics on the Table*. At the same time he continued his statistical work, particularly in the area of robust estimation.

I have, of course, known Steve since the 1960s, when he was a graduate student in our department. Later, he was chair of the University of Chicago statistics department when (in 1991) the university gave me an honorary degree. I feel sure that he was the driving force behind this award. One source of continued contact was our shared interest in the history of statistics; he has been an invaluable resource for my occasional historical writing.

In addition to his work as statistician and historian of science, Stigler has also provided much administrative service to the profession. He has served as theory and methods editor of JASA, as president of the Institute of Mathematical Statistics (IMS) and of the International Statistical Institute (ISI), as member of the board of the Social Science Research Council, and for the last twenty years as member of the board of trustees of the Center for Advanced Study in the Behavioral Sciences. In 2005, he was elected to the American Philosophical Society.

13
New Tasks and Relationships

By the early 1970s, my friend Joe Hodges had gone into administration, and our longtime collaboration had come to an end. I continued to do research, but other projects came to the fore and research became less dominant. In fact, I too temporarily became ensnared by administrative duties when in 1973 I agreed to take my turn at chairing the department. Since this involves responsibility for the professional well-being of a large number of people (students, teaching assistants, faculty, and staff), it is a fairly demanding job.

Nearly at the same time, in the summer of 1973, an event occurred that was to profoundly change my life. It was the arrival of a sabbatical visitor from Kansas, the psychologist Juliet Shaffer, who wanted to use the year to improve her knowledge of statistics. Four years later she became my wife, and for the last thirty wonderful years we have been lovers, friends, colleagues, and collaborators.

A third event that started at that time but came to fruition only the following year was a direct consequence of my becoming chair. This enabled me to bring to Berkeley for a year Fred Mosteller, a remarkable statistician whom up to then I had only known by reputation. The friendship that developed during his Berkeley year later resulted in my collaborating with him on the second and third editions of the volume of essays known as SAGTU—*Statistics: Guide to the Unknown.*

A very different project started a few years later when Constance Reid agreed to my suggestion that she write a biography of Neyman. Since she was not a statistician, she asked me to help her with some of the more technical issues, particularly with the letters Pearson had received from Neyman during the years of their collaboration. Although unfortunately only a few of Pearson's letters to Neyman have survived, nevertheless the surviving correspondence provides a vivid day-to-day account of their joint work.

Finally, the 1970s led to a friendship with the magician, mathematician, and statistician Persi Diaconis, when in 1974 he joined the Stanford statistics department. It has resulted in a continuing exchange of ideas, joint efforts in common causes, and mutual support, all of which have greatly enriched my life.

59. Juliet P. Shaffer (b. 1932)

In the summer of 1973, I received a letter from a psychology professor at the University of Kansas. She wanted to use a sabbatical, she wrote, to improve her knowledge of statistics, and to this end was planning to spend the upcoming year in Berkeley. Her stay would be supported by a fellowship that required her to have a sponsor. Would I be willing to serve in this capacity?

She added that she knew I was very busy and promised me that she would not take up much of my time. It is a promise she did not keep because four years later we were married.

Juliet (Julie) Popper Shaffer was born and raised in Brooklyn. At Midwood High School, she managed, through special arrangements, to take the full four-year mathematics curriculum, although at the time it was intended for boys only. She also joined the math club, the only girl in her class to do so. After graduating from Midwood, she turned down a scholarship from Cornell in order to go to Swarthmore.[1]

At Swarthmore, she started out as a chemistry major, switched to pre-med, and finally ended up as a psychology major with a minor in mathematics and

[1] Much of this information is provided by Robinson (2005).

philosophy. She did her graduate study in psychology at Stanford, where she obtained her Ph.D. with a thesis titled "Social and Personality Correlates of Children's Estimates of Height." On the way she took a number of statistics courses, not only those offered by McNemar in the psychology department, but also courses by Lincoln Moses, Al Bowker, and other members of the statistics faculty.

After receiving her degree, Julie spent a postdoctoral year at Indiana University working with William Estes, and then accepted a tenure-track appointment in psychology at the University of Kansas, where she remained for twenty years, rising to the rank of professor. At Kansas, she taught courses in both general and mathematical psychology, and in addition taught most of the statistics courses offered by her department.

When she moved to Berkeley, enrollment in psychology was low and psychology departments did little hiring. However, Julie obtained visiting appointments to teach statistics, during 1975–76 at the University of California at Davis and the following year in our department. The very mathematical orientation of the Berkeley department was a drawback for her, but at the same time her extensive applied experience provided the department an opportunity to strengthen its applied side.

In fact, as one of her courses, she started a statistical consulting service, staffed by the graduate students taking the course. During the ten years that she was in charge of this course, the service provided statistical advice to about two thousand clients, mostly—but not exclusively—from within the university. To head this service, Julie was appointed lecturer in 1977 and senior lecturer in 1981, a position in which she remained until her retirement in 1994.

Shortly after her retirement, Julie was offered a position as principal research scientist and coordinating director of the Large Scale Assessment Group at ETS (Educational Testing Service) in Princeton. So we spent the years 1995 to 1997 in Princeton.

Julie's research up to 1970 was in psychology, and during the next decade she still published occasional papers in that field. But starting in her last years at Kansas, the focus of her work moved to statistics, and in particular to contingency tables, analysis of variance, and multiple comparisons. Eventually her research centered on the last of these subjects and she became one of the leaders in that field.

The central problem of multiple comparisons, particularly multiple testing, is easy to describe. Suppose s independent tests are performed at level α (say .05), for example tests of the effectiveness of s possible treatments of some medical condition, and suppose that one of them turns out highly significant. Can we then with reasonable confidence contend that this particular hypothesis is false? We could obviously do so if we had tested just this one hypothesis. However, the situation changes radically if we take account of the fact that we are testing not just that one treatment but, independently, s of them. Even if none of them has any beneficial effect, the probability that at least one of them (and hence the most significant one) will give a significant result is 1 minus the probability of no false rejections and hence

$$(*) \qquad P(\text{at least one false rejection}) = 1 - (1 - \alpha)^s.$$

As s becomes large, $(1 - \alpha)^s$ tends to zero and the probability of at least one false rejection to 1. If $s = 50$, for example, (*) = .92.

The question of how to handle this problem of multiplicity is difficult, but if it is ignored we are duped into many false rejections. What clearly is needed is an approach that does not treat each of the s hypotheses separately but considers them jointly as a set (the technical term is family).

The problem, despite its practical importance and theoretical interest, was long ignored. The first person to study it systematically was John Tukey, who in 1953 produced a book-length manuscript entitled, *The Problem of Multiple Comparisons*. However, he did not publish it but only distributed it in mimeographed form to a limited audience. It was finally published in 1994 in volume 8 of Tukey's *Collected Works*.

In this manuscript, Tukey formulated the concept of family, proposed various measures of error control for families, suggested procedures with satisfactory error control, and so on. Partly as a result of his work, the importance of the subject was gradually realized, and eventually led to a flood of publications. The first published book on the topic was Miller's *Simultaneous Statistical Inference* (1966). More recent monographs are *Multiple Comparison Procedures* (Hochberg and Tamhane, 1987) and *Resampling Based Multiple Testing* (Westfall and Young, 1993), and by now many others.

Shaffer's first papers in this area appeared in the early 1970s. They were followed by two joint papers with me in 1977 and 1979. Perhaps her (so far) two most importance contributions had their origin in a question she was asked by a Kansas colleague. As she explains (Robinson, 2005):

> He had carried out a perception experiment with three conditions. Multiple comparison methods indicated that the smallest and largest were significantly different, but the middle one was not significantly different from either of the others. He found that conclusion unpleasant, since if the first and third were really different, the middle one obviously had to be different from at least one of them. Thinking about this issue made me wonder whether an additional criterion in evaluating multiple comparison procedures, aside from error rate and power, should be the interpretability of the conclusions reached by using them. This resulted after some time in a paper sketching out these ideas and some evidence related to them (1981). Although I did not continue that line of research, the ideas on possible patterns of differences were useful in suggesting some improvements on the Holm (1979) sequentially rejective multiple comparison procedure (Shaffer, 1986).

These improvements turned out to be substantial, but their full usefulness was limited by the difficulty of their implementation. This difficulty was largely overcome in recent papers by Rasmussen (1991, 1993), Westfall (1997), and Donoghue (2004), who provided additional theory, some helpful heuristics, and efficient algorithms.

Shaffer also initiated work on another aspect of multiple testing. When testing the null hypothesis that a parameter is zero, in case of rejection one frequently also makes the determination whether it is positive or negative. In doing so, one runs the risk of a directional error (also called type III error), that is, of deciding that the effect is positive when in fact it is negative or vice versa. In a 1980 paper, Shaffer showed the unexpected result that taking these additional errors into account can boost the error rate beyond the nominal level α. She also found conditions under which this cannot happen. A definitive solution proved quite difficult, and her paper sparked a substantial literature.

Julie's more than twenty papers on multiple comparisons include not only theoretical and methodological contributions, but also frequently cited expository papers, in particular a review paper in the *Annual Review of Psychology* for 1995 and the article "Simultaneous Testing" in volume 8 of the *Encyclopedia of Statistical Sciences*. A more recent (somewhat more specialized) paper was a survey of "Optimality Results in Multiple Hypothesis Testing" (2004).

Her remarkable career took Julie from psychology to applied statistics, to quite theoretical work in multiple comparisons, to applications of statistics to education and more recently to genomics. She has served in various editorial positions, including that of editor of the *Journal of Educational Statistics* (1986–1989), and at present is associate editor of *The American Statistician*. In addition, she has served as a member of many panels and committees, including the visiting committee to the Harvard statistics department (1993–1999), and chair of the American Statistical Association (ASA) representatives to sections of the American Association for the Advancement of Science (1996–2002). Since 1996, she has been a member of the Defense Advisory Committee on Military Personnel Testing of the U.S. Department of Defense.

Julie Shaffer's work has been recognized by election to fellowship in both ASA and American Psychological Association (APS) and to membership in the International Statistical Institute (ISI). In 2004, she received the F.N. David award from the Committee of Presidents of Statistical Societies (COPSS).

My own work was strongly influenced by Julie in a number of ways. Fairly early, she rekindled my interest in multiple comparisons. It is a subject on which I had worked in the 1950s but which I then abandoned in favor of nonparametrics. She also exerted a strong continuing influence through her critically reading my writing (as I did hers), which resulted in many improvements. But her greatest impact on my work was to provide the impetus for two books that without her I would not have written.

The first of these had its origin many years earlier in Colin Blyth's lecture notes. After I had converted the notes on hypothesis testing into a book (in 1959), it would have been natural to do the same with the estimation notes. However, that project did not appeal to me, since I did not find the theory, much of it based on squared error loss, very persuasive. Now Julie gradually convinced me that there was a need for such a book, and so in 1983 I published, *Theory of Point Estimation* as a companion to my testing book.

At about that time, Julie also persuaded me to launch another, very different, project. She had noticed a serious problem with our applied graduate courses such as analysis of variance, contingency tables, and multivariate analysis. Many of these courses involved a substantial amount of asymptotics. Since most of the students did not have the background in probability needed for this work, these courses tended to spend two or three weeks introducing the necessary probability tools. However, the ideas were too different, and the time period too short, to provide a real understanding of this material. Confronted with Julie's repeated expressions of concern, I told her that I saw a way out. It would be possible, I believed, to teach the needed large-sample theory at a fairly elementary mathematical level (in fact requiring only basic calculus) by presenting the concepts, results, and applications, but omitting the proofs of some of the basic theorems. It would be somewhat like taking an aerial tramway to a mountaintop rather than making the climb under your own power. You miss part of the experience but you can still fully appreciate the view.

Our discussions led to my giving this approach a try, and so from 1980 to my retirement in 1988 I taught a course (in alternate years) in large-sample theory with minimal prerequisites. It drew students from our program but also from other departments such as economics, sociology, education, the engineering sciences, and so on. The enrollment was never large (between ten and twenty students), but the reactions were very positive, some students telling me that the course had made material accessible to them that they thought would forever be out of their reach.

With Julie's encouragement and support, after retiring I expanded the notes I had distributed to the students in the course into a book, which was essentially completed by 1995 when we moved to Princeton. There the authorities at ETS asked me to give lectures based on the still-unpublished book. When preparing these lectures (one every two weeks), I often found it possible to make improvements and during our two-year stay at ETS I completely rewrote the manuscript.

I have often been asked about the dynamics of marriage to a colleague (a situation that is less rare today than it used to be). For us it has worked out wonderfully well. It has enabled us to appreciate each other's work instead of being excluded from this important area of our lives. In addition, we have been able to be of great help to each other, through discussions, suggestions, and criticism. And of course we have had the pleasure of occasional joint papers. All in all, it has greatly enriched our relationship.

60. Frederick Mosteller (1916–2006)

A wonderful resource for scientists at the University of California since 1955 has been the Miller Institute for Basic Research in Science. One of the benefits it offers is a year (since 1988 only a semester) to devote to research, free

of all teaching and administrative obligations. I was lucky enough to be given such a Miller year in 1962–63 and again in 1972–73. Between those two years, I served on the advisory board of the Miller Institute from 1966 to 1969.

In addition to funding such local leaves, the institute also provides departments with the opportunity to bring visiting faculty to Berkeley under similarly attractive conditions. When I became department chair in 1973, it occurred to me that this might be a means for our department to get to know an outstanding statistician who to my knowledge had never been to Berkeley, one of the few prominent statisticians who had not participated in any of the Berkeley Symposia. The person in question was Frederick Mosteller of Harvard, and at some meeting that we both attended I mentioned the possibility of a Miller appointment to him. After looking into his various projects and commitments, Fred agreed to come to Berkeley as Miller Professor for the academic year 1974–75.

At the time, Fred was editing two books: *Costs, Risks and Benefits of Surgeries* (with Bunker and Barnes), and *Statistics and Public Policy* (with Fairley). During his year in Berkeley, he gave several fascinating lectures on some of his own contributions to these volumes, particularly on the problem of assessing the effectiveness of medical innovations and of large-scale social action programs.

The first of these two books was reviewed by Hiatt,[2] who describes it as

> a remarkable book the import [of which] has been far reaching. . . . As Fred Mosteller has done so often in his extraordinary career, he and his colleagues in this book identify some crucial problems, describe how they have come to pass, add insights concerning their complexity and possible solutions, and end with a series of constructive proposals. Surely the book is in part responsible for the fact that today the proposals are accepted in large measure and widely followed.

It is not possible here to discuss all of the more than sixty books that Fred has authored or edited (often jointly with others). I have already mentioned (in Section 55) some of his joint books with Tukey (four in all, three of them with David Hoaglin as third coauthor or editor) on various aspects of data analysis. Concerning his collaboration with Tukey, Fred once told me that just like I, he too often did not know some of the terms John was using in their discussions. In such cases, he would stop John in midsentence to ask for an explanation. Of course, he could do this more easily than I because they had known each other since Fred's student days at Princeton.[3]

Fred's work with Lincoln Moses (and others) on the National Halothane Study (1969) was mentioned in Section 37. It is summarized in the essay, "Safety of Anesthetics" by Moses and Mosteller in Tanur et al. (1972). In this investigation, Fred had to deal with the problem of cross-classified data. The work led to the Ph.D. theses of two of Fred's students, Yvonne Bishop and Stephen Fienberg, and eventually a major book on the subject. About Mosteller's part in this book, Steve Fienberg (2006) writes:

> He organized a group of us to write a book around the recent developments in categorical data analysis. . . . This project ultimately produced *Discrete Multivariate Analysis—Theory and Practice* [1975]. He was the guiding light behind the project and our constant editor and sometimes contributor, but in typical fashion he insisted that only Yvonne Bishop, Paul Holland, and I be listed as "authors." Ultimately, he agreed to let us acknowledge his efforts by listing him as a "collaborator" on the title page.

While in the Halothane study the substantive problem was primary and then led to the development of some needed methodology, the reverse was the case with another project that resulted in the book with David Wallace *Inference and Disputed Authorship* (1964, 1986). As the authors explain in the preface:

> We apply a 200–year-old mathematical theorem to a 175–year-old historical problem more to advance statistics than history. . . . For us the question of whether Hamilton or Madison wrote the disputed Federalist papers has served as a laboratory and demonstration problem for developing and comparing statistical methods.

To emphasize this intention, the second edition bore the new title, *Applied Bayesian and Classical Inference: The Case of the Federalist Papers*.

---

[2] Reprinted in Fienberg et al. (1990).

[3] Some of their recollections from this time can be found in Anscombe (1988).

The books on surgical and social innovations, the Halothane study, and the Federalist papers illustrate Fred's scientific work. Equally important is another area of his activities, his work as an educator. He believes that an understanding of the ideas of probability theory and statistics is important for people in all walks of life, and he has put much effort into making these ideas as widely available as possible.

An early project of this kind was his 1961 text (with Rourke and Thomas), *Probability and Statistical Applications*. Requiring only two years of high school algebra and no calculus, the book was intended as a high school text, with the aim of engendering

> first, an understanding of the kinds of regularity that occur amid random fluctuations; second, experience in associating probabilistic mathematical models with phenomena in the real world; third, skill in using these mathematical models to interpret such phenomena and in predicting, with appropriate measures of uncertainty, the outcomes of related experiments; and fourth, some insight into statistical inference, both classical and Bayesian.

Fred used a version of this book as text for his 1960–61 television course, "Continental Classroom." Although the course was intended primarily for college and university students taking the course for credit, it was also used by some high schools and was enjoyed by many members of the general public. Fred reports (Mosteller, 1962) that "it has been estimated that during a week about 1.2×10^6 different people viewed the lessons."

In a strange way, I became involved with another of Fred's projects; however, it was not directly through Fred, whom I did not know at the time, but through Bill Kruskal at Chicago. One day in 1971, Bill, who some years earlier had spent a year at Berkeley, called me in my capacity as editor of the series in probability and statistics for the publishing house Holden-Day. The manuscript he wanted to talk about was a collection of essays put together by a joint committee of the ASA and the National Council of Teachers of Mathematics (Fred Mosteller, chair; Judith Tanur, editor), which was intended to show a general public the usefulness of statistics. Each essay was concerned with a particular application, and the cases came from a wide variety of fields.

Kruskal mentioned that the manuscript had been offered to the principal publishers of statistics books but that none had been interested. The book sounded very promising to me, and the publisher agreed. After seeing the manuscript, we quickly came to terms and *Statistics: Guide to the Unknown* (SAGTU) appeared in 1972 under the Holden-Day imprint.

The book was a great success and after a few years it was time to think of a new edition. It seemed to me that a deficiency of the volume, particularly for teaching purposes, was the absence of problems. I therefore suggested that I organize a set of problems for each of the essays, and I then carried out this project with the help of some of my graduate students. I also proposed to Fred that two new essays by him, based on the talks he had given in Berkeley during his Miller year on surgical and social innovations, would make perfect additions to the volume, and he agreed to provide them. With these additions, the second edition came out in 1978.

While these changes were, I believe, helpful, another idea of mine turned out to be very unsuccessful. I thought there would be a market for smaller (and hence less expensive) books with essays in only one area that would be suitable as supplementary material for statistics courses in that area, so we published three booklets of a little over one hundred pages, each containing a subset of about a dozen essays in, respectively, business and economics, the biological and health sciences, and political and social issues. However, they were a failure. The market I had foreseen just was not there.

In the mid-1980s, Fred felt it was time for a third edition of SAGTU. Sixteen years had elapsed since the original publication and some of the essays had begun to show their age. They needed to be retired or at least updated, and authors had to be found to cover a number of topics of current interest. Fred asked me to work with him on this revision. Thus, for a number of years I visited him every few months for this purpose. These Harvard trips usually included my giving a seminar talk either in the statistics or biostatistics department, and having an enjoyable dinner with Fred and his wife, Virginia.

It was interesting to watch Fred in action and to meet some of the members of his group, the people who assisted him in the research, computing, and writing on the several projects he was handling at any given time. The much-changed third edition came out in 1989.

Fred's great achievements derived from a combination of three abilities: he was a superb applied statistician and data analyst who was able to spot important problems and was willing to tackle them; he was an outstanding and dedicated teacher and communicator; and finally, he was a masterful organizer, leader, and manager.

As a result of this last capacity, he was much in demand as an administrator. Particularly noteworthy is his administrative work at Harvard, where in the course of his career he chaired four different departments.

Fred's connection with Harvard began in 1946 when, after obtaining his Ph.D. under Wilks and Tukey at Princeton, he was appointed lecturer in the newly formed Department of Social Relations. He was promoted to associate professor in 1948 and to professor of mathematical statistics in 1951. In 1953–54, he served as acting chair of the department.

In 1957, Harvard established the Department of Statistics, and Fred served as its chair from 1957 to 1969 and again from 1975 to 1977. He followed this by chairing the Department of Biostatistics from 1977 to 1981, and then in 1981 was asked instead to chair the Department of Health Policy and Management, which was facing some difficulties. Of his accomplishments in chairing these different departments, one stands out as particularly unusual. In 1977, he managed to bring to the Department of Biostatistics (in joint appointments with the Sidney Farber Cancer Center) Marvin Zelen, together with most of the group Zelen had built up at the State University of

New York at Buffalo, thus enriching the department by ten new faculty members. Two additional members of the group joined the following year.

Recognition of Fred's distinction and leadership abilities has led to his becoming president of the Psychometric Society (1957), ASA (1967), IMS (1974), and the International Statistical Institute (1992). From 1975 to 1981, he served on the board of directors of the American Association for the Advancement of Science (AAAS), and in 1980 he served as its president. In addition, from 1964 to 1985 he was a member of the board of directors of the Russell Sage Foundation. His effectiveness and influence in these last two positions is described in Fienberg et al. (1990, pp. 54–57).

Fred has received many honors. He has been elected to the three principal American academies: the National Academy of Sciences, the American Academy of Arts and Sciences, and the American Philosophical Society. He has received honorary degrees from the University of Chicago and from Carnegie Mellon, Yale, Wesleyan, and Harvard. In addition, some of his friends and colleagues have published a book about him: *A Statistical Model: Frederick Mosteller's Contributions to Statistics, Science, and Public Policy* (Fienberg et al., 1990). It contains a biographical essay by Tukey, a bibliography, and six chapters on Fred's various contributions. A volume of *Selected Papers of Frederick Mosteller* (Fienberg and Hoaglin, eds.) was published in 2006.

61. Constance Reid (b. 1918)

In 1976, I was reading with great interest the recently published biography of Richard Courant, the mathematician who had been responsible for my coming to Berkeley. Its author was Constance Reid, the sister of my former fellow student Julia Robinson. It seemed to me that Mrs. Reid, who had also written a biography of the great mathematician David Hilbert, would be an ideal person to write a biography of Neyman. Since I did not know her, I asked Julia to inquire whether her sister might be interested in such a project. Julia replied that she (Julia) was strongly opposed to the idea. She believed that mathematicians should be remembered through their work, and that their lives had no relevance and should remain private. Nevertheless, she agreed to forward my suggestion. However, the answer was negative—Mrs. Reid did not want to write another mathematical biography.

A few months later, I received a phone call from Constance saying that she might be interested after all, although she was thinking of an article rather than a book. But she would need some cooperation from Neyman. Just what would be involved? She thought two meetings of one to two hours each would suffice.

So I went to see Neyman, the books on Hilbert and Courant under my arm, and told him of the project. "It's a free country," he barked. Although he had often expressed his lack of interest in the past and that only the future concerned him, I was startled by the violence of his reaction. I told him that

we had no interest in proceeding if he objected. At this, he became more conciliatory and asked what would be expected of him. I repeated what Constance required and he relented. "I always enjoy talking to young ladies," he said. "All right."

As it turned out, he enjoyed their conversations so much that for the next year he and Constance met every Saturday morning, followed the session with lunch, and then reconvened in the afternoon. Thus, the book was based on an extensive oral record as well as many documents, including the crucial correspondence with Egon Pearson from the 1920s and early 1930s. She had obtained this correspondence by going to London to see Pearson and persuading him to copy the letters and let her use them for her work. When, after a year's preparation, she finally told Neyman that the time had come for her to start writing and that they would have to discontinue their Saturday meetings, he was very disappointed.

Since Constance had no background in statistics, she asked Neyman whether he would object to her showing the Neyman–Pearson letters to me. His reaction was the same as when I first approached him about the project, "It's a free country," to which he added, "No objection."

It was a great thrill for me to see these letters, which made it possible to follow, step by step, the gradual development of what was to become the basic theory of hypothesis testing, and the respective contributions made by the two authors. And as I read, a clear picture emerged: during the early years of their collaboration, Pearson was the leader and originator, who explained to Neyman what he was doing and where the work was leading him. Neyman, to whom all this was quite new, frequently misunderstood, and his principal contribution at this stage was to force Pearson to greater clarity, and to help with working out a variety of examples.

This early work resulted in a joint 1928 paper of one hundred pages setting forth the likelihood ratio method of test construction, with many applications. This method, which Pearson had proposed to Neyman at the beginning of their collaboration, seemed to give the right results, and Pearson felt that it provided the general answer he had been looking for.

But Neyman was not satisfied. He wanted not just an intuitively plausible method but a formulation that was logically convincing. The tables had now turned, with Neyman taking the lead and Pearson having to be persuaded. Pearson himself, in an account of this part of the work, confirmed that "my part was to help shaping the material; sharpening the arguments; standardizing the notation and terminology; working on the illustrative examples; and deciding on the best forms for the diagrams." The resulting paper appeared in 1933, and for the first time provided a logical basis for hypothesis testing. The optimality approach that it initiated was to become a central theme of mathematical statistics.

More details of this fascinating story are given in Constance Reid's book, which appeared in 1982 to very favorable reviews. It gives a lively picture of Neyman, which Constance considered a portrait rather than a biography, and to which she gave the title *Neyman—from Life*. Neyman himself did not see the book. He died of heart failure in 1981.

Before the Hilbert, Courant, and Neyman trilogy, Constance had written a number of other books, including the very successful *From Zero to Infinity—What Makes Numbers Interesting* (1955, 1968, 1992). She followed the three biographies with two more, one in 1993 on E.T. Bell, the author of *Men of Mathematics,* and one on her sister Julia (1996).

The last of these had a forerunner in a biographical essay written during the last month of Julia's life. In view of Julia's opposition to such biographical writing, this publication is somewhat of a surprise. That she finally agreed to it was due to the fact that, as reported in Section 5, she had become a public figure and a role model.

The book, *Julia—A Life in Mathematics,* includes several articles on her work by mathematicians, one of them by Yuri Matijasevich, who had completed her proof of the Robinson conjecture regarding Hilbert's Tenth Problem (see Section 5). However, the core of the book is Constance Reid's essay, "The Autobiography of Julia Robinson." How can an autobiography be written by someone else? Constance explains in the preface:

> I could never write about Julia without writing more intimately than she or I would wish, and it took me a while to come up with the solution of writing her "autobiography."

What I wrote would then be entirely what she would want to have written about her own life. I would be writing in her spirit, not my own. . . .

When I started to write, she was back in the hospital. Although she was hopeful of a second remission [from leukemia], she was also realistic about her chances. Every few days I read aloud to her what I had written—which was based on an interview we had had on June 30. She listened attentively and amended or deleted as appropriate, sometimes just a word. She heard and approved all that I wrote. . . . She died on July 30, 1985, at the age of 65.

The book is a moving testament to a wonderful person and great mathematician and provides an insightful picture of a mathematician's life. It caps Constance Reid's remarkable career. Although she never studied mathematics beyond elementary algebra and plane geometry—no analytic geometry, no calculus—she was able to write successfully about mathematicians and their work. In the process, she got to know and become friends with many mathematicians and acquired much knowledge about various aspects of mathematics. As a result, she was one of the subjects in the collection of portraits, *Mathematical People* (Albers and Alexanderson, 1985). She had become a preeminent mathematical writer and a member of the mathematical community.

62. Persi Diaconis (b. 1945)

Of the many people who are the subjects of this book, Persi Diaconis is undoubtedly the one with the most unusual career path. He ran away from home at age fourteen and spent the next ten years on the road as a practicing magician. He had been interested in magic tricks since he was five, had learned to perform some tricks, and at school joined the magic club. He spent much time at the magic store and became known in the magic community. He explains what happened next[4]:

When I was 14, America's greatest magician was a man named Dai Vernon. We met at a magician's cafeteria and he invited me to go on the road with him as sort of an assistant, and I jumped at the chance. I just went off. I didn't tell my parents; I just left.

Two years later, Vernon settled on the West Coast and Diaconis continued on his own.

When at twenty-four he decided to go back to school, he graduated from high school in a strange way, of which he gives the following account (in De Groot, 1986):

I came back to New York and kept getting mail as if I had graduated. Letters from the army saying, "Dear Graduate, perhaps you would be interested in . . . And I had won some scholarships—a Merit Scholarship and some others. And I thought, "Gee, this

[4] Quoted from De Groot (1986).

is funny. I didn't even graduate from high school and there are all these opportunities that I cannot take." But I kept getting these letters, so then I went into school and I said, "Did I somehow graduate?" This is a giant New York City high school, George Washington, and the assistant principal said, "Oh, Diaconis. Yeah, the teachers got together and decided it would not do you any good to cause you trouble, and they just decided to give you grades and graduate you."

Thus, Diaconis was able to go to college. He went to night school at the City College of New York, and graduated in two-and-a-half years. For his choice of a graduate program, he had two aims. He wanted to study mathematics and he wanted to go to Harvard. However, these two goals were at odds with each other, since no one from City College had gotten into mathematics at Harvard. So he applied instead to the Harvard statistics department, where he was accepted. He had originally thought that he might be able to transfer to mathematics after a semester, but it turned out that he liked statistics, so he became a statistician.

Three years after entering the program, he obtained his Ph.D. in 1974 with a thesis, written without supervision, on a problem that he had found interesting: the distribution of leading digits in various arithmetic sequences. After getting his degree, he accepted a position at the Stanford statistics department, where he remained until 1987, with an interruption of two visiting years at Harvard. From 1987 to 1996, he served on the mathematics faculty at Harvard and, after two years at Cornell, in 1998 returned to Stanford with a joint appointment in mathematics and statistics. He continues to be very active in this position today.

The mixture of appointments and interests in mathematics and statistics throughout his career raises a question that he answers in his 1986 interview with Morris De Groot: "What am I?":

> I am a statistician. That's my training and my interest, and that's the language that I speak and the way I think.

Despite the implicit disclaimer, mathematics was and continues to also be central to Persi's work and thought, not only as an indispensable tool but also for its own interest and beauty. He has in fact written a number of papers in pure mathematics. And the mathematical community has accepted him as one of their own, as can be seen from his selection as Hedrick Lecturer (1989) of the Mathematical Association of America, as Gibbs Lecturer (1997) of the American Mathematical Society, and as plenary speaker at the International Congress of Mathematics in 1998.

Besides statistics and mathematics, magic continues to be a theme in Persi's life. He has close friends in the magic community and over the years he has built up one of the world's greatest private library in magic. In addition, aspects having their origin in his magic experience continue to show up both in his research and his teaching. At present, for example, he, together with his frequent collaborator Ron Graham, are close to completing a book, *From Magic to Mathematics and Back*.

The paper that in 1991 brought Persi to the front page of the *New York Times* grew out of his experience as a magician. It was concerned with the question: How many shuffles does it take to get a new deck of cards close to random order, that is, so that each of the 52! orders is equally likely? He showed in a joint paper with Bayer (1992) that the first five shuffles don't get you very far, but that then there is a sudden considerable improvement, and that by the end of seven shuffles one is fairly close to randomness.

This "cutoff" phenomenon of a sudden drop after a certain number of steps was also found in some other situations and led to what is one of my favorites among Persi's papers, "The Cutoff Phenomenon in Finite Markov Chains" (1996). It surveys instances in which the cutoff phenomenon does and does not occur, and explores the underlying cause.

A few years before the shuffle paper, Persi had been on the front page of the *New York Times* with a 1989 paper (with Fred Mosteller) on coincidences. We all have experienced coincidences that are truly astounding and seem to defy explanation. So a scientific study of this phenomenon is of great general interest. The principal findings of the Diaconis-Mosteller paper are summarized in the abstract:

> Once we set aside coincidences having apparent causes, four principles account for large numbers of remaining coincidences: hidden cause; psychology, including memory and perception; multiplicity of end points, including the counting of "close"

or nearly alike events as if they were identical; and the law of truly large numbers, which says that when enormous numbers of events and people and their interactions cumulate over time, almost any outrageous event is bound to occur.

This work on coincidences is an ongoing project, with a book planned for the near future.

Many of Persi's papers are concerned with issues relating to his philosophical position—the fact that he is a subjective Bayesian in the sense of Savage and De Finetti. An important part of this work is a long series of papers with David Freedman on the consistency of Bayes estimates. One of the basic properties of these estimates, supported by various theoretical results, is that their asymptotic behavior is independent of the prior distribution, and that they are guided to the correct value by the data as the sample size increases. It therefore came as a shock when in 1963 Freedman (as mentioned in Section 35) provided an example in which this is not the case. In continuing work (summarized in 1986 and 1997), Diaconis and Freedman have explored the circumstances under which Bayes estimates are or are not consistent.

Of Diaconis' nearly two hundred publications, I shall mention only one other, which is particularly close to my own interests. It is a joint paper with his wife Susan Holmes, "Gray Codes for Randomization Procedures" (1994), and deals with the following one-sample testing problem:

Let $Z_1, \ldots, Z_n$ be a sample from a distribution $F(z - \theta)$, with F continuous and symmetric about the origin. To test the hypothesis H: $\theta = 0$, we can apply the randomization t-test, which has an exact level independent of F. When N is large, calculation of the critical value becomes prohibitive, and one resorts to an approximation. One such approximation is the critical value of the t-distribution, another that of the normal distribution. The authors investigate which of the two gives the better approximation. They show that this depends on the values of $Z_1, \ldots, Z_n$, and find that the answer to the question is provided by the second term of an asymptotic expansion.

I first met Persi when he was a graduate student at Harvard and I a member of the visiting committee assessing the state of the Harvard statistics department. Since getting his Ph.D., he has throughout much of his career been my Stanford neighbor and friend. During his years on the Harvard faculty (1981–82, 1985–86, and 1987 to 1997), I would often stay with him at his bachelor quarters near Harvard Square when visiting Cambridge to work with Fred Mosteller.

Over the years, we have been engaged in various formal and informal collaborative efforts. In particular, we wrote a joint chapter for Fred Mosteller's 1990 Festschrift on Fred's contributions to *Mathematical Statistics*. We also wrote a review of the *Encyclopedia of Statistical Sciences* for *Math Reviews* (although for some unknown reason the review appeared under my name only). We serve as each other's experts: he when I need information about some mathematical issues, I by translating or summarizing early German material on magic. We also share an interest in the history of statistics and often discuss historical issues. In addition, Persi is my window on the current statistical scene. Since my retirement nearly twenty years ago I am out of the loop, but Persi knows everything and everybody and keeps me informed.

For years now we have had an ongoing conversation on the state of the field and where it is going. Although we are on opposite sides of the Bayes-frequentist divide, we see eye-to-eye on the basic issue of the value of theory. With the great complexity of many of the statistical problems now at the forefront, theory is often replaced by haphazard consideration of many ad hoc proposals, and this change of attitude has been accompanied by a general denigration of theory. Persi and I have accumulated much material for a paper, "In Praise of Theory," which we hope eventually to publish.

Persi has become the poster boy for statistics. Recently, when the Swiss newspaper *Neue Züricher Zeitung* wanted to publish an article about the field of statistics, they flew a reporter to Stanford to interview him. He is in constant demand as a lecturer by many different groups, and he has honorary degrees from the universities of Chicago, Toulouse, and Uppsala. In 1982, he received a MacArthur Fellowship, one of only three or four statisticians to have been given this "genius award." His not really having finished high school does not seem to have hurt his career too badly.

14 England

One drawback of the personal approach taken in this book is its exclusively American perspective. The people who were my colleagues at Berkeley and Stanford, whom I encountered at meetings, with whom I served on committees, with very few exceptions lived and worked in the United States. Had I lived in England, I would have written instead about Maurice Bartlett, George Barnard, Henry Daniels, Maurice Kendall, and other British colleagues. Similarly, the organization with which I was involved was the Institute of Mathematical Statistics and the journal in which I published and for which I acted in various editorial capacities was the *Annals*. Had I lived in England, I would have more likely been involved with the Royal Statistical Society and its journals.

As a result, this book gives the unfortunate impression that work in statistics was only being carried out in America. The intention of this chapter and the next is to dispel this impression and broaden the perspective. These chapters are more fragmentary, but at least give an indication of the work in some other countries. England holds a special place in the history of statistics. After the early probabilistic and statistical work by such outstanding continental mathematicians as Jacob Bernoulli, Gauss, Laplace and Poisson, the principal center of activity moved to England. It was there that Galton, Edgeworth, Yule, and Karl Pearson developed what gradually became a separate discipline, its first institutional manifestation being Pearson's Department of Applied Statistics at University College, London.

Their work prepared the ground for the new statistical methodology developed by R.A. Fisher, which he accompanied with a wealth of new theoretical concepts and results. And this in turn was followed by the work of Egon Pearson (Karl Pearson's son) and Jerzy Neyman, who moved from Poland to London in 1934. Thus, England was the cradle of what today constitutes classical statistics.

This British dominance ended when in 1938 Neyman and Wald left Europe for the United States and founded statistical centers at Berkeley and Columbia, respectively, and with the outbreak of the Second World War, which saw a greatly heightened level of activity in both England and the U.S. This chapter reflects my principal encounters with British statistics.

63. R.A. Fisher (1890–1962)

The basic statistical methodology that today is still being used the world over was created by Ronald Aylmer Fisher in the 1920s and 1930s. But although it was at the core of my own work, it took me a long time to realize Fisher's crucial influence; it was not part of my statistical education. In fact Neyman, who taught the statistics courses I took at Berkeley, rarely mentioned Fisher's name. That was partly due to the fact that Neyman emphasized theory rather than methodology, and partly to the great animosity that had developed between the two men. It took many years before I appreciated Fisher's achievements. For example, my 1959 book on hypothesis testing only fleetingly refers to Fisher's fundamental paper of 1922, although the book is based on the paradigm Fisher established in the paper, because at the time I was not aware of this fact.

The new formulation that Fisher presented in that paper was motivated by what he saw as the purpose of statistics:

> Briefly, and in its most concrete form, the object of statistical methods is the reduction of data. A quantity of data, which usually by its mere bulk is incapable of entering the mind, is to be replaced by relatively few quantities which shall adequately represent the whole, or which, in other words, shall contain as much as possible, ideally the whole, of the relevant information contained in the original data.

In the next paragraph, Fisher states how this aim is to be achieved:

> The object is accomplished by constructing a hypothetical infinite population, of which the actual data are regarded as constituting a random sample. The law of distribution of this hypothetical population is *specified by relatively few parameters*, which are sufficient to describe it exhaustively in respect to all qualities under discussion. [Emphasis added.]

Here, Fisher defines a new paradigm that has become the framework for much of statistics as we know it today, namely as the science of inference in parametric models. (Even the use of the term *parameter* in this context is new.)

The paper contains an astonishing number of other new concepts, many of them flowing from his idea of statistics as data reduction with no or little loss of information. They include sufficiency, the amount of information contained in a data set, the concepts of consistency and efficiency, and finally maximum likelihood as an efficient method of estimation.

The paper is remarkable not only for its originality, the breadth of its vision and its enormous influence; it is also surprising for seemingly having come out of the blue, with Fisher's previous publications giving no indication of what was to come. The origins of the paper have been investigated in a recent paper by Stigler (2005), in which he also emphasizes its enormous importance for the development of the field.

Stigler characterizes Fisher's paper as an astonishing work, which "announces and sketches out a new science of statistics, with new definitions, a new conceptual framework and enough hard mathematical analysis to confirm the potential and richness of this new structure." Fisher's paper, he writes, "was to become a watershed for twentieth century mathematical statistics for most of the last three-quarters of the twentieth century."

How could it have taken me so long to discover the significance of such a fundamental work?

The data-reduction point of view of Fisher's 1922 paper led to important further developments which he presented in 1934 under the uninformative title, "Two New Properties of Mathematical Likelihood." In the first part, he investigates the circumstances under which there exists a single sufficient statistic for a one-parameter family of distributions, and shows that the only families for which this is the case are those later called exponential families. These families (in their later more general multivariate form) were central to my testing and estimation books.

The second part of the paper deals with estimation in the presence of ancillary statistics, that is, statistics whose distribution is independent of the unknown parameters. (It is a subject on which I later wrote a paper, joint with my former student Fritz Scholz). Fisher's 1934 paper was the beginning of work by Fisher and others on the problem of conditional inference. Basically, this is the question of what is the proper frame of reference for frequentist inference.

In estimating the probability of surviving an operation, for example, should we consider the class of all patients having undergone this surgery, or only the patients of similar age and state of health, and so on. On the one hand, the cases should be relevant to the case at hand; on the other, the group should not be so small that accurate estimation becomes impossible. Conditional inference, including in particular Fisher's later concept of relevant subsets, became the subject of a new chapter in the second edition of my testing book.

I learned of some of Fisher's other results as a student, but through Neyman's eyes, not those of Fisher. Thus Neyman taught the distributions of the t- and F-statistics, but he derived them not by Fisher's geometric arguments but analytically through transformation of variables. Learning about Jacobians and acquiring facility with this technique later stood me in good stead, although at the time it was rather painful.

Neyman's graduate course also included certain aspects of Fisher's analysis of variance and regression analysis, although again not from Fisher's point of view but rather in terms of the Gauss-Markov theorem and of hypothesis testing in general linear models. Trying later to read Fisher's treatment of the subject, I found it hard to penetrate. That others too found it difficult is illustrated by a 1987 paper by Speed, "What Is An Analysis of Variance?" which is followed by the comments of eleven discussants, no two of whom quite agree on its meaning.

Surprisingly, Fisher, who based his new methodology on the concept of parametric models, also initiated ideas that were forerunners of the later development of an alternative nonparametric approach. The most important of these were (in modern terminology) randomization models and the related possibility of distribution-free permutation tests. An optimum theory of such permutation tests was later worked out by Charles Stein and me (1949); randomization models play a central role in my nonparametric book of 1975.

Another nonparametric innovation was provided in the 1938 volume of *Statistical Tables* by Fisher and Yates, which included tables for the use of what is now called the Normal Scores test. In their introduction to these tables, the authors explain:

> It is often necessary to draw statistical conclusions from data giving the order of a number of magnitudes, without the knowledge of their quantitative values. . . . Not infrequently, also, an experimenter who possesses quantitative values may suspect that the metric used is unsuitable to the comparisons he wishes to make, and prefer to draw conclusions only from the order of the magnitudes observed.

From this and other comments, it is clear that Fisher considered the normal theory t-test as primary for day-to-day use, and its permutation and rank versions as modifications needed in special circumstances. All the more impressive that he originated these two nonparametric alternative approaches to the problem.

It is impossible even to sketch here all of Fisher's new ideas, but I shall mention one other area of his work, with which I struggled for a long time without much success. It is fiducial inference, which Fisher considered a crucial element of the structure he was building. I had the same difficulty with it that others have found: a sudden switch, midstream, from considering the parameters as constants to treating them as random variables. The unsuccessful efforts of others with this issue is illustrated in Fisher's correspondence with the French probabilist Maurice Fréchet and with John Tukey (published in Bennett, 1990).

Fisher's life and work are well documented. First of all there is the biography by his daughter Joan Fisher Box, *R.A. Fisher: The Life of a Scientist* (1978). A window is also provided by the two volumes of his correspondence edited by J.H. Bennett. And then there is the work itself. Fisher's papers are collected in five magnificent volumes. They comprise both the statistical papers and those on genetics. (Fisher was a great geneticist as well as statistician, an aspect that I am neglecting in this account.)

In addition to the papers, there are Fisher's books. He wrote three books on statistics that were enormously influential: *Statistical Methods for Research Workers, The Design of Experiments,* and *Statistical Methods and Scientific Inference,* first published in 1925, 1935, and 1956, respectively. Their extraordinary impact and durability can be judged by the fact that they are still in print today, in a single volume combining the latest editions of the three works.

Finally, there exists a great deal of secondary literature, including the volume, *R.A. Fisher: An Appreciation* (Fienberg and Hinkley, 1980). Perhaps the best overview is provided by Jimmy Savage in his (posthumous) paper, "On Rereading R.A. Fisher" (1976).

Savage explains the motivation for his essay by Fisher's influence on his statistical education. The present section is similarly motivated, because my first statistical education as a student of Neyman was supplemented by the later influence of Fisher's ideas. The nature of these two phases of my education was very different. Neyman's work is characterized by extraordinary clarity. He presents his results by stating the assumptions they require, followed by the theorem and its proof and some illustrations. The work throughout is theoretical and highly mathematical.

In Fisher's writings, the assumptions are often omitted, the theorem not precise, the proof absent. The mathematical aspects are minimized. In consequence, his claims are often correct in essence but their limitations not noted. Fisher is concerned with the big picture, not with what he would consider mathematical nitpicking.

In his books, a new topic is usually introduced through a data set and an indication of its context, so that the motivation is applied rather than theoretical. As Savage points out, "Mathematics is ruthlessly omitted from Fisher's didactic works, 'Statistical Methods for Research Workers' and 'The Design of Experiments,' " and about Fisher's style Savage writes that, "He has a tendency to be aphoristic and cryptic."

As a result, I and many others have found his books and papers difficult and often frustrating, yet in the end have found the effort to be well worth it and to provide many rewards.

During the 1990s, I became interested in the history of statistics and found occasions to write about some aspects of Fisher's work. The first such instance was the surprising selection of me as the Fisher Lecturer for 1988—surprising in view of the hostility between Neyman and Fisher and my close association with Neyman.

My selection was accompanied by a request for a topic half a year before the lecture. Without giving it much thought I expected that it would be interesting to study Fisher's attitude on modeling, and I chose model specification as my topic. A few weeks later, I started the project by consulting the excellent index to Fisher's *Collected Papers*. To my surprise (and dismay), I found no entry under "model" and only one entry for "specification," namely to his 1922 paper in which he states that the specification (of the model) is "entirely a matter for the practical statisticians." Despite this discouraging statement, Fisher offers some comments on the subject in the paper, so it was not a complete blank.

On the other hand, I found very interesting material from Neyman on modeling (including the unpublished manuscript of a talk). The unlooked-for consequence was that my Fisher lecture had very little to say about Fisher but a lot about the ideas of his great antagonist Neyman.

The antagonism that over the years had developed between Neyman and Fisher, the two principal architects of classical statistics, resulted in more serious consequences than an awkwardness for my Fisher lecture. It tended to accentuate their differences and obscure the fact that Neyman's work (in collaboration with Pearson) was basically a continuation of Fisher's. Although the philosophical differences between Fisher and Neyman were profound, this had little effect on statistical practice. On the whole, their two approaches complement rather than contradict each other. Fisher denied the usefulness of the Neyman-Pearson concept of the power of a test, while Neyman and Pearson ignored the importance of conditioning and thus choosing the most appropriate reference for their frequency calculations.

What has been emphasized by many authors is the difference between the calculation of p-values and the use of a predetermined significance level α, the former attributed to Fisher and the latter to Neyman and Pearson. However, in practice most users combine the two by calculating a p-value and then rejecting or accepting the hypothesis as the p-value is below or above α. This is in fact Fisher's own frequent practice. In 1993, I presented an account along these lines in an expository paper, "The Fisher, Neyman-Pearson Theories of Testing Hypotheses: One Theory or Two?"

The third of my Fisher papers was motivated by the statement of F.N. David mentioned in Section 30: "Gosset was really the big influence in statistics." It seemed to me that it would be interesting to investigate this claim, and I did so in a 1999 paper, " 'Student' and Small-Sample Theory."

Gosset's influence on Fisher can be traced through their correspondence, although—as in the case of the Neyman-Pearson correspondence—mainly the letters of one of the authors (in this case Gosset's) have been preserved. However, they, together with Fisher's comments on some of the letters, provide a detailed picture that I summarized in my paper. They show Gosset's great influence on Fisher's distributional research; as David says, he (Gosset) asked the questions. But Fisher, of course, did much more than put them into statistical language: he found the answers.

I encountered Fisher in person only once. In 1947, Neyman took me (then a newly minted faculty member) with him to a meeting of the International Statistical Institute (ISI) in Washington. At one point, as I was standing next to Neyman, Fisher passed us and brusquely asked Neyman why I was not wearing a name tag. Neyman replied that I was not a member of the ISI. "Then he should not be at the meeting," Fisher said and walked on.

64. Egon S. Pearson (1895–1980) I: Collaboration and Friendship with Neyman (1894–1981)

Neyman and Pearson

The Neyman–Pearson theory of hypothesis testing about which I learned as a student and which is the basis of much of my work has been discussed in Sections 7 and 61. However, the creators of this theory were not only collaborators, but over the twelve years of their joint work they also became close personal friends. This section is concerned with the more personal side of this story, which can be pieced together from Pearson's 1966 article, "The Neyman-Pearson Story" and from Constance Reid's conversations with both authors reported in her book, *Neyman—from Life*.

The partnership united two men of strikingly different appearance, background, and personality. They first met in 1924, when Neyman, a Russian-born Pole, came to Karl Pearson's Department of Applied Statistics for a year of postdoctoral study. Egon Pearson, Karl Pearson's son, was a junior lecturer in the department, with duties somewhat like those of a teaching assistant.

At the time, Neyman's written English was full of mistakes, and he spoke with a strong accent (which he never lost). He led a Bohemian lifestyle and often had to borrow money to tide him over to the next paycheck. Egon describes the impression he made on the occasion of a concert they attended together (Reid, p. 61):

> Jerzy got up from his seat, clapped his hands and shouted, "Bravo!" He looked so foreign with the little moustache and the pince-nez. People looked around. I was embarrassed, but I didn't take it against him.

In contrast, Egon was a member of the British establishment. The son of the distinguished and powerful Karl Pearson, he had been educated at Winchester, one of the great English public (i.e., private) schools. While Neyman was excitable and impetuous, Egon was reserved and disciplined.

Not much is known about the contact between Neyman and Egon Pearson during Neyman's stay at Karl Pearson's department, but one incident (recounted in Reid, pp. 56–57) stands out.

Neyman had brought with him some reprints of papers he had written, two in French, the others in Polish with French and German summaries. Karl Pearson read them and said he would publish one of the papers but that it contained an error. The statement in question claimed that the mean and variance are independent for only one of the Pearson curves, namely the normal. As Neyman recalled to Constance Reid:

> And at that time it seemed that Karl Pearson did not understand the difference between independence and lack of correlation. He was talking to me in this room with the desks. People whom I hardly knew. It was the first weeks essentially. And I tried with my inadequate English to explain to him.

Pearson angrily said, "That may be true in Poland, Mr. Neyman, but it is not true here!" and stalked out. Neyman also left and stayed away from the laboratory for over a week. He was very worried. Would Pearson even let him continue in the department? In this quandary, Neyman turned to another junior member of the staff (J.D. Irwin), who explained the issue to Egon, and Egon was able to convince his father.

And Reid adds: "After the incident with the professor, Neyman felt that there was a change in Egon Pearson's attitude toward him."

The year 1925–26 was difficult not only for Neyman but also for Egon. He began to realize that the work of R.A. Fisher (culminating in his 1925 book) required a rethinking of the current philosophy of inference, but that this would set him at odds with his father, who "was not able or never saw the need to" make such a shift. In a posthumously published (1990) account of his relations with Karl Pearson, he commented,

> I knew how much I owed to those years of apprenticeship, when I realized the breadth of his vision and received the stimulus of his lectures. But the time had come when it was necessary for me to go through the painful process of experiencing growing doubts in my earlier belief in parental infallibility.

For assistance with his concerns, on May 5, 1926, Egon wrote to Gosset, who in 1908, under the pseudonym "Student" had initiated the development of small-sample theory. In his letter, he raised the question:

> Could one find some principle appealing to intuition which would guide one in choosing between tests?

Gosset's reply[1] a week later contained the spark that ignited a revolution in statistical theory. He suggested that when faced with an unlikely result one would be inclined to consider the hypothesis not to be true if there exists "an alternative hypothesis which will explain the sample with a more reasonable probability."

Egon found the suggestion persuasive and it led him to think of the two kinds of error, and of likelihood ratio tests as a solution to his problem. However, he felt that his mathematics was not adequate for dealing with the precise formulation and the implications of these ideas.

He was looking for someone with stronger mathematical background and ability, and perhaps also for moral support in his effort to make himself independent from his father, of whom he stood in awe and who had dominated him for so long. In any case, it seemed to him that "Neyman was the right man." Sometime in late spring, he invited Neyman to spend a weekend at a Pearson family cottage. It may have been then, toward the end of Neyman's stay in London, Egon writes, that,

> I spoke to him about a very general statistical problem which I had for some time been puzzling around. I suggested that if he was interested we might collaborate in going further with the investigation.

[1] Reprinted in Pearson and Kendall (1970, p. 396).

Neyman's year in London had not been a particularly happy one. He was lonely (his wife Olga, a painter, was spending the year in Paris), his inadequate English made communication difficult, and he was greatly disappointed in the mathematical level of Karl Pearson's department. He had therefore decided to spend his second year in Paris to work in pure mathematics under Lebesgue and Borel. He might have been lost to statistics if he had not toward the end of 1926, after half a year of silence, received a letter from Egon.

Included with the letter were several pages of notes on the ideas about hypothesis testing on which Egon had been working. Although the letter has not survived, it seems clear from Neyman's response that it must have renewed the suggestion of collaborating on these problems.

Neyman responded enthusiastically and thus started the Neyman–Pearson collaboration, carried out mainly by correspondence with Neyman, first in Paris, then in Poland, and through occasional visits back and forth and some joint holidays. Its principal results were the joint papers of 1928 and 1933, which were briefly discussed in Section 59.

The year 1933 brought not only the crucial second Neyman–Pearson paper but also the retirement of Karl Pearson. Egon was appointed to succeed him as head of the Department of Applied Statistics (while Karl Pearson's other position as director of the Galton Laboratory went to Fisher). As a result, the following year Egon was able to bring Neyman into his department. However, their great work had been done and his new duties left Egon much less time for research. As he wrote in his 1966 account of their collaboration:

> I think that by 1934 we had found the answers that satisfied us to most of the tractable problems, . . . our joint work continued in London, . . . but the curtain had come down on that particular episode.

Neyman and Pearson's joint work in London resulted in 1936 in the first volume of a new journal they were founding, *Statistical Research Memoirs,* which contained two Neyman–Pearson papers and a number of others by students and coworkers. In the same year, Karl Pearson died at the age of seventy-nine. Although retired, he had edited the journal *Biometrika* (founded in 1901) up to the time of his death. The trustees appointed Egon to succeed him. Karl Pearson had not been sympathetic to the work of Neyman and Pearson (one of the principal reasons for their starting their own journal). Now a new attitude could be expected.

At the time, Neyman, working separately from Egon, was completing a long paper setting forth his theory of confidence intervals, and naturally submitted it to *Biometrika*. It must have come as a tremendous shock when Egon, after some back and forth, finally decided—very apologetically—to reject it as too long and too mathematical.

Even in retrospect, the decision is hard to understand. The two friends had worked together for ten years. Their points of view had always been somewhat different, but they had managed to make compromises and find common ground. If the paper was too long and too mathematical, Egon surely could have suggested some modifications that would have made it acceptable.

One factor that seems likely to have motivated this rejection was the recent death of Karl Pearson. This was one of his son's first big editorial decisions and it seems understandable that at this moment he did not want to publish a major paper that his father would never have accepted.

While this seems a natural explanation, another factor might have affected this difficult decision: the realization that Neyman's optimality approach, which Egon had somewhat reluctantly shared during their collaboration, was basically not congenial to him, and that "this episode" had come to an end.

Despite this divergence, the two remained friends, and when in 1938 Neyman left London for California they stayed in touch. Unlike Egon, Neyman did not want to abandon their collaboration. He pressed for continued joint work on the Statistical Research memoirs and on a book they had planned, on "Whither Mathematical Statistics?" but Egon demurred. He explained that he was too burdened with administrative work that did not leave him "with the energy to do any joint work." After seeing Egon in 1950 on a visit to England, Neyman finally realized that the "old resonance" between them seemed to be lacking (Reid, p. 223).

A collection of the joint papers of Neyman and Pearson was published in 1966, together with two separate volumes of selected papers by each of the two authors (in 1966 and 1967). They provide a record of great achievements. A festschrift for Neyman, edited by F.N. David, was published in 1966. The volume opened with a paper by E.S. Pearson, "The Neyman–Pearson Story: 1926–34," with Egon's account of their collaboration. The concluding paragraph lets in a rare ray of emotion:

> Sorting out the papers and letters which had been stored away, I can recapture some of the intellectual thrill of that time; the exhilaration which goes with the belief that one is chipping away along the fringe of the unknown. What value is or will be placed on our joint work suddenly seems relatively unimportant. It is the experience within oneself and the joint friendship which have really mattered in life. In this respect, at least, how extraordinarily lucky it was that I decided to launch some of my unsolved puzzles on that rather language-tied research Fellow in the summer of 1926!

Neyman, on his part, briefly commented on their collaboration in a paper, "Frequentist Probability and Frequentist Statistics" (1977). He sent a copy to Egon, who immediately replied[2]:

> Dear Jurek, I received your letter of 24th with your Synthèse paper, and was so delighted that I have started devouring it, although only received about five hours ago! Shall I briefly tell you why? Will comment in detail shortly, but this is a quick reaction. There is a tale or fable about us.

[2] Unpublished letter.

> From 1926–36 we were working together in excited cooperation. My clumsily defined ideas, sharpened by your mathematical formulation, and we went on and on together, until by about 1936–37 we had solved between us what seemed the basic problems, and so found a statistical philosophy. But the time came when to find new mountains to scale, you were forced to tackle more and more mathematically complex problems—tests of "Type" A1 or B2, etc., etc., and I began to lose interest because I was always aiming at attacking types of problems with probability tools which seemed to get fairly simply into gear with the way which the human reason worked. And "types" Ax, By, etc., etc., seemed to me stepping out of this field.

The passage makes it clear that Pearson not only initiated their joint effort but also terminated it. The collaboration between two such different partners with very different goals must not have been easy, and we must be grateful that it held together as long as it did.

65. Egon S. Pearson II: Other Work

Egon Pearson was a major figure in British statistics, quite apart from his work with Neyman. He served as head of his department from 1934 until his retirement in 1960, and as managing editor of *Biometrika* from 1936 to 1966. In both of these capacities, he exerted great influence. His bibliography

(Bartlett, 1981) comprises 135 entries dealing with a great variety of subjects. I shall here consider mainly his work on robustness and on the history of statistics.

Pearson's interest in robustness began as the result of a comment in Gosset's letter to him of May 11, 1926:

> I am more troubled really [this refers to Pearson's question of how to choose a test discussed in the preceding section] by the assumption of normality and have tried from time to time to see what happens with other population distributions.

Pearson (1990, p. 100) describes his response in his recollections:

> I very readily seized on the idea of developing a systematic attack on the problem, using what could be termed experimental sampling [i.e., simulation]. Even with the help of Tippett's tables of random sampling numbers (published in 1927), this exploration was inevitably slow and patchy. . . .
>
> A first report on it appeared in Biometrika 20, 356–360 (1928). . . . By June 1929 I had already accumulated enough evidence to convince me that certain tests involving the ratio of two estimates of variance (using what Fisher called the test statistic z) were much more sensitive to non-normality than others.

While he was working on this problem, Pearson was asked by the journal *Nature* to review the second edition of Fisher's *Statistical Methods*. Mindful of his findings, Pearson—in an otherwise favorable review—commented on the fact that Fisher rarely drew much attention to, and often even didn't mention, that many of his tests were based on the assumption of normality. In particular, he pointed out that

> the tests, for example, connected with the analysis of variance [by this he meant tests concerning variances] are far more dependent on normality than those involving Student's z (or t) distribution is almost certain, but no clear indication of the need for caution in their application is given to the worker. It would seem wiser in the long run, even in a textbook, to admit the incompleteness of theory in this direction, rather than risk giving the reader the impression that the solution of all his problems has been achieved.

Fisher was furious and drafted an apparently highly intemperate response. In the end he did not send it and it has not survived. That Fisher withdrew his letter was due to the good offices of Gosset, who was a close friend of both Fisher and the Pearsons. After some negotiations, Gosset himself published a response in *Nature* that had everyone's approval.

Fisher could not let the matter go without stating his own point of view. In a letter to *Nature* under the title, "Statistics and Biological Research" (reprinted in his collected papers), he affirmed his conviction:

> On the practical side there is little enough room for anxiety, especially among biologists, who are used to checking the adequacy of their methods by control experiments. . . . I have never known difficulty to arise in biological work from imperfect

normality of the variation, even though I have examined the data for this particular cause of difficulty.

However, Pearson did not let Fisher have the last word. He concludes the correspondence with a reply (*Nature,* October 19, 1926) in which he gives examples of published data that are far from normal and points out that Fisher's personal experience is not universally applicable:

It is not questioned that in a very wide field of biological work the normal distribution is adequate. Those who work within its bounds are fortunate but they should admit the possibility that others may meet in practice cases of distinctly non-normal variation; and therefore wish to know more precisely at what point the criteria based on means, standard deviations, and correlation coefficients fail to be distributed in sampling according to "normal theory," and to understand a little more clearly the nature of the consequences of the inefficiency introduced by using these "statistics."

Surprisingly, Pearson does not return to his most important point, the extreme sensitivity to non-normality of the F-test for variances. There was considerable further work confirming Pearson's conclusion, both empirical and theoretical, by Pearson himself, by Gayen and Geary, and particularly by Box (1953). However, as far as I know, Fisher never acknowledged this difficulty.

Among Pearson's most important contributions is his work on the history of statistics, much of it directed toward the preservation of his father's legacy. His first major effort in this direction consisted of two long articles entitled, "Karl Pearson—An Appreciation of Some Aspects of His Life and Work." They were published in *Biometrika* in 1936 and 1937 following Karl Pearson's death in 1936, and were then republished as a book of 170 pages in 1938.

In the preface to the book, Egon Pearson explains his intention:

It is in no sense a life of Karl Pearson; to deal adequately with so large a subject would need far more time than the two seven-week vacations which have been all that I could give to it. Besides, I am fully conscious of the difficulties which a son must face in attempting to write the life of his father. Nevertheless it was important, while memories were fresh and records easy to trace, that some account of facts should be put down on paper. . . . In the task of collecting and recording I had certain advantages; as one of the "three rampaging urchins [Egon and his two sisters] of my mother's Biometric Lay, I could recall at first hand something of that spirit which inspired the founders of the Biometric School in the early years of the century, and much later, as a member for twelve years of my father's Department of Applied Statistics, I had ample opportunity to study his aims and methods. Let this be my reason for writing.

To this work, in 1948 Egon added a volume, *Karl Pearson's Early Statistical Papers,* and his last publication (in 1978, at age 83) consisted of an edition of his father's 1921–1933 lectures, *The History of Statistics in the 17th and 18th Centuries.*

A year after Karl Pearson's death, Egon was saddened by the death of the universally beloved William Sealy Gosset (1876–1937), who had greatly influenced Egon's work. Egon wrote an extensive appreciation, "William

Sealy Gosset: "Student" as a Statistician," for the 1939 volume of *Biometrika*. Of his own relation with Gosset, he wrote:

> My real understanding of Gosset as a statistician began, as no doubt for many others, when I joined that wide circle of his scientific correspondents. . . . In looking back through this correspondence I realize more clearly now than I could ever have done at the time what its value to me has been, and I can see how many of his ideas scattered through these letters have since almost unconsciously become part of my own outlook. I think this must be true also in the case of other persons with whom he corresponded, so that one can say that the last thirty years' progress in the theory and practice of mathematical statistics owe far more to "Student" than could be realized by a mere study of his published papers.

Of great value are the extracts from some of Gosset's letters provided at the end of the paper. Later, Egon edited and published some of Gosset's correspondence with Karl Pearson and with Fisher as number XX (1968) of the *Biometrika* "Studies in the History of Probability and Statistics." It was a series Egon had started to publish in 1955 with a paper by F.N David. From the beginning, it had been his hope to eventually reissue those contributions by various authors in a single volume. This hope was realized in 1970 with the issue of *Studies in the History of Statistics and Probability,* volume 1, edited by Egon Pearson and Maurice Kendall. The editors admitted that the "articles are clearly no substitute for a unified historical appreciation, but . . ., together, we believe, they give a very fair idea of the whole domain." A second volume, edited by Kendall and Plackett, appeared in 1977 with many of the articles from journals other than *Biometrika*.

A last historical work under Pearson's name was published posthumously in 1990. Based on notes by Pearson, it was edited by Plackett and Barnard under the title: *Student: A Statistical Biography of William Sealy Gosset*. Pearson had planned this to be his magnum opus and at various times had given it the working titles, "The Growth of Modern Mathematical Statistics—The Part Played by Student," and "All This—and Student Too." The book published ten years after his death has chapters on Gosset, Karl Pearson, Ronald Fisher, and Egon Pearson, and it is full of valuable personal information.

In their introduction, the editors provide the following assessment of Pearson's own place in history, in which they also mention some aspects of his work not discussed here:

> Egon Sharpe Pearson has a secure place in any account of statistical methodology during the 20th Century. Between 1925 and 1938, his collaboration with Jerzy Neyman established the Neyman–Pearson theory of testing hypotheses. The continuing importance of this feature of statistical inference owes much to his interests in the connection between theory and practice, which are also shown by his work on editing statistical tables. His enthusiasm for the use of quality control in industry led to the Royal Statistical Society forming an Industrial and Agricultural Research Section in 1933, and greatly assisted the introduction of control charts in wartime. He was

Managing Editor of Biometrika from 1936–1966, in which role the subject was immeasurably helped by his conscientious editing and kindly advice to contributing authors. His many honors attest to the esteem in which he was widely held.

The introduction continues with his work as "an outstanding historian of statistics." Surprisingly, it does not mention his important robustness work.

I met Egon Pearson briefly twice. On a visit to London in the 1950s, he invited me to his office, and reminisced about his collaboration with Neyman. He mentioned how intense and passionate about work Neyman was, and that when he came to London in 1934, Neyman was greatly disappointed to find that Egon had gotten married and therefore was not always available.

The second time I saw Pearson was at a party at Betty Scott's house the only time Pearson visited Berkeley, in the 1960s. One member of our department—it may have been Evelyn Fix—proposed a toast that she concluded with: "We love you, Professor Pearson," to which he replied rather dryly: "How is that possible? You only just met me."

66. David Cox (b. 1924)

When Egon Pearson retired from the editorship of *Biometrika* in 1966, his successor was David Cox, then professor of statistics at Imperial College, London. Cox remained as editor for the next twenty-five years. At the time, he must have seemed the natural choice in view of his broad knowledge of both probability theory and statistics and his great productivity, which by now has resulted in over 300 publications in many different areas and which is still continuing. I shall comment on only two of these areas.

Cox's most famous paper is entitled, "Regression Models and Life Tables" (1972). It formulates (and shows how to analyze) a model for failure time data involving a number of secondary (explanatory) variables, which has become known as Cox's Proportional Hazard Model. To explain the term *hazard* in this context, suppose that the lifetime X of a unit has probability density $p(x)$ and cumulative distribution function $F(x) = P(X \leq x)$. Then the hazard function, given by $p(x)/[1 - F(x)]$, is the conditional density of the lifetime given that the unit has survived to time x. This way of specifying the distribution of X is particularly useful for survival data. Cox's model assumes a simple but fairly general form for the hazard function.

Cox, after describing the genesis of the model in Reid (1994), continues:

> Then the question was how to actually do the statistical analysis. I wrote down the full likelihood function and was horrified at it because it's got exponentials of integrals of products of all sorts of things, unknown functions and so forth. I was stuck for quite a long time—I would think the best part of five years or maybe even longer. Then suddenly I thought that the obvious thing to do was to concentrate on that part of the likelihood that actually gave you the information about the regression coefficients that you were interested in. It was absolutely obvious how to do that, and so just write down the answer.

The paper has been reprinted in volume 2 of *Breakthroughs in Statistics* (Kotz and Johnson) with an introduction by Ross Prentice. As Prentice states: "Within a few years of publication, this procedure became a data analytic standard in a number of application areas, most notably in the biomedical sciences. The procedure has also stimulated considerable related methodological development."

In generalization of the simplification described in the passage from Cox quoted above, in 1975 Cox developed a general theory of partial likelihood that can often be used to simplify inferences concerning the parameters of interest in the presence of other parameters.

A very different influential paper, "Some Problems Connected with Statistical Inference" (1958), discusses a number of general issues, including in particular the desirability of conditioning in order to confine the inference to situations relevant to that at hand. Cox discusses the problem both in a Neyman–Pearson setting and from a Fisherian point of view. He makes the latter very persuasive by the following example.

Suppose an observation X is drawn either from a normal distribution with mean θ and variance σ_1^2 or from a normal distribution with mean θ and variance σ_2^2, with a probability of ½ for each. It is assumed that σ_1^2 and σ_2^2 are known and that σ_1^2 is much larger than σ_2^2. Cox considers the problem of testing the hypothesis $H{:}\theta = 0$, but for simplicity let us here consider instead the problem of estimating θ. Our estimator is X and the question is how to report its variance, that is, the accuracy of X. Unconditionally, this variance is $(\sigma_1^2 + \sigma_2^2)/2$, but suppose we know that X was drawn from the population with variance σ_1^2. Then, for most purposes, the large σ_1^2 would seem to be the more relevant value. The fact that we might have drawn X from the population with smaller variance (but did not do so) should not provide much comfort.

An important and influential part of Cox's work consists of the fifteen books he wrote, many of them with collaborators. Most of the books are fairly short, typically 200 to 250 pages, and they cover many different subjects of probability theory and statistics. They are not textbooks. Instead, as Cox explains[3]:

> If you've thought about a subject a considerable time and feel you have something to say about it that isn't in the literature, it is entirely sensible to write it down as a book of some sort.

Some of his statistical books in this vein are:

The Statistical Analysis of Series of Events (1966, with Lewis)
The Analysis of Binary Data (1970)
Analysis of Survival Data (1984, with Oakes)
Inference and Asymptotics (1994, with Barndorff-Nielsen)
Multivariate Dependencies (1996, with Wermuth)

My favorite of Cox's books actually is a textbook of about five hundred pages, *Theoretical Statistics* (1974, with David Hinkley). It is a broadly based introduction to statistical theory, which emphasizes "general concepts rather than mathematical rigour or detailed properties of particular techniques." The book covers parametric and nonparametric tests, point and interval estimation, asymptotic theory, Bayesian methods, and decision theory. It is very reader-friendly and, after more than thirty years, still very useful. Somewhat similar in outlook is his much shorter 2006 book, *Principles of Statistical Inference*.

My own relations with David Cox got off to a bad start. While I was editor of the *Annals,* he submitted a paper (jointly with Wally Smith) on a probabilistic subject that I knew nothing about. The associate editor judged the paper to be basically flawed and, following his recommendation, I rejected it. Later it turned out that the objections raised by the associate editor were unfounded. It was a very unfortunate discouragement of an author at the beginning of his career, but David, when much later I apologized, claimed to have forgotten the incident and in any case seems to have forgiven me.

David taught in Berkeley during the summer of 1956 and presented papers at the fourth and sixth Berkeley Symposia of 1960 and 1970, respectively, and at the second Lehmann Symposium in 2004. In the other direction, I lectured in London twice in the 1950s during European sabbaticals. But of all my

[3] Quoted from Reid (1994), p. 451.

encounters with David, the incident that stands out most occurred in 1985, when I accompanied my wife to a psychometric conference in Cambridge. David spent an afternoon with us, in the course of which he showed us around the Cambridge Statistical Laboratory. Everyone in the laboratory who passed us turned to David and said "congratulations." After several of these felicitations, we asked him for their cause. He waved us off: "Oh, it's nothing," he said. But as the congratulations kept coming, we insisted. He blushed deeply and admitted that he had just been knighted.

David Cox's knighthood was only the most conspicuous of an unprecedented array of honors he has received. They include Fellow of the Royal Society (FRS) and foreign membership in the Royal Danish Academy, the Indian National Academy, and the three principal American academies. He has served as president of the Bernoulli Society, the Royal Statistical Society, and the International Statistical Institute, and from 1988 to 1994 held the position of Warden of Nuffield College, Oxford.

David received the Guy Medal in Gold of the Royal Statistical Society, and the Gold Medal for Cancer Research from Sloan-Kettering. Up to now, he has received twenty honorary doctorates. In 1991, a Festschrift was published, *Statistical Theory and Modelling: In Honor of Sir David Cox, FRS,* edited by Hinkley, Reid, and Snell. A second, edited by Davison, Dodge, and Wermuth, *Celebrating Statistics,* was brought out for his eightieth birthday. Last year saw the publication of two volumes of his collected papers, with comments by Cox.

It has been a truly remarkable career.

15
Contacts Abroad

The statistical theory and methods that Fisher and Neyman–Pearson developed in England during the 1920s and 1930s, spread after World War II not only to the United States but also to many other countries around the world. In this process, Berkeley played a significant role.

On the one hand, the Berkeley Symposia in Statistics and Probability, which took place at five-year intervals from 1945 to 1970 were the most important international meetings of the period. Although the talks were by invitation only, Neyman's broad contacts ensured substantial international participation. In the long run, even more influential were the large number of graduate students from many different countries who received their training in the new statistics at Berkeley.

There tended to be a pattern to their flow. One or two early students from some country liked their Berkeley experience and recommended it to others. After receiving their degrees, some of them stayed in the U.S. But more important were the others who went back to take up positions in their home countries. They eventually established their own graduate programs, so that after a while it was no longer necessary for students from that country to study abroad. The flow of these students then receded, to be replaced by a wave from some other country. Later, these contacts resulted in occasional invitations of some of us to the home countries of our students. On these visits, we gave lectures, were entertained, and were shown some of the sights.

This chapter considers some aspects of this development, and my involvement with it, for the five countries with which I had the most contact: Switzerland, India, China, Israel, and the Netherlands.

67. Bartel L. van der Waerden (1903–1996)

In 1956, I was eligible for my first sabbatical year and decided to spend it in Zürich the beautiful and culturally rich city in which I had lived during my high school and first university years. A drawback of Zürich was that

neither of its two academic institutions, the university or the Eidgenössische Technische Hochschule (ETH), had a program in statistics.

I knew that there was one person in Zürich who had a strong interest and considerable knowledge about the subject, namely the great algebraist Bartel L. van der Waerden. About him there was, however, a concern. Doubts had been raised regarding the fact that van der Waerden, although of Dutch origin and nationality, had remained as professor in Leipzig (Germany) throughout the Nazi period. The Dutch had held it strongly against him. If he had been a Nazi sympathizer, I wanted nothing to do with him.

For advice, I turned to my thesis advisor and friend George Polya at Stanford, who knew about such things. Polya assured me that I need have no qualms. van der Waerden was perhaps somewhat naïve, but he surely had done nothing reprehensible; I could associate with him in good conscience.

Accordingly, soon after my arrival in Zürich I looked up van der Waerden, and it turned out that he was delighted to see me. He was just reading a proof of a book he had written on mathematical statistics and he had a question to which he hoped I might have the answer. He knew that Student's t-test was uniformly most powerful among unbiased tests, but assumed that it was in fact uniformly most powerful among all tests and had stated so in the book. Did I know a proof?

This was the problem Charles Stein and I had considered in our 1948 paper (see Section 13), and we had shown the conjecture to be false. I had come just in time for a correction to be included in the book.

Statistics was only a sideline for van der Waerden. As he told me, he had been drawn into the subject through requests by scientific colleagues in Leipzig for help with their statistical problems. To answer their questions, he had taught himself by reading Fisher. Later he also wrote a few papers on the subject. However, they were not comparable in importance to his seminal contributions in several areas of pure mathematics. He was known to me at the time principally for his path-breaking book, *Modern Algebra,* of which Saunders MacLane wrote in 1997 that "it is, in my view, the most influential text in algebra of the twentieth century."

His statistical book was also excellent, although less influential. It was roughly comparable to Cramér's text, but different in a number of significant ways. On the one hand, it omitted the theories of measure and integration. On the other, since it was written ten years later it was able to include more recent developments, in particular, for example, nonparametric tests such as the Wilcoxon and van der Waerden's own X-test (which is asymptotically equivalent to the normal scores test). A strong feature of the book is the examples, which are taken from real situations. I liked the book so much that I arranged for two Berkeley graduate students to do a translation, which appeared in 1968.

Of van der Waerden's other books I shall only mention his two-volume *Science Awakening,* the first volume a history of Greek mathematics and its precursors (1954), and the second entitled, *The Birth of Astronomy* (1974). Written from a broad perspective—mathematical, historical, and philosophical—they are a pleasure to read. These books are only a small part of van der Waerden's extensive and influential body of work on the history of mathematics and astronomy.

After the war, van der Waerden returned to Holland to accept an earlier offer from the University of Utrecht. However, the government refused to approve the appointment because of his having remained in Germany during the whole Nazi period. He briefly worked for Shell and then accepted an offer from the City University of Amsterdam, which at first was privately funded. Three years later, he moved to a better position at the University of Zürich, where he remained until his retirement in 1973.

During my year in Zürich, I saw a lot of van der Waerden, usually for afternoon coffee at his house, where I also met his wife, Camilla. At one of these meetings, in the spring of 1956, he told me about the mathematical conference center Oberwolfach in the Black Forest, and of the upcoming statistics conference there, which he was planning to attend. He suggested that I accompany him and also give a talk.

My first reaction was very negative. For me, Germany at that time was the country that had killed six million Jews, including some of my relatives, and that had driven me out. I did not want to become involved with German statistical activities. But van der Waerden was persuasive, and eventually I did go with him. I decided to give my talk in German, which turned out to be unexpectedly difficult. Although German was my mother tongue, I did not know any of the technical terms that I had learned in Berkeley.

During the meeting, I was able to set aside my feelings and to relate to the people I met as individuals who presumably were no better or worse than citizens of other countries. However, later I continued to feel that as one who had escaped the horror, I had an obligation to those who had not been so lucky, not to pretend that nothing had happened. Reconciliation was up to the next generation. I resolved not to again participate in professional activities in Germany. On the other hand, I was always happy to welcome individual German visitors to our department in Berkeley, and developed good relations with several of them.

This first Swiss sabbatical had been so pleasant and productive that I decided to return for another half-sabbatical in the fall term of 1959. Again I saw much of van der Waerden, who also invited me to give a talk at the Zürich Mathematical Colloquium. Another Zürich friend was Walter Saxer, who was a specialist in insurance mathematics at the ETH. It was he who conveyed to me the offer of a chair in mathematical statistics at the ETH, reported in Section 43.

The van der Waerden I knew in Zürich was a very modest person—one would never have guessed his importance both as a mathematician and as a historian of mathematics, and I was not fully aware of them. My relation with him was primarily through his interest in statistics. His being the sole representative of that field in Zürich changed in the 1960s, when first Peter Huber and later also Frank Hampel took up positions in Zürich.

68. C.R. Rao (b. 1920)

India experienced an early development in statistics due to the work of a remarkable leader, Prasanta Chandra Mahalanobis (1893–1972). This is not the place to write about his achievements,[1] except to mention that in 1931 he founded the Indian Statistical Institute, to which he attracted, among many others, R.C. Bose, S.N. Roy, and C.R. Rao, all three of whom became outstanding statisticians. He also founded the journal *Sankhya* (in 1933) and edited it until his death. (Henry Scheffé and I published our two papers on completeness and minimal sufficient statistics in *Sankhya*.)

The person who did the most to continue Mahalanobis's work as a leader of statistics in India was Calyampudi Radhakrishna Rao. After receiving a master's degree in mathematics in 1940 from Andhra University, he was

[1] For a biography, see Rudra (1996). An account of the development of statistics in India is provided by Ghosh, Maiti, Rao and Sinha (1999).

advised that job opportunities were better in statistics and got another master's degree, this time in statistics, from Calcutta University in 1943, and accepted a job at the Indian Statistical Institute. In 1946, he went to Cambridge by invitation to work at the University Museum of Archeology and Ethnology on a project using statistical methodology developed at the institute. During his two-year stay in Cambridge, he also worked under R.A. Fisher and obtained a Ph.D. from Cambridge University. On return from Cambridge, he joined the faculty of the institute in 1948, where he became professor in 1949, director of research and training in 1964, and—after Mahalanobis's death—secretary and director of the institute in 1972. In 1979, Rao took mandatory retirement from the institute and moved to the United States, first to the University of Pittsburgh (1979–1988) and then to Pennsylvania State University, where—although retired—he continues to be active.

Rao's bibliography (Bera, 2003) contains more than 450 items. I shall here discuss only a few of his papers and books that have been of particular relevance to me.

One of his earliest papers, "Information and Accuracy Attainable in the Estimation of Statistical Parameters" (1945), was remarkable in containing three major ideas:

i. The first is an inequality that provides a nonasymptotic lower bound for the variance of an unbiased estimate. The inequality, now called the

Cramér–Rao inequality, was discovered independently by Fréchet (1943), Rao (1945), and Cramér (1946).[2] It has become a staple of mathematical statistics and has been extended in many different ways by Rao himself and by others. As an application, Hodges and I (1951) found that the inequality provides a powerful tool for proving admissibility of estimators. More recently, applications of Cramér–Rao inequality have been found in quantum physics, signal processing, and in proving some limit laws in probability.

The independent discovery of the inequality by Fréchet in France, Rao in India, and Cramér in Sweden suggests that the time was ripe for it. This is supported by Rao's own account of how he came to the result (De Groot, 1987; Bera, 2003). After he had lectured on Fisher's asymptotic version of the inequality, a student in the class asked, "Why don't you prove it for finite samples?" and within 24 hours Rao did just that.

ii. The 1945 paper contained a second important result also relating to unbiased estimation. Rao showed that if T is a sufficient statistic and δ an unbiased estimator of, say, $g(\theta)$, then the conditional expectation $E(\delta \mid T)$ of δ given T is also an unbiased estimator of $g(\theta)$ and its variance is less than that of δ unless δ is a function of T.

A corollary is the very useful fact that an unbiased estimate can be improved by taking its expectation given a sufficient statistic. This process has been called Rao–Blackwellization by Berkson (1955) and the theorem itself the Rao–Blackwell theorem by Lehmann and Scheffé (1950). The reason for the addition of Blackwell's name is that he obtained the same results (independently) in 1947.

iii. The results (i) and (ii) were in the spirit of the time and soon found many generalizations and applications. This was not the case for Rao's third contribution in this paper, which introduced ideas from differential geometry into statistics, including the concepts of metric, distance, and measure now associated with his name. This work was before its time and came into its own only in the 1980s.

A second important paper by Rao (with which I was much concerned in my expository work) is of an asymptotic nature and deals with testing rather than estimation. It added a new general method of testing to the likelihood ratio test of Neyman and Pearson (1928) and the Wald test (1943): what is now known as the Rao score test (1948). These three tests are sometimes referred to as "the holy trinity."

For the case of a simple hypothesis H: $\theta = \theta_0$ concerning a real-valued parameter θ, against the alternatives $\theta > \theta_0$, Rao's test rejects when the derivative of the logarithm of the likelihood evaluated at θ_0 is sufficiently large. In many situations the three tests are asymptotically equivalent, but for finite samples

[2] The name, first proposed by Neyman and Scott (1948), has stuck despite its historical inaccuracy.

they can vary widely. Each has its advantages and drawbacks. These are discussed in large-sample books such as Sen and Singer (1993) and Lehmann (1999), and also in Lehmann and Romano (2005).

Rao's papers of 1945 and 1948 have each been reprinted in *Breakthroughs in Statistics* (Kotz and Johnson), the 1945 paper in volume 1 with an introduction by Pathak, and that of 1948 in volume 3 introduced by Sen.

In the early 1960s, Rao returned to problems of estimation but with two important differences. For one, he was now concerned with large-sample properties such as first- and second-order efficiency. In addition, he was considering estimation not as point estimation in the classical sense of calculating a single value coming close to an unknown parameter being "estimated," but (following Fisher) as a process of data condensation that tries to "preserve an estimate as a substitute for the whole sample for possible future use" (Rao, 1962). In the discussion of this paper, Rao states, "With such a criterion, estimation need not be confined to what are called point estimates."

In view of this interpretation, he defined efficiency of an estimator not in the traditional way in terms of asymptotic variance, but rather in terms of its closeness to the derivative of the log likelihood. He then proved the superiority of the maximum likelihood estimator from this point of view.

Although Rao repeatedly stated his position clearly, it was misunderstood and his definitions were criticized as irrelevant to the (traditional) purpose of estimation. In the controversy that followed, the discussants talked past each other until Efron, in a 1982 paper, "Maximum Likelihood and Decision Theory," gave a comprehensive comparative account of the two approaches.

Rao wrote papers in many other areas of statistics, especially in combinatorial experimental designs known as orthogonal arrays, which are widely used in industrial experimentation, but I shall now turn to some of his more than a dozen books. The most influential of these was probably a text titled, *Linear Statistical Inference and Its Applications*. Despite its title,[3] which suggests a somewhat limited coverage, it is really a very general introduction to statistical inference covering both estimation and testing, exact theory for finite samples, and large-sample theory. An unusual feature of the book is that its mathematical preparation consists not only of a chapter on measure theoretic probability but also a chapter of nearly eighty pages on various aspects of linear algebra and vector spaces, including some of Rao's own work on generalized inverses of matrices. The level of mathematical rigor is high throughout, as is the book's readability.

A quite different book written by Rao in conjunction with the Russian mathematicians Kagan and Linnik deals with a very special topic indicated by its title, *Characterization Problems in Mathematical Statistics* (Kagan et al., 1973),

[3] Not Rao's original title but one proposed by the publisher as more catchy.

that is, with properties that uniquely characterize probability distributions and certain other statistical structures. Rao's interest in such problems began when he was a student, and in fact he wrote a master's thesis on the subject. Later, he published papers on properties characterizing the normal distribution, the Poisson distribution, the gamma distribution, certain linear structures, and so on. The book provides a comprehensive treatment of such results and the methods for obtaining them. It is the source that I consult when faced with problems in this area.

A third and again very different book with the title *Statistics and Truth* is the written version of three lectures given by Rao in memory of the great Indian mathematician Ramanujan.[4] It is a wide-ranging, nontechnical overview of the history, nature, and usefulness of statistics. The first chapter discusses the fundamental concept of randomness and the great change from a deterministic to an indeterministic worldview in the latter half of the nineteenth century. This is followed in Chapter 2 by a consideration of the various ways in which statistics extracts information from data. Finally, Chapter 3, after discussing the usefulness of statistics, illustrates how this comes about in eighteen very different, but all interesting, examples. The book offers an attractive introduction to statistics for the general reader, and I greatly appreciated it when Rao sent me an inscribed copy.

Of Rao's remaining books, I shall only mention that the following four, related to the broad subject of linear models, reflect his interest and contributions to the algebraic side of statistics:

Generalized Inverses of Matrices and Their Applications (with Mitra, 1971)
Estimation of Variance Components and Its Applications (with Kleffe, 1988)
Linear Models: Least Squares and Alternatives (with Toutenberg, 1995)
Choquet-Deny Type Functional Equations with Applications to Stochastic Models (with Shanbhag, 1994)

Rao's great success and influence as an administrator, researcher, expositor, and teacher has led to his receiving a large number of honors. They include presenting the Wald Lectures (1975), "Estimation of Parameters in Linear Models," and a Festschrift, *Statistics and Probability: Essays in Honor of C.R. Rao* (Kallianpur, Krishnaiah, and Ghosh, Eds 1982). He has received thirty honorary degrees. He is a Fellow of the UK Royal Society (FRS) and a member of several national academies, including the (American) National Academy of Sciences. He has served as president of the Institute of Mathematical Statistics, International Biometric Society, and International Statistical Institute, and the list goes on. Particularly prestigious awards were the (U.S.) President's National Medal of Science and the second highest civilian award of Padma Vibhushan by the government of India.

[4] For a biography of Ramanujan, see Kanigel, *The Man Who Knew Infinity: a Life of the Genius Ramanujan* (1991).

I first met Rao when he taught in the Berkeley summer session of 1954. In 1960, he attended the fourth Berkeley Symposium and in 1970 the sixth. During the 1960s, we had some correspondence concerning my many Indian Ph.D. students, quite a number of whom took up positions in the U.S. rather than returning to India. Rao seemed to hold me responsible, and from time to time would scold me for it.

More important perhaps than our direct contact was the interaction in our work. In particular, for example, several of my early papers grew out of Rao's paper of 1945, and at the time of writing this section I am in fact also working on a paper that has its origin in Rao's work in the 1960s on efficiency.

69. Zhongguo Zheng (b. 1938)

My contact with India was primarily through my close to twenty Indian Ph.D. students. The ties that connected me to the statistics community of the People's Republic of China were due mainly to my relations with two Chinese statisticians. To begin with, as mentioned in Section 11, the great Chinese scholar P.L. Hsu had been instrumental in helping me to get my Ph.D. when he spent the fall term of 1945 in Berkeley. Unfortunately, I never saw him again. After a year-and-a-half with Hotelling, he returned to China, where he died in 1970.

When years later American statisticians learned of his death, the *Annals of Statistics* commissioned several memorial articles: an article on his life by Anderson, Chung, and Lehmann; and one each on Hsu's work on inference (Lehmann), multivariate analysis (Anderson), and probability (Chung).[5] They appeared in the 1979 volume of the *Annals*.

The same year brought me a new, very different, contact with China. In December 1979, a Chinese visitor arrived for a two-year stay in our department. He was Zhongguo Zheng, a forty-one–year-old lecturer at Peking University who came to Berkeley to learn about modern developments in statistics and probability. He had been trained in Beijing: six years as an undergraduate (the standard time at Peking University) and four years as a graduate student. He completed his studies in 1965 with a thesis on random walks but without a degree—the university at that time did not grant doctoral degrees.

Those were the turbulent days of the Cultural Revolution, and for the next seven years Zheng was sent to the countryside to do physical work. During that time, as he wrote in a recent letter, "no teaching, no research work, no study." He then returned to the university to teach but, as he writes,

> The student's level was quite low. Also, the university had stopped to order any English journals. So, for a very long period, we had no chance to do research. That is the reason why for a very long time after graduation I did not write any papers.

Zhongguo made up for this later. Since 1985, he has published more than one hundred papers—mainly, but not exclusively, in Chinese journals—on a great variety of statistical topics, particularly in the area of estimation. Most of them are theoretical—recently, for example, in graph theory—but there are also occasional papers dealing with specific applied problems.

Since I was Zhongguo's sponsor for his stay in Berkeley, we invited him to dinner soon after his arrival. We were astonished to learn that this flight to the U.S. had been the first time he had been on a plane, and that he had never used a fork and knife (fortunately we had chopsticks). But he quickly adjusted to American ways. We saw him frequently during his two years in Berkeley, and we became friends.

Some years later, Zhongguo's visit had an unexpected and thrilling consequence for us: he arranged that my wife and I were invited for a two-week visit to China in September 1986 as guests of the University of Peking and the Chinese Academy of Sciences. We would stay at the guest house of the University, and both Julie and I would give a series of lectures for students and faculty of the two institutions.

We were told that translators would not be required; the students could understand English if it was spoken sufficiently slowly. Despite this warning, the discussion after my first lecture showed that I had spoken much too fast.

---

[5] These articles were reprinted in Hsu's *Collected Papers* (1983).

As a result, I adjusted my pace, wrote everything on the blackboard, and asked faculty members to intervene when help was needed. The same language difficulty caused the introduction at Julie's first lecture of Juliet Shaffer as "Professor Scheffé."

On the other hand, the student guides on our various sightseeing tours had fairly good command of English. They provided not only much understandable information, but also were able (and willing) to engage in interesting and unexpectedly frank conversation.

Sightseeing generally does not much appeal to me, but the many wonders in and around Beijing easily overcame this lack of enthusiasm. There were splendors everywhere: palaces, temples, sculptures, and parks. It was a culture of incredible richness and antiquity about which, despite some preparation, we knew very little and which left us with a feeling of unreality, of being in a dream or fairy tale.

And there was the devastating contrast between this magnificence and the struggling everyday lives of our hosts. These two weeks became such an extraordinary experience because as colleagues we saw the working conditions at the university and were generously invited into homes where we met spouses and children. At that time, conditions in Beijing were much more primitive than they are today. In one apartment, we were proudly shown a telephone. Our host told us that it was a rarity but of course, he added as an afterthought, it is not connected.

Our sponsor who was responsible for our arrangements was Zhongguo, who was now an associate professor at the University of Peking. I brought him a copy of the second edition of my testing book, which had just appeared but had not yet reached China. He insisted on in turn giving me his copy of the first (pirated) edition printed in China. He inscribed it for me: "To the author of the book with best wishes."

A few days after our arrival, Zhongguo invited us for dinner at his home, an apartment consisting of two bedrooms but no living room. He lived there with his wife and two daughters, and it also served as his workplace since the university did not provide faculty members with offices. His desk stood in the larger bedroom but for the occasion had been pushed into a corner to make room for a card table seating four people. The fourth seat was for another guest, not for Zhongguo's wife, who was too busy to join us. In a tiny kitchen space, on two burners fed by bottled gas, she prepared a feast for us, with course following course, sixteen in all. It was a wonderful meal but we missed her company.

We were also invited to a more formal dinner by the head of the Academy Institute of Systems Science (which included statistics). He and his wife lived in a larger apartment in a brand-new apartment building that was considered state of the art but had no hot water. Again, the meal was very elaborate, but this time it was prepared with the help of a servant. In the traditional Chinese manner, our host heaped delicacies onto our plates. One dish of which he gave both Julie and me a large portion, we could not identify. Since no one at the table knew the English word, our hostess got up to look it up in a dictionary. She came back, beaming: "Earthworms!"

Our contact with Zhongguo has continued over the years. In 1987, he spent another three-and-a-half months in Berkeley, and in 2000 he and his wife stayed with us for a week as tourists. They were on their way to visit their older daughter, who had settled in the U.S. Most recently, a project on which Zhongguo had worked for some time came to fruition. In 2004, his translation of my estimation book (second edition, with Casella) was published by China Statistics Press.

70. Joseph (Yossi) A. Yahav (b. 1935)

Between 1949 and 1971, nine statistics students from Israel obtained a Ph.D. at Berkeley, and most of them then returned to Israel to take up positions in their home country. Four of these students, Joe Putter (in 1953), Henry Konijn (in 1954), Shulamith Gross (in 1966), and Dan Anbar (in 1971), wrote their theses with me, but the one to whom I eventually became closest was Yossi Yahav, who had worked with Blackwell and who obtained his degree in 1963 with a thesis on optimal stopping.

Yahav remained in Berkeley for another two years as acting assistant professor and then took up the position of head of the Department of Statistics at Tel Aviv University. After ten years, he moved to the Hebrew University of Jerusalem, where in addition to being a faculty member he held a number of administrative positions: dean of the Faculty of Social Sciences (1980–84), head of the Department of Statistics (1986–88) and Department of Agricultural Economics (1988–90), and vice president for administration and finance (1992–94). Throughout much of his appointment at the Hebrew University, his position was split, with half the time at the Department of Statistics and the other half at the Department of Agricultural Economics (located at Rehovot).

In 1994, he accepted an appointment by the Israeli government as the government statistician and head of the Central Bureau of Statistics. This officer advises the government on all of its statistical activities. The bureau includes a Department of Macro Economics, which does all the statistical work related to the preparation of the budget and its consequences. It is also in charge of the census, and in fact Yahav's first year in this position was almost completely devoted to the census that took place in November 1995.

Despite this extensive administrative work, Yahav throughout the 1960s and 1970s published a substantial number of papers on a variety of subjects, among them dynamic programming, sequential analysis, estimating the size of a population, and subset selection.

Yahav's achievements are particularly impressive in view of his many health problems, including a bout with Hodgkin's lymphoma, which was successfully treated by Henry Kaplan at Stanford.

His friendship and joint work with Peter Bickel brought Yossi frequently to Berkeley. He held visiting faculty positions in our department in 1969–70 and again in 1984–86. For many years, he spent part of each summer in Berkeley on one of Bickel's grants or contracts.

The close contact of the Israeli statistics community, but most particularly of Yossi, with the Berkeley statistics department led to two happy developments in 1988: an honorary degree for Peter Bickel from Hebrew University, and earlier in the year an invitation for Julie and me to visit Israel as guests of the Hebrew University, to each give a series of lectures in Jerusalem and Tel Aviv. We presented lectures and gave consultations, met old friends and new colleagues, and attended dinner parties. From this perspective, this was a familiar world, somewhat more elaborate but not all that different from such a visit in the United States.

But then there was the incredible experience of Israel. If our stay in Beijing had seemed like a fairy tale, this trip gave a sense of place and reality to stories that had long been in our imagination. Whenever we had free time, Yossi took us on excursions. One day, for example, he drove us to Masada, the fortress in which the Zealots held out against a Roman siege for several years and committed suicide when the Romans completed a ramp to storm this seemingly impenetrable mountain stronghold. And then there was Jerusalem itself, the Western Wall, the Dome of the Rock, and so on, but I must keep this from becoming a travelogue.

The impressions from this visit were so powerful that two years later we decided to go again. As before, Yossi was our wonderful host, and this time we lectured not only in Jerusalem and Tel Aviv but also in Haifa. This gave us an opportunity to see some of northern Israel, including an excursion to the Sea of Galilee, Nazareth, and up to the Syrian border.

Experiencing life in Israel gave us a new feeling for the meaning of a Jewish state, in which Jewish traditions reigned rather than Christian ones. We also gained a better understanding of the geopolitical situation of the country. Driving to the borders with Jordan in the east and Syria in the north made it clear how close these neighbors are—something that is hard to realize when one is used to the great American distances.

I shall conclude this section on a lighter note by recounting a quip of Yossi's when he attended a talk by Dennis Lindley in Barlow's Bayesian seminar in the Department of Industrial Relations (see Section 51). Lindley had solved a problem assuming a certain prior but was not satisfied with the solution. He therefore proposed to change the prior. Yossi, mindful of Lindley's insistence on the true (personal) prior being obtained through a searching process of introspection, called out: "Wouldn't it be easier to change the data?"

71. Willem (Bill) R. van Zwet (b. 1934)

A systematic development of mathematical statistics in Holland is due mainly to David van Dantzig (1900–1959).[6] Before World War II, he had been a pure mathematician who obtained his degree in topological algebra under van der Waerden. After the war, he changed fields and worked in probability theory and statistics. He is perhaps best remembered today for his theory of collective marks and for two papers entitled, "Statistical Priesthood," which were attacks on Savage's subjective approach to probability and on Fisher's fiducial probability, respectively.

To facilitate a unified approach to both mathematical and statistical research, and their applications, in 1946 van Dantzig (jointly with van der Corput and Koksma) founded the Mathematical Centre in Amsterdam. (I was later to give lectures at the Centre on a number of visits to the Netherlands.) Van Dantzig spent a semester in Berkeley in 1950; however, I was teaching on the East Coast at that time and I never met him. Nor did I meet his successor, Jan Hemelrijk, who greatly expanded the activities of the Centre.

While I did not meet either van Dantzig or Hemelrijk, over the years I developed close contact with Hemelrijk's student Bill van Zwet, who

[6] For an account of van Dantzig's contributions, see Hemelrijk (1960).

between 1967 and 1993 spent parts of many summers in Berkeley. During most of that time, he was supported by grants or contracts of Peter Bickel, of whom he became a close friend and frequent collaborator. In addition, he was in Berkeley in 1997 on a Miller professorship. From 1990 to 1998, he spent much time at the University of North Carolina as William Newman Professor.

Van Zwet obtained his master's degree with van Dantzig, and his Ph.D. (in 1964) with Hemelrijk with a thesis, *Convex Transformations of Random Variables*. Since then, he has published on a wide variety of statistical subjects, both theoretical and applied. Particularly noteworthy are his many papers on asymptotic expansions, which require very delicate analysis. More recently, his work has included asymptotic investigations of resampling, on which he gave the Wald Lectures in 1992, and of inference in contact processes.

In addition to his research, van Zwet has been very active in administration, both at the University of Leiden, where he was a member of the faculty from 1965 until his retirement in 1999, and internationally. At Leiden, he served as chair of the Department of Applied Mathematics from 1974 to 1978 and as dean of the Faculty of Mathematics and Natural Sciences in 1982–83.

He played a prominent role in the Institute of Mathematical Statistics, serving as editor from 1986 to 1988, the first time the *Annals* were edited from outside the United States, and as president in 1991–92. Perhaps even more important was van Zwet's work with the International Statistical Institute, for which he chaired the Organizing Committee of the Centenary session (1981–85) and the Program Committee (1989–93), and for which he served as president from 1989 to 1993.

Van Zwet was also heavily involved with the founding of the Bernoulli Society, for which he served as editor-in-chief (2000–2003) and as president (1987–89). Finally, it was his initiative that ultimately led to the creation of Eurandom, a European Institute of Statistics, which got off the ground in 1997. Van Zwet was its scientific director for the first three years.

Van Zwet's many honors include an honorary degree from Charles University in Prague, membership in the Royal Netherlands Academy of Sciences, the Médaille de la Ville de Paris, and Knighthood in the Order of the Netherlands' Lion.

I, of course, knew van Zwet from his many visits to Berkeley. In addition, I had the great pleasure of his company when in 1997 he stayed with Julie and me for several weeks during his tenure as Miller Professor. In the evenings, after dinner, we used to discuss the problems of the world over a glass of genever, a supply of which he had brought from the Netherlands. However, this was more than ten years after he had brought about an amazing event, which was one of the highlights of my life. Extracts from a diary that I kept during that momentous occasion are given in the next section.

72. Van Zwet's Gift

The letter came without warning. "Dear Sir," it said,

> The University at Leiden—the oldest in the Netherlands—was opened on the 8th of February 1575. Each year on the 8th of February a sober ceremony will take place to celebrate the foundation of the university, during which sometimes a doctorate honoris causa is conferred.
>
> In 1985 the university will celebrate her 410th anniversary and because of this anniversary celebration it has been decided to confer four doctorates honoris causa to scientists whose research has greatly contributed to the development of teaching and research at Leiden University.
>
> I have the honour and pleasure to inform you that, on the recommendation of the Council of the Faculty of Sciences, the Board of Faculty Deans of Leiden University has decided to confer upon you an honorary doctorate in sciences, in recognition of your distinguished services to scholarship and society. Dr. W.R. van Zwet, professor of mathematical statistics in this university, will be the sponsor.
>
> I congratulate you on the university's recognition of your distinction and at the same time I express the hope that you will be willing to accept the proposed honorary degree.

The letter was signed A.A.H. Kassenaar, rector magnificus.

When I passed the letter over to Julie, she smiled. She had known about it for months, but had kept her promise of secrecy. The Dutch authorities had consulted her (via a colleague in our department) to make sure that there was no Nazi taint in my German background. Had I perhaps, even for a short while, been a member of the Hitler-Jugend?

Lehmann in Leiden

I was bowled over—never had I expected to receive such an honor from so distinguished a European university. Later I learned some of its history. The town of Leiden had been besieged for five months by the Spanish Army. When in October 1574, relief finally came, William the Silent offered Leiden the choice between remission of some of its taxes or a university. Realizing that the former would be only temporary, they opted for a university. It was the first in the country (followed by Groningen in 1614, Amsterdam in 1632, and Utrecht in 1636), and it soon attracted many famous scholars (including Descartes). Some of its development is sketched by Will and Ariel Durant in volume 7 of the *Story of Civilization,* in which they state, "By 1640, Leiden was the most renowned seat of learning in Europe." It still considers itself superior to the other Dutch universities, and until fairly recently salaries for professors at Leiden were twenty-five percent higher than those of other Dutch professors.

And so in February 1985, we left for a midwinter trip to Leiden. The following are excerpts from my Leiden diary:

Monday, February 4:

At the university, Bill [Bill van Zwet, the moving force behind this event] showed us the ceremonial room where doctoral examinations are held. It is the "senaatskamer," a very formal affair with painted portraits of famous professors and a portrait of the founder of the university, William the Silent. Then we saw the "sweat-room" next door, where students are supposed to wait for the results. If successful, you sign your name on the wall. The walls are thus filled with signatures and messages—graffiti of the centuries—up to the top, which can be reached only by means of a high ladder that rests in a corner. Next came the auditorium, in which newly appointed professors give their inaugural lectures. It contains two lecterns: a high one for full professors, and one lower down for new appointees of associate rank.

Then the assistant Pedel brought the scrolls for the honorary degree, of which Bill had to sign the original. The sponsor of the psychiatrist Rutter was also there to sign his scroll and I committed a faux pas by asking him whether this was the first honorary degree he had sponsored. He looked at me as if I had fallen from the sky, and said this was an honor which with great luck one could achieve once in one's life. Leiden is very sparing with its degrees.

Tuesday, February 5:

The next morning, I felt just awful: nauseous, achy, with a fever. There was no way in which I could make it to the afternoon's events: a mini-statistical meeting at which four Dutch statisticians were to talk about work of theirs that was related to mine. I was very unhappy, both because the speakers and the audience would be disappointed if I did not show up, and for my own sake. Bill managed to scare up a university doctor, who came to the hotel, examined me (when he put the stethoscope to my stomach, he complained it was hurting his ears), and pronounced it to be a virus which would probably require three days to run its course. To enable me to attend the afternoon meeting, he prescribed anti-nausea pills and painkillers. After the medications took effect, I felt I might be able to make it, and I was ready when Bill picked me up.

The meeting was labeled, *"Eredoctorat E.L. Lehmann,"* and notifications had been sent to the various Dutch statistical centers—this was in line with Bill's idea that this honorary degree would raise the visibility of statistics in the Netherlands. The announced purpose was to present some lectures that were related to *"het werk von Lehmann."* Afterwards, there was to be an informal reception to provide an opportunity to *"met de Heer and Mevrouw Lehmann Kennis te maken."* Poor Julie—throughout the week she had to give up her identity and answer to "Mevrouw Lehmann."

Thursday, February 7:

Not having eaten any solid food since Monday night, I thought I had better try some breakfast. We were joined by Professor Wevers, a theologian from Toronto and one of the other three honorees, who told us a nice story. Two of his sons are musicians and one of them, a composer, recently dedicated a symphony to his father, which is to have its first performance next month—a somewhat mixed blessing, since Wevers does not enjoy anything later than Mozart. However, his other musician son reassured him: "You can tell that he really wrote it for you, Dad, because he wrote it in a key!"

After breakfast, we walked to the tailor, Mr. Sloos, a block away to see whether we could rent some tails. Mr. Sloos, tall, with a beautifully groomed blond beard and wearing a gray morning coat, is the picture of sartorial splendor. He wonderfully combines the proverbial scraping and bowing of the obsequious tailor with the slightly amused disdain of an elegant man for a klutz like me. I was reprimanded for coming so late—"the day before the ceremony, most of the tuxedoes and tails have already been rented out, lots of people want them tomorrow." Eventually, he condescended to take my measurements and assured me all would be ready the next day. "Don't forget," he reminded me, "you will need black shoes and socks." I assured him

I had what was needed. "But the socks must be black," he insisted. He obviously had visions of my disgracing his outfit by wearing blue or brown socks. The charge for jacket, vest, pants, semi-soft shift, and white tie was forty dollars. (What a waste of money, was Bill's comment.)

This is perhaps the time to talk about the background of this degree, because behind all the pomp and circumstance lie two years of hard-fought struggles, both within the department and between departments. Roughly, each department is given a chance at such a degree every 25 years; they must then unite behind a single candidate with whom they can do battle against other competing departments. Mathematicians had lost out on the past three occasions, so the last honorary degree in mathematics had been awarded in 1884 (to the mathematician Stieltjes, born in Leiden although teaching in Paris, and well known for the Stieltjes integral and the Stieltjes moment problem).

This time, there were apparently two factions. The majority of the department are geometers who understandably wanted a pure mathematician. Bill wanted a statistician, partly because he thought it would be good for statistics. He may also have believed that a statistical candidate would have a better chance. I could have told the mathematicians that theirs was a lost cause, since Bill is extremely clever and a superb fighter. He made me somewhat more palatable to the mathematicians by describing my work as contributing to the "mathematization of statistics."

Once I became their candidate, the mathematicians apparently rallied behind me—perhaps any mathematician was better than none! This attitude showed itself at a wonderful dinner partly given for us by the mathematics department, one of the high points of the week, and in particular by the very gracious speech by the department chairman Jaap Murre. He emphasized that it did not matter whether a person was pure or applied, or what their specialty was, the only important thing was quality, and he went on to explain that I was now one of theirs. Later in the evening, he told me that next time I came to visit Leiden he would—thank God!—no longer be chairman. However, he would insist as a personal privilege that we come to his house for dinner and a long conversation.

The dinner, which ended past midnight after lasting for over five hours, was one of the high points of the week. (The other two were the Tuesday scientific meeting and the actual conferment of the degree on Friday.) I only wish I had not been recovering from stomach flu so I could have better enjoyed the wonderful food.

Friday, February 8:

After last night's dinner, I could not even think of breakfast, but went down with Julie to have some tea. We were joined by Pierre Pescatore, the candidate of the law school, who told us about his triple career as diplomat, academic, and one of the seven Justices of the European Community. From what was said about him later, I gather that he is the person largely responsible for the theoretical underpinning of the European Court.

At two o'clock, a university car came to pick us up for the 410th birthday party of the University of Leiden. For the ceremony, I was supposed to wear a cap, gown and hood from Berkeley. When I had tried to rent a hood in Berkeley, the university store had had difficulty finding one (they of course prefer to sell them, but I doubted that I would ever need it again). I told them that in that case I would wear my wife's, who got her degree from Stanford. (Julie really does own hers.) This threat produced one quite rapidly.

In the car, we were joined by the van Zwets and by Jaap Fabius, a former Berkeley student who had recently succeeded Bill as dean. We were taken to the side entrance of

Pieterskerk, Leiden's main church, built in the 14th Century over a period of 30 years by Rotger of Cologne, who was also the architect of the Cologne cathedral. It was filled with flowers, a student orchestra and chorus, and a large audience. Bill, Jaap, and I went to the robing area to put on our finery. Here I finally met Professor Kassenaar, the jovial Rector of the university, who welcomed me back from the grave. I also had the opportunity to have a brief talk with Michael Rutter, the only one of the honorees I had not yet met. He is a London professor of psychiatry known for his work on autism, and he completely outshone the rest of us with his scarlet Oxford robe.

Shortly after 2:30, the Master of Ceremonies raised a silver scepter, and the Rector; the orator (the Leiden professor van Rood, who was to give a talk on "the molecular basis of recognition"); the ere-doctores and their promoters; the deans; and the faculty (in the order printed in the program) followed in solemn procession through the church to their assigned seats. The four of us and our sponsors sat in the first row, with Julie, Bill's wife Lucy, and the other wives directly behind us (which was good for Julie's picture-taking).

The ceremony began, wonderfully, with music from Bach's Cantata No. 71, "Gott ist mein König." Then van Rood ascended the pulpit to deliver his speech, about which there had been some controversy. Bill had tried to persuade the administration to have the talk given in English, as the now-universal language of science, but had been rebuffed. He felt that the insistence on a 45–minute speech in Dutch indicated a provincial attitude that did not bode well for the future of the university. As a compromise, we found on our seats, together with the program, an English summary of the talk. But despite this help, and although it is fairly easy to read Dutch, we could not understand a word of van Rood's talk.

The four of us were then motioned to chairs behind a small table on a podium facing the audience, and the deans took up their stations on our right. The order was determined by the age of the faculties, so Wevers stepped up first. His theological sponsor addressed him in Dutch, extolling his virtues and accomplishments, and ended with the official Latin citation. The dean of the theological faculty then pinned on the doctoral cape; the Rector, by a formal address, made the conferment official; and then it was Pescatore's turn. Although his native language is French, his sponsor addressed him in English, explaining that it was now the universal language of scholars, exactly the point made by Bill.

After Pescatore, I came next. Bill's address, of course, was also in English. The Latin summary at the end (which coincides with the text on the scroll) was rather amusing, since it was full of statistical terms translated for the occasion, such as *"methodi sine parametro"* (nonparametrics) and *"asymptotica secundi ordinis"* (second order asymptotics). There had been much discussion of the correct Dutch pronunciation of Latin. Bill had worked on this with his older son, who was taking Latin in high school, and was later told by several classical scholars that his Latin had been the best.

Next, Dean Fabius pinned the cape on me, and after the Rector's official benediction I was a Dr. h.c. from Leiden. After Rutter had also been doctored, Wevers thanked the university on behalf of all of us in a brief speech in Dutch, which the university had requested from him. Finally, we went back to our original seats, from where we were treated to a beautiful performance of "La Fuite en Egypte," by Berlioz.

After the ceremony, everybody congratulated everybody else, and then we were shepherded, with wives and sponsors, toward more picture-taking by the press and, without my realizing it, were formed into a receiving line. I had managed to grab a glass of Genever (my favorite drink in Holland) from a tray that was being passed around, and now had a hard time shaking hands with an unending stream of well-wishers, keeping my precariously perched cap from sliding down with each energetic handshake, and holding on to my drink. The people who were filing by were the Rectors of other Dutch universities wearing beautiful ornamental chains; and statisticians from Amsterdam, Utrecht and further away. There were applied statisticians from agriculture, economics, and psychology, most of whom I did not know. The British Ambassador and the Ambassador of Luxembourg, who were there for Rutter and Pescatore, introduced themselves and briefly talked to me. The American Embassy was less forthcoming. A somewhat scruffy individual shook my hand, said, "Congratulations. Representing the American Embassy," and disappeared. I wondered whether they had sent one of the Embassy chauffeurs.

Eventually, the formal part of the reception was over and we could talk with friends, but soon we were told that the official car was waiting to take us back. By the time we got to the hotel, it was past five, and Bill was to pick us up at 6:45 for the last event, the annual dinner for the Leiden faculty and their spouses, organized by the Faculty Club. Bill had tried to avoid this dinner, but was firmly told that we, and he, were expected to be there. This was the occasion for which tails had been prescribed, and the putting on of these clothes was the main task remaining. I did not get very far before realizing that either Mr. Sloos had overestimated me after all or that he had forgotten something—there were no cufflinks. Fortunately, there was still time to call Bill and ask him to bring a pair, so disaster was averted.

The dinner for about 300 people was anticlimactic. Too many courses were interspersed with entertainment in Dutch, which was lost on us. During a break after dinner, before another round of entertainment, we left early—although after 11. The next morning, when Bill took us to the airport, even he admitted to being a bit tired. It had been a big week, but for me a once-in-a-lifetime, wonderful experience.

Afterword

When as a twenty-two-year-old I arrived in the United States, I knew no one and was isolated and rootless. As a Nazi refugee, I had lost my country, my language, and my friends. What I most longed for is indicated by the title of an early draft of this book, "In Search of Community," a community to which I could belong.

It has been my wonderfully good fortune over the years to find two such communities. On the personal side it has been my family: my wife, Julie, my children and stepchildren and their spouses, their children and spouses, and even a great-granddaughter.

Professionally, I became a member of another community, that of the statisticians among whom I worked and who became my friends: my teachers, colleagues, and students. To describe this, my statistical community, has been the aim of this book.

Bibliography

Albers, D. J. and Alexanderson, G. L. (1985). *Mathematical People*. Birkhäuser, Boston.

Albers, D. J., Alexanderson, G. L. and Reid, C. (1990). *More Mathematical People*. Harcourt Brace Jovanovich, Boston.

Anderson, T. W. (1955). The integral of a symmetric unimodal function over a symmetric convex set and some probability inequalities. *Proceedings of the American Mathematical Society* 6, 170–176.

Anderson, T. W. (1958; 3rd Ed. 2004). Multivariate Analysis. John Wiley. New York.

Anderson, T. W. (1965). Samuel Stanley Wilks, 1906–1964. *Annals of Mathematical Statistics* 36, 1–23.

Anderson, T. W. (1990). *Collected Papers* (2 volumes). John Wiley, New York.

Anderson, T. W. and Darling, D. A. (1952). Asymptotic theory of certain "goodness of fit" criteria based on stochastic processes. *Annals of Mathematical Statistics* 23, 193–212.

Anderson, T. W. and Darling, D. A. (1954). A test of goodness of fit. *Journal of the American Statistical Association* 49, 765–769.

Anderson, T. W., Chung, K. L. and Lehmann, E. L. (1979). Pao-Lu Hsu, 1909–1970. *Annals of Statistics* **7**, 467–470.

Andrews, D. F., Bickel, P. J., Hampel, F. R., Huber, P. J., Rogers, W. H. and Tukey, J. W. (1972). *Robust Estimates of Location*. Princeton University Press.

Anscombe, F. J. (Ed. 1988). Frederick Mosteller and John W. Tukey: a conversation. *Statistical Science* 3, 136–144.

Arrow, K. J. and Lehmann, E. L. (2005). Harold Hotelling 1895–1973. In *Biographical Memoirs of the National Academy*, Vol. 87. National Academies Press, Washington, D.C.

Arrow, K. J., Blackwell, D. and Girshick, M. A. (1949). Bayes and minimax solutions of sequential decision problems. *Econometrica* 17, 213–244.

Bahadur, R. R. (1966). A note on quantiles in large samples. *Annals of Mathematical Statistics* 37, 577–580.

Bahadur, R. R. (1960). Stochastic comparison of tests. *Annals of Mathematical Statistics* 31, 276–295.

Bahadur, R. R. and Lehmann, E. L. (1955). Two comments on "sufficiency and statistical decision functions." *Annals of Mathematical Statistics* 26, 139–142.

Bahadur, R. R. and Savage, L. J. (1956). The nonexistence of certain statistical procedures in non-parametric problems. *Annals of Mathematical Statistics* 27, 1115–1122.

Barndorff-Nielsen, O. E. and Cox, D. R. (1994). *Inference and Asymptotics*. Chapman & Hall, London.

Bartlett, M. S. (1981). Egon Sharpe Pearson, 1895–1980. *Biographical Memoirs of Fellows of the Royal Society* 27, 425–443.

Barton, D. E. and David, F. N. (1960). *Combinatorial Chance*. Charles Griffin, London.

Bather, J. (1996). A conversation with Herman Chernoff. *Statistical Science* 11, 335–350.

Bayer, D. and Diaconis, P. (1992). Trailing the dovetail shuffle to its lair. *Annals of Applied Probability* 2, 294–313.

Bellhouse, D. R. (2004). The Reverend Thomas Bayes, FRS: a biography to celebrate the tercentenary of his birth (with discussion). *Statistical Science* 19, 3–43.

Benjamini, Y., Bretz, F. and Sarkar, S. (Eds.) (2004). *Recent Developments in Multiple Comparison Procedures*. Institute of Mathematical Statistics, Beachwood, OH.

Bennett, J. H. (Ed.) (1983). *Natural Selection, Heredity and Eugenics: Selected Correspondence of R. A. Fisher with Leonard Darwin and Others*. Clarendon Press, Oxford.

Bennett, J. H. (Ed.) (1990). *Statistical Inference and Analysis: Selected Correspondence of R.A. Fisher*. Clarendon Press, Oxford.

Bera, A. K. (2003). The ET interview: Professor C. R. Rao. *Econometric Theory* 19, 331–400.

Berger, J. O. (1980). *Statistical Decision Theory*. Springer-Verlag, New York.

Berger, J. O. (1984). The robust Bayesian viewpoint. In Kadane, Ed.

Berger, J. O. (1985). The frequentist point of view and conditioning. In *Proceedings of the Berkeley Conference in Honor of Jerzy Neyman and Jack Kiefer* (Le Cam and Olshen, Eds.), Vol. 1.

Berger, J. O. and Wolpert, R. L. (1984). *The Likelihood Principle*. Institute of Mathematical Statistics, Hayward, CA.

Berkson, J. (1955). Maximum likelihood and minimum χ^2 estimates of the logistic function. *Journal of the American Statistical Association* 50, 130–162.

Bernardo, J. M. (1979). Reference posterior distributions for Bayesian inference (with discussion). *Journal of the Royal Statistical Society (B)* 41, 113–147.

Bernardo, J. M. and Smith, A. F. M. (1994). *Bayesian Theory*. John Wiley, Chichester.

Bickel, P. J. and Doksum, K. A. (1976). *Mathematical Statistics: Basic Ideas and Selected Topics*. Holden-Day, San Francisco.

Bickel, P. J. and Lehmann, E. L. (1975–76). Descriptive statistics for nonparametric models I-III. *Annals of Statistics* 3, 1038–1069 and 4, 1139–1158.

Bickel, P. J., Doksum, K. A. and Hodges, J. L. (Eds.) (1983). *A Festschrift for Erich L. Lehmann*. Wadsworth, Belmont, CA.

Bickel, P. J., Klaassen, C. A. J., Ritov, Y. and Wellner, J. A. (1993). *Efficient and Adaptive Estimation for Semiparametric Models*. Johns Hopkins University Press, Baltimore.

Billard, L. and Ferber, M. (1991). Elizabeth Scott: Scholar, teacher, administrator. *Statistical Science* 6, 206–216.

Bishop, Y. M. M., Fienberg, S. E. and Holland, P. W. (1975). *Discrete Multivariate Analysis*. MIT Press, Cambridge, MA.

Blackwell, D. (1947). Conditional expectation and unbiased sequential estimation. *Annals of Mathematical Statistics* 18, 105–110.

Blackwell, D. and Bowker, A. (1955). Meyer Abraham Girshick 1908–1955 *Annals of Mathematical Statistics* 26, 365–367.

Blackwell, D. and Girshick, M. A. (1954). *Theory of Games and Statistical Decisions*. John Wiley, New York.

Blyth, C. R. (1951). On minimax statistical decision procedures and their admissibility. *Annals of Mathematical Statistics* 22, 22–42.

Bose, R. C. (Ed.) (1970). *Essays in Probability and Statistics (Dedicated to the Memory of S. N. Roy)*. University of North Carolina Press, Chapel Hill.

Box, G. E. P. (1953). Non-normality and tests for variances. *Biometrika* 40, 318–335.

Box, G. E. P. and Andersen, S. L. (1955). Permutation theory in the derivation of robust criteria and the study of departures from assumption. *Journal of the Royal Statistical Society (B)* 17, 1–34.

Box, J. F. (1978). *R. A. Fisher: The Life of a Scientist*. John Wiley, New York.

Brillinger, D. R. (1975). *Time Series: Data Analysis and Theory*. Holt, Rhinehart and Winston, New York.

Brillinger, D. R. (1983). A generalized linear model with "Gaussian" regressor variables. In Bickel, Doksum, and Hodges, Eds. Wadsworth, Belmont, CA.

Brillinger, D. R. (1988). Some statistical methods for random process data from seismology and neurophysiology. *Annals of Statistics* 16, 1–54.

Brillinger, D. R. (1992). Nerve cell spike train data analysis: a progression of technique. *Journal of the American Statistical Association* 87, 260–271.

Brillinger, D. R. (2002). John W. Tukey: his life and professional contributions. *Annals of Statistics* 30, 1535–1575.

Brillinger, D. R., Fernholz, L. T. and Morgenthaler, S. (Eds.) (1997). *The Practice of Data Analysis: Essays in Honor of John W. Tukey*. Princeton University Press, Princeton, NJ.

Brown, B. W. and Hollander, M. (1999). A conversation with Lincoln E. Moses. *Statistical Science* 14, 338–354.

Brown, L. D. (1971). Admissible estimators, recurrent diffusions, and insoluble boundary value problems. *Annals of Mathematical Statistics* 42, 855–903.

Brown, L. D. (1986). *Fundamentals of Statistical Exponential Families (with Applications in Statistical Decision Theory)*. Institute of Mathematical Statistics, Hayward, CA.

Brown, L. D. (1993). Minimaxity more or less. In *Statistical Decision Theory and Related Topics,* V 1–18 (Gupta and Berger, Eds.). Springer, New York.

Brown, L. D. (2000). An essay on statistical decision theory. *Journal of the American Statistical Association* 95, 1277–1282.

Brown, L. D., Cai, T. T. and DasGupta, A. (2001). Interval estimation for a binomial proportion (with discussion). *Statistical Science* 16, 101–133.

Brown, L. D., Cai, T. T. and DasGupta, A. (2003). Interval estimation in exponential families. *Statistica Sinica* 13, 19–50.

Bunker, J. P., Barnes, B. A. and Mosteller, F. (Eds.) (1977). *Costs, Risks, and Benefits of Surgery*. Oxford University Press, New York.

Bunker, J. P., Forrest, W. H., Mosteller, F. and Vandam, L. D. (Eds.) (1969). *The National Halothane Study*. Government Printing Office, Washington, D.C.

Chakravarti, I. M. (1980). *Asymptotic Theory of Statistical Tests and Estimation (In Honor of Wassily Hoeffding)*. Academic Press, New York.

Chernoff, H. (1949). Asymptotic Studentization in testing of hypotheses. *Annals of Mathematical Statistics* 20, 268–278.

Chernoff, H. (1972). *Sequential Analysis and Optimal Design*. SIAM, Philadelphia.

Chernoff, H. (1973). The use of faces to represent points in k-dimensional space graphically. *Journal of the American Statistical Association* 68, 361–368.

Chernoff, H. and Lehmann, E. L. (1954). The use of maximum likelihood estimates in χ^2-tests for goodness of fit. *Annals of Mathematical Statistics* 25, 579–586.

Chernoff, H. and Moses, L. E. (1959). *Elementary Decision Theory*. John Wiley, New York

Chernoff, H. and Savage, I. R. (1958). Asymptotic normality and efficiency of certain nonparametric test statistics. *Annals of Mathematical Statistics* 29, 972–994.

Cochran, W. G. (1953). *Sampling Techniques*. John Wiley, New York.

Cochran, W. G. (1983). *Planning and Analysis of Observational Studies* (Moses and Mosteller, Eds.). John Wiley, New York.

Cochran, W. G. and Cox, G. M. (1950). *Experimental Designs*. John Wiley, New York.

Courant, R. and Robbins, H. (1941). *What Is Mathematics?* Oxford University Press, London.

Cox, D. R. (1958). Some problems connected with statistical inference. *Annals of Mathematical Statistics* 29, 357–372.

Cox, D. R. (1970). *The Analysis of Binary Data*. Methuen, London. (2nd ed., with Snell, 1989. Chapman & Hall, New York.)

Cox, D. R. (1972). Regression models and life tables (with discussion). *Journal of the Royal Statistical Society (B)* 34, 187–220.

Cox, D. R. (1975). Partial likelihood. *Biometrika* 62, 269–276.

Cox, D. R. (2006). *Principles of Statistical Inference*. Cambridge University Press.

Cox, D. R. and Hinkley, D. V. (1974). *Theoretical Statistics*. Chapman & Hall, London.

Cox, D. R. and Lewis, P. A. W. (1966). *The Statistical Analysis of Series of Events*. Methuen, London.

Cox, D. R. and Oakes, D. (1984). *Analysis of Survival Data*. Chapman & Hall, London.

Cox, D. R. and Wermuth, N. (1996). *Multivariate Dependencies*. Chapman & Hall, London.

Cramér, H. (1936). Über eine eigenschaft der normalen verteilungsfunktion. Mathematische Zeitschrift 41, 405–414.

Cramér, H. (1937). Random Variables and Probability Distributions. *Cambridge Tracts in Mathematics, volume* 36 Cambridge University Press, Cambridge.

Cramér, H. (1946). *Mathematical Methods of Statistics*. Princeton University Press, Princeton, NJ.

Cramér, H. (1976). Half a century with probability theory: some personal recollections. *Annals of Probability* 4, 509–546.

Cramér, H. (1994). *Collected Works* (2 volumes). Springer-Verlag, Berlin.

Daggett, R. and Freedman, D. (1985). Econometrics and the law: a case study in the proof of antitrust damages. In Le Cam and Olshen, Eds., Vol. 1. Wadsworth, Belmont, CA.

Dalenius, T., Karlsson, G. and Malmquist, S. (Eds.) (1970). *Scientists at Work (Festschrift in Honor of Herman Wold)*. Almquist and Wiksell, Uppsala

Daniel, C. and Lehmann, E. L. (1979). Henry Scheffé 1907–1977. *Annals of Statistics* 6, 1149–1161.

Daniell, P. J. (1920). Observations weighted according to order. *American Journal of Mathematics* 42, 222–236.

Darmois, G. (1945). Sur les limites de la dispersion de certains estimations. *Revue Internationale de Statistique* 13, 9–15.

DasGupta, A. (2005). A conversation with Larry Brown. *Statistical Science* 20, 193–203.

David, F. N. (1962). *Games, Gods, and Gambling*. Charles Griffin, London.

David, F. N. (Ed. 1966). *Research Papers in Statistics: Festschrift for J. Neyman*. John Wiley, London.

David, F., Kendall, M. and Barton, D. (1966). *Symmetric Functions and Allied Tables*. Cambridge University Press, Cambridge.

Davison, A. C., Dodge, Y. and Wermuth, N. (2005). *Celebrating Statistics*. Oxford University Press, Oxford.

De Groot, M. H. (1986). A conversation with Persi Diaconis. *Statistical Science* 1, 319–334.

De Groot, M. H. (1987). A conversation with C. R. Rao. *Statistical Science* 2, 53–67.

De Groot, M. H. (1988). A conversation with George A. Barnard. *Statistical Science* 3, 196–212.

Diaconis, P. (1985). Discussion of Huber (1985). *Annals of Statistics* 13, 494–496.

Diaconis, P. (1996). The cutoff phenomenon in finite Markov chains. *Proceedings of the National Academy of Science* 93, 1659–1664.

Diaconis, P. and Freedman, D. (1986). On the consistency of Bayes estimates (with discussion). *Annals of Statistics* 14, 1–67.

Diaconis, P. and Freedman, D. (1997). Consistency of Bayes estimates for nonparametric regression: a review. In Pollard, et al., Eds.

Diaconis, P. and Holmes, S. (1994). Gray codes for randomization procedures. *Statistics and Computing* 4, 287–302.

Diaconis, P. and Holmes, S. (Eds.) (2004). *Stein's Method: Expository Lectures and Applications*. Institute of Mathematical Statistics, Hayward, CA.

Diaconis, P. and Mosteller, F. (1989). Methods for studying coincidences. *Journal of the American Statistical Association* 84, 853–861.

Doksum, K. A. (1974). Tailfree and neutral random probabilities and their posterior distributions. *Annals of Probability* 2, 183–201.

Doksum, K. A. and Lo, A. (1990). Consistent and robust Bayes procedures for location based on partial information. *Annals of Statistics* 18, 443–453.

Donoghue, J. R. (2004). Implementing Shaffer's multiple comparison procedure for a large number of groups. In Benjamin, Bretz, and Sarkar, Eds.

Donoho, D. L. and Huber, P. J. (1983). The notion of breakdown point. In Bickel, Doksum, and Hodges, Eds.

Doob, J. L. (1972). William Feller 1906–1970. *Proceedings of the Sixth Berkeley Symposium on Mathematical Statistics and Probability*, Vol. 2, xv-xx. University of California Press, Berkeley.

Doob, J. L. (1988). Commentary on probability. In Duren, Ed., Part II.

Duren, P. (Ed.) (1988–1989). *A Century of Mathematics in America* (3 volumes). American Mathematical Society, Providence, RI.

Efron, B. (1978). The geometry of exponential families. *Annals of Statistics* 6, 362–376.

Efron, B. (1979). Bootstrap methods: another look at the jackknife. *Annals of Statistics* 7, 1–26.

Efron, B. (1981). Nonparametric standard errors and confidence intervals (with discussion). *Canadian Journal of Statistics* 9, 139–172.

Efron, B. (1982). Maximum likelihood and decision theory. *Annals of Statistics* 10, 340–356.

Efron, B. (1982). *The Jackknife, the Bootstrap and Other Resampling Plans*. SIAM, Philadelphia.

Efron, B. (1986). Why isn't everyone a Bayesian? *American Statistician* 40, 1–11.

Efron, B. and Morris, C. N. (1973a). Combining possibly related estimation problems (with discussion). *Journal of the Royal Statistical Society (B)* 35, 379–421.

Efron, B and Morris, C. N. (1973b). Stein's estimation rule and its competitors—an empirical Bayes approach. *Journal of the American Statistical Association* 68, 117–130.

Efron, B. and Thisted, R. (1987). Did Shakespeare write a newly discovered poem? *Biometrika* 74, 445–455.

Efron, B. and Tibshirani, R. J. (1993). *An Introduction to the Bootstrap*. Chapman & Hall, New York.

Eisenhart, C. (1989). S. S. Wilks' Princeton appointment, and statistics at Princeton before Wilks. In Duren, Ed., Part III. American Mathematical Society, Providence, RI.

Eisenhart, C., Hastay, M. W. and Wallis, W. A. (Eds.) (1947). *Selected Techniques of Statistical Analysis*. McGraw-Hill, New York.

Ericson, W. A. (1981). *The Writings of Leonard Jimmie Savage*. The American Statistical Association and the Institute of Mathematical Statistics.

Fairley, W. B. and Mosteller, F. (Eds.) (1977). *Statistics and Public Policy*. Addison-Wesley, Reading, MA.

Fan, J. and Koul, H. (Eds.) (2006). *Frontiers in Statistics*. Imperial College Press, Hackensack.

Feferman, A. B. and Feferman, S. (2004). *Alfred Tarski—Life and Logic*. Cambridge University Press, Cambridge.

Feller, W. (Vol. 1, 1950 and 1957; Vol. 2, 1966). *An Introduction to Probability Theory and Its Applications*. John Wiley, New York.

Fienberg, S. E. and Hinkley, D. V. (Eds.) (1980). *R. A. Fisher: An Appreciation*. Springer-Verlag, New York.

Fienberg, S. E., Hoaglin, D. C. Kruskal, W. H. and Tanur, J. M. (1990). *A Statistical Model: Frederick Mosteller's Contributions to Statistics, Science, and Public Policy*. Springer-Verlag, New York.

Fisher, N. I. and van Zwet, W. R. (2005). Wassily Hoeffding, 1914–1991. In *Biographical Memoirs of the National Academy*, Vol. 86. National Academies Press, Washington, D. C.

Fisher, R. A. (1922). On the mathematical foundations of theoretical statistics. *Philosophical Transactions of the Royal Society of London (A)* 222, 309–368.

Fisher, R. A. (1925). *Statistical Methods for Research Workers*. Oliver and Boyd, Edinburgh.

Fisher, R. A. (1934). Two new properties of mathematical likelihood. *Proceedings of the Royal Society (A)* 144, 285–307.

Fisher, R. A. (1935). *The Design of Experiments*. Oliver and Boyd, Edinburgh.

Fisher, R. A. (1935). The logic of inductive inference (with discussion). *Journal of the Royal Statistical Society* 98, 39–54.

Fisher, R. A. (1955a). Science and Christianity. *Friend* 113, 995–996.

Fisher, R. A. (1955b). Statistical methods and scientific induction. *Journal of the Royal Statistical Society (B)* 17, 69–78.

Fisher, R. A. (1957). *Statistical Methods and Scientific Inference*. Oliver and Boyd, Edinburgh.

Fisher, R. A. and Yates, F. (1938). *Statistical Tables (for Biological, Agricultural and Medical Research)*. Oliver and Boyd, London.

Fix, E. and Hodges, J. L. (1955). Significance probabilities of the Wilcoxon test. *Annals of Mathematical Statistics* 26, 301–312.

Fix, E. and Hodges, J. L. (1989). Discriminatory analysis—nonparametric discrimination: consistency properties (1951). *International Statistical Review* 57, 238–247.

Fix, E. and Neyman, J. (1951). A simple stochastic model of recovery, relapse, death, and loss of patients. *Human Biology* 23, 205–241.

Fix, E. and Neyman, J. (1954). Statistical adventures in Thailand. In *Idea and Experiment, Vol. 3*, 12–15. University of California Press, Berkeley.

Fix, E., Hodges, J. L. and Lehmann, E. L. (1959). The restricted chi-square test. In Grenander, Ed.

Fréchet, M. (1943). Sur l'extension de certains évaluations statistiques au cas de petits échantillons. *Revue Internationale De Statistique* 11, 183–205.

Freedman, D. (1963). On the asymptotic behavior of Bayes estimates in the discrete case I. *Annals of Mathematical Statistics* 34, 1386–1403.

Freedman, D. (1987). As others see us: a case study in path analysis (with discussion). *Journal of Educational Statistics* 12, 101–223.

Freedman, D. (1991). Statistical models and shoe leather. In *Sociological Methodology* (P. Marsden, Ed.). American Sociological Association, Washington, D.C.

Freedman, D. (1997). From association to causation via regression. *Advances in Applied Mathematics* 18, 59–110.

Freedman, D. (2005). *Statistical Models—Theory and Practice*. Cambridge University Press.

Freedman, D. and Navidi, W. (1986). Regression models for adjusting the 1980 census (with discussion). *Statistical Science* 1, 3–39.

Freedman, D., Pisani, R. and Purves, R. (1978). *Statistics*. W. W. Norton, New York.

Freeman, H. A., Friedman, M., Mosteller, F. and Wallis, W. A. (Eds.) (1948). *Sampling Inspection*. McGraw-Hill, New York.

Freeman, P. R. and Smith, A. F. M. (Eds.) (1994). *Aspects of Uncertainty: A Tribute to D. V. Lindley*. John Wiley, New York.

Friedman, M. (1937). The use of ranks to avoid the assumption of normality implicit in the analysis of variance. *Journal of the American Statistical Association* 32, 675–701.

Gani, J. (Ed.) (1982). *The Making of Statisticians*. Springer-Verlag, New York.

Gardner, D. P. (1967). *The California Oath Controversy*. University of California Press, Berkeley.

Ghosh, J. J., Maiti, P., Rao, J. and Sinha, B. K. (1999). Evolution of statistics in India. *International Statistical Review* 67, 13–34.

Ghosh, J. K., Mitra, S. K., Parthasarthy, K. R. and Prakasa Rao, B. L. S. (Eds.) (1993). *Statistics and Probability: A Raghu Raj Bahadur Festschrift*. John Wiley Eastern, New Delhi.

Gigerenzer, G., Swijtink, Z., Porter, T., Daston, L., Beatty, J. and Krüger, L. (1989). *The Empire of Chance*. Cambridge University Press.

Giri, N. and Kiefer, J. (1964). Local and asymptotic minimax properties of multivariate tests. *Annals of Mathematical Statistics* 35, 21–35.

Giri, N., Kiefer, J. and Stein, C. (1963). Minimax character of Hotelling's T^2 test in the simplest case. *Annals of Mathematical Statistics* 34, 1524–1535.

Girshick, M. A. and Savage, L. J. (1951). Bayes and minimax estimates for quadratic loss functions. *Proceedings of the Second Berkeley Symposium on Mathematical Statistics and Probability*. University of California Press, Berkeley.

Gosset, W. S. (1970). Letters from W. S. Gosset to R. A. Fisher, 1915–1936 (with summaries by R. A. Fisher and a foreword by L. McMullen). Printed for private circulation.

Grenander, U. (1995). A survey of the life and works of Harald Cramér. *Scandinavian Actuarial Journal* 1, 2–5.

Grenander, U. (Ed. 1959). *Probability and Statistics (the Harald Cramér Volume)*. John Wiley, New York.

Hajek, J. (1998). *Collected Works*. John Wiley, Chichester.

Hald, A. (1990). *A History of Probability and Statistics and Their Applications Before 1750*. John Wiley, New York.

Hald, A. (1998). A History of Mathematical Statistics from 1750 to 1930. John Wiley, New York.

Hampel, F. (1987). Design, modelling and analysis of some biological data sets. In Mallows, Ed.

Hampel, F. (1996). On the philosophical foundations of statistics: bridges to Huber's work, and recent results. In Rieder, Ed.

Hampel, F. (1997). Some additional notes on the "Princeton robustness year." In Brillinger, Fernholz and Morgenthaler, Eds.

Hampel, F. (1998). Is statistics too difficult? *Canadian Journal of Statistics* 26, 497–513.

Hampel, F. R., Ronchetti, E. M., Rousseeuw, R. J. and Stahel, W. A. (1986). *Robust Statistics (The Approach Based on Influence Functions)*. John Wiley, New York.

Hardy, G. H. and Heilbronn, H. (1938). Edmund Landau. *J. London Math. Soc.* 1–13, 302–310.

Harshbarger, B. (1976). History of the early development of modern statistics in America (1920–1944). In Owen, Ed.

Hedges, L. V. and Olkin, I. (1985). *Statistical Methods for Meta-Analysis*. Academic Press, Orlando.

Hemelrijk, J. (1960). The statistical work of David van Dantzig. *Annals of Mathematical Statistics* 31, 269–275.

Hinkley, D. V., Reid, N. and Snell, E. J. (Eds.) (1991). *Statistical Theory and Modeling (in Honour of Sir David Cox, FRS)*. Chapman & Hall, London.

Hoaglin, D. C., Mosteller, F. and Tukey, J. W. (Eds.) (1983). *Understanding Robust and Exploratory Data Analysis*. John Wiley, New York.

Hoaglin, D. C., Mosteller, F. and Tukey, J. W. (Eds.) (1985). *Exploring Data Tables, Trends, and Shapes*. John Wiley, New York.

Hochberg, Y. and Tamhane, A. (1987). *Multiple Comparison Procedures*. John Wiley, New York.

Hodges, J. L. (1967). Efficiency in normal samples and tolerance of extreme values for some estimates of location. *Proceedings of the Fifth Berkeley Symposium on Mathematical Statistics, and Probability*, Vol. 1, 163–186. University of California Press, Berkeley.

Hodges, J. L. and Lehmann, E. L. (1950). Some problems in minimax point estimation. *Annals of Mathematical Statistics* 21, 182–197.

Hodges, J. L. and Lehmann, E. L. (1951). Some applications of the Cramér-Rao inequality. *Proceedings of the Second Berkeley Symposium on Mathematical Statistics and Probability*. University of California Press, Berkeley.

Hodges, J. L. and Lehmann, E. L. (1952). The use of previous experience in reaching statistical decisions. *Annals of Mathematical Statistics* 23, 396–407.

Hodges, J. L. and Lehmann, E. L. (1955). Testing the approximate validity of statistical hypotheses. *Journal of the Royal Statistical Society (B)* 16, 261–268.

Hodges, J. L. and Lehmann, E. L. (1956). The efficiency of some nonparametric competitors of the t-test. *Annals of Mathematical Statistics* 27, 324–335.

Hodges, J. L. and Lehmann, E. L. (1962). Rank methods for combination of independent experiments in analysis of variance. *Annals of Mathematical Statistics* 33, 482–497.

Hodges, J. L. and Lehmann, E. L. (1963). Estimates of location based on rank tests. *Annals of Mathematical Statistics* 34, 593–611.

Hodges, J. L. and Lehmann, E. L. (1970). Deficiency. *Annals of Mathematical Statistics* 41, 783–801.

Hodges, J. L. and Lehmann, E. L. (2005). *Basic Concepts of Probability and Statistics*, 2nd ed. SIAM, Philadelphia.

Hoeffding, W. (1948). A class of statistics with asymptotically normal distributions. *Annals of Mathematical Statistics* 19, 293–325.

Hoeffding, W. (1951). "Optimum" nonparametric tests. *Proceedings of the Second Berkeley Symposium on Mathematical Statistics and Probability*. University of California Press, Berkeley.

Hoeffding, W. (1952). The large-sample power of tests based on permutations of observations. *Annals of Mathematical Statistics* 23, 169–192.

Hoeffding, W. (1968). Some recent developments in nonparametric statistics. *International Statistical Review* 36, 176–187.

Hoeffding, W. (1994). *The Collected Works* (Fisher and Sen, Eds.). Springer-Verlag, New York.

Holm, S. (1979). A simple sequentially rejective multiple test procedure. *Scandinavian Journal of Statistics* 6, 65–70.

Holmes, S.; Morris, C.; and Tibslirani, R. (2003). Bradley Efron: A conversation with good friends. Statistical Science 18, 268–281.

Hotelling, H. (1930). British statistics and statisticians today. *Journal of the American Statistical Association* 25, 186–190.

Hotelling, H. (1931a). The generalization of Student's ratio. *Annals of Mathematical Statistics* 2, 360–378.

Hotelling, H. (1931b). Recent improvements in statistical inference. *Journal of the American Statistical Association* 28 (March supplement), 79–89.

Hotelling, H. (1933). Analysis of a complex of statistical variables into principal components. *Journal of Educational Psychology* 24, 417–441, 498–520.

Hotelling, H. (1936). Relations between two sets of variables. *Biometrika* 28, 321–377.

Hotelling, H. (1940). The teaching of statistics. *Annals of Mathematical Statistics* 11, 457–470.

Hotelling, H. (1949). The place of statistics in the university. *Proceedings of the Berkeley Symposium on Mathematical Statistics and Probability*. University of California Press, Berkeley.

Hotelling, H. and Pabst, M. (1936). Rank correlation and tests of significance involving no assumption of normality. *Annals of Mathematical Statistics* 7, 29–43.

Howie, D. (2002). *Interpreting Probability*. Cambridge University Press, Cambridge.

Hsu, P.-L. (1983). *Collected Papers*. Springer-Verlag, New York.

Huber, P. (1964). Robust estimation of a location parameter. *Annals of Mathematical Statistics* 35, 73–101.

Huber, P. (1965). A robust version of the probability ratio test. *Annals of Mathematical Statistics* 36, 1753–1758.

Huber, P. (1973). Robust regression: asymptotics, conjectures, and Monte Carlo. *Annals of Statistics* 1, 799–821.

Huber, P. (1985). Projection pursuit (with discussion). *Annals of Statistics* 13, 435–525.

Huber, P. J. (1981). *Robust Statistics*. John Wiley, New York.

Huber, P. J. (1997). Speculations on the path of statistics. In Brillinger, Fernholz, and Morgenthaler, Eds.

Huber, P. J. (2002). John W. Tukey's contributions to robust statistics. *Annals of Statistics* 30, 1640–1648.

Jaynes, E. T. (1983). *Papers on Probability, Statistics and Statistical Physics*. Kluwer, Dordrecht.

Jeffreys, H. (1939). *Theory of Probability*. Oxford University Press, Oxford.

Johnson, N. L. and Balakrishnan, N. (Eds.) (1997). *Advances in the Theory and Practice of Statistics: A Volume in Honor of Samuel Kotz*. John Wiley, New York.

Johnson, N. L., Kotz, S. and Balakrishnan, N. (1994–95). *Continuous Univariate Distributions*, 2nd ed. (2 volumes). John Wiley, New York.

Johnson, N. L., Kotz, S. and Kemp, A. W. (1992). *Univariate Discrete Distributions*, 2nd ed. John Wiley, New York.

Jung, J. (1955). On linear estimates defined by a continuous weight function. *Arkiv for Matematik*. 3, 199–209.

Jureckovà, J. and Sen, P. K. (1996). *Robust Statistical Procedures*. John Wiley, New York.

Kac, M. (1972). William Feller, in memoriam. *Proceedings of the Sixth Berkeley Symposium on Statistics and Probability* 2.

Kadane, J. B. (Ed.) (1984). *Robustness of Bayesian Analysis*. North Holland, Amsterdam.

Kagan, A. M., Linnik, Y. V. and Rao, C. R. (1973). *Characterization Problems in Mathematical Statistics*. John Wiley, New York.

Kallenberg, W. C. M., et al. (1984). *Testing Statistical Hypotheses: Worked Solutions*. Mathematical Centrum, Amsterdam.

Kallianpur, G., Krishnaiah, P.R. and Ghosh, J. K. (Eds.) (1982). *Statistics and Probability (Essays in Honor of C. R. Rao)*. North Holland, Amsterdam.

Kanigel, R. (1991). *The Man Who Knew Infinity: A Life of the Genius Ramanujan*. Scribner's, New York.

Karlin, S., Amemiya, T. and Goodman, L. A. (1983). *Studies in Econometrics, Time Series and Multivariate Statistics (In Honor of T. W. Anderson)*. Academic Press, New York.

Kendall, M. and Plackett, R. L. (Eds.) (1977). *Studies in the History of Statistics and Probability, Vol. 2*. Charles Griffin, London.

Kendall, M. G. (1943, 1946). *The Advanced Theory of Statistics* (2 volumes). Charles Griffin, London.

Kendall, M. G. (1948). *Rank Correlation Methods*. Charles Griffin, London.

Kerr, C. (2003). *The Gold and the Blue, Vol. 2*. University of California Press, Berkeley.

Kiefer, J. C. (1958). On the nonrandomized optimality and randomized nonoptimality of symmetrical designs. *Annals of Mathematical Statistics* 29, 675–699.

Kiefer, J. C. (1959a). K-sample analogues of the Kolmogorov-Smirnov and Cramér-von Mises tests. *Annals of Mathematical Statistics* 30, 420–447.

Kiefer, J. C. (1959b). Optimum experimental designs (with discussion). *Journal of the Royal Statistical Society (B)* 21, 273–319.

Kiefer, J. C. (1984–85). *Collected Works* (3 volumes). Springer-Verlag, New York.

Kiefer, J. C. and Wolfowitz, J. (1959). Asymptotic minimax character of the sample distribution function for vector chance variables. *Annals of Mathematical Statistics* 30, 463–489.

Kiefer, J. C. and Wolfowitz, J. (1960). The equivalence of two extremum properties. *Canadian Journal of Mathematics* 12, 363–366.

Kolmogorov, A. (1933). Grundbegriffe der wahrscheinlichkeitsrechnung. *Ergebnisse der Mathematik* 2, 196–262. (English translation: *Foundations of the Theory of Probability* [1950]. Chelsea, New York.)

Kotz, S. and Johnson, N. L. (Eds.) (1982–1988). *Encyclopedia of Statistical Sciences.* John Wiley, New York.

Kotz, S. and Johnson, N. L. (1987). The making of an encyclopedia. *Journal of Official Statistics* 3, 93–99.

Kotz, S. and Johnson, N. L. (Eds.) (1992, 1997). *Breakthroughs in Statistics* (3 volumes). Springer-Verlag, New York.

Kotz, S., Balakrishnan, N. L. and Johnson, N. (2000). *Continuous Multivariate Distributions, Vol. 1.* John Wiley, New York.

Kruskal, W. and Neyman, J. (1995). Stochastic models and their applications to social phenomena. *Probability and Mathematical Statistics* 15, 21–27.

Kruskal, W. H. and Tanur, J. M. (Eds.) (1978). *International Encyclopedia of Statistics.* The Free Press, New York.

Laird, N. (1989). A conversation with F. N. David. *Statistical Science* 4, 235–246.

Landau, E. (1927). *Vorlesungen über Zahlentheorie.* S. Hirzel, Leipzig.

Landau, E. (1930). *Grundlagen der Analysis.* Akademische Verlagsgesellschaft, Leipzig.

Landau, E. (1934). *Einführung in die Differentialrechnung und Integralrechnung.* Noordhoff, Groningen.

Le Cam, L. (1953). On some asymptotic properties of maximum likelihood estimates and related Bayes' estimates. *University of California Publications in Statistics* 1, 277–330.

Le Cam, L. (1960). Locally asymptotically normal families of distributions. *University of California Publications in Statistics* 3, No. 2, 37–98.

Le Cam, L. (1986). *Asymptotic Methods in Statistical Decision Theory.* Springer-Verlag, New York.

Le Cam, L. (1986). The central limit theorem around 1935. *Statistical Science* 1, 78–96.

Le Cam, L. (1995). Neyman and stochastic models. *Probability and Mathematical Statistics* 15, 37–45.

Le Cam, L. and Lehmann, E. L. (1974). J. Neyman: on the occasion of his 80th birthday. *Annals of Statistics* 2, vii-xiii.

Le Cam, L. and Olshen, R. (Eds.) (1985). *Proceedings of the Berkeley Conference in Honor of Jerzy Neyman and Jack Kiefer* (2 volumes). Wadsworth, Monterey, CA.

Le Cam, L. and Yang, G. L. (1990). *Asymptotics in Statistics.* Springer, New York.

Le May, C. (1965). *Mission with Le May: My Story.* Doubleday, New York.

Lee, A. J. (1990). *U-Statistics.* Marcel Dekker, New York.

Lehmann, E. L. (1947). On families of admissible tests. *Annals of Mathematical Statistics* 18, 97–104.

Lehmann, E. L. (1959). *Testing Statistical Hypotheses.* John Wiley, New York. (3rd ed., with Romano, 2005, Springer, New York.)

Lehmann, E. L. (1966). Some concepts of dependence. *Annals of Mathematical Statistics* 37, 1137–1153.

Lehmann, E. L. (1975, 2006). *Nonparametrics: Statistical Methods Based on Ranks.* Holden-Day, San Francisco; Springer, New York.

Lehmann, E. L. (1981). An interpretation of Basu's theorem. Journal of the American Statistical Association 76, 335–340.

Lehmann, E. L. (1983). *Theory of Point Estimation.* John Wiley, New York. (2nd ed., with Casella, 1998, Springer, New York.)

Lehmann, E. L. (1985). The Neyman-Pearson theory after 50 years. In *Proceedings of the Neyman-Kiefer Conference* (Le Cam and Olshen, Eds.). Wadsworth, Monterey, CA.

Lehmann, E. L. (1990). Model specification: the views of Fisher, Neyman, and later developments. *Statistical Science* 5, 160–168.

Lehmann, E. L. (1993). The Fisher, Neyman-Pearson theories of testing hypotheses: one theory or two? *Journal of the American Statistical Association* 78, 1242–1249.

Lehmann, E. L. (1997). Testing statistical hypotheses: the story of a book. *Statistical Science* 12, 48–52.

Lehmann, E. L. (1999). "Student" and small-sample theory. *Statistical Science* 14, 418–426.

Lehmann, E. L. (1999). *Elements of Large-Sample Theory.* Springer, New York.

Lehmann, E. L. and Loh, W.-Y. (1990). Pointwise vs. uniform robustness of some large-sample tests and confidence intervals. *Scandinavian Journal of Statistics* 17, 177–187.

Lehmann, E. L. and Rojo, J. (1992). Invariant directional orderings. *Annals of Statistics* 20, 2100–2110.

Lehmann, E. L. and Scheffé, H. (1950, 1955). Completeness, similar regions, and unbiased estimation. *Sankhya* 10, 305–340 and 15, 219–236.

Lehmann, E. L. and Scholz, F. (1992). Ancillarity. In *Current Issues in Statistical Inference: Essays in Honor of D. Basu* (Ghosh and Pathak, Eds.), *IMS Lecture Notes*, Vol. 17. Institute of Mathematical Statistics.

Lehmann, E. L. and Stein, C. (1948). Most powerful tests of composite hypotheses. *Annals of Mathematical Statistics* 19, 495–516.

Lehmann, E. L. and Stein, C. (1949). On the theory of some non-parametric hypotheses. *Annals of Mathematical Statistics* 20, 28–45.

Lévy, P. (1934). Sur les intégrales dont les elements sont des variables aléatoires indépendentes. *Annali della Scuola Normale Superiore di Pisa (2)* 3, 337–366.

Lindley, D. (1965). *Introduction to Probability and Statistics (from a Bayesian Viewpoint)* (2 volumes). Cambridge University Press, Cambridge.

Lindley, D. (1990a). The present position in Bayesian statistics (with discussion). *Statistical Science* 5, 44–89.

Lindley, D. (1990b). A survey of George Barnard's statistical work. In *Bayesian and Likelihood Methods in Statistics and Econometrics* (Geisser, et al., Eds.). North Holland, Amsterdam.

Lindley, D. V. (1971a). *Bayesian Statistics: A Review.* SIAM, Philadelphia.

Lindley, D. V. (1971b). *Making Decisions*. John Wiley, New York.

Lindley, D. V. (2006). *Understanding Uncertainty*. John Wiley, New York.

MacLane, S. (1997). Van der Waerden's modern algebra. *Notices of the American Mathematical Society* 44, 321–322.

Mallows, C. (Ed.) (1987). *Design, Data, and Analysis (by Some Friends of Cuthbert Daniels)*. John Wiley, New York.

Maritz, J. S. and Lwin, T. (1989). *Empirical Bayes Methods*, 2nd ed. Chapman & Hall, London.

Marshall, A. W. and Olkin, I. (1979). *Inequalities: Theory of Majorization and Its Applications*. Academic Press, New York.

Mehra, K. and Sarangi, J. (1967). A symptotic efficiency of certain rank tests for comparative experiments. *Annals of Mathematical Statistics* 38, 90–107.

Miller, R. G. (1966). *Simultaneous Statistical Inference*. McGraw-Hill, New York.

Monge, P. and Cappella, J. (Eds.) (1980). *Multivariate Techniques in Communication Research*. Academic Press, New York.

Moore, C. (2007). Mathematics at Berkeley. A. K. Peters. Wellesley, M.A.

Morgenstern, O. (1951). Abraham Wald, 1902–1950. *Econometrica* 19, 361–367.

Moses, L. and Mosteller, F. (1968). Institutional differences in post-operative death rates. *Journal of the American Medical Association* 203, 492–494.

Moses, L. and Mosteller, F. (1972). Safety of anesthetics. In Tanur, et al., Eds.

Moses, L. E. (1986). *Think and Explain with Statistics*. Addison-Wesley, Reading, MA.

Mosteller, F. (1962). Continental classroom's TV course in probability and statistics. *The American Statistician* 16, No. 5, 20–25.

Mosteller, F. (1964). Samuel S. Wilks: statesman of statistics. *The American Statistician* 18, No. 2, 11–17.

Mosteller, F. (2006). *Selected Papers*. Springer, New York.

Mosteller, F. and Tukey, J. W. (1977). *Data Analysis and Regression*. Addison-Wesley, Reading, MA.

Mosteller, F. and Wallace, D. L. (1964). *Inference and Disputed Authorship: The Federalist*. Addison-Wesley, Reading, MA.

Mosteller, F., Rourke, R. E. K. and Thomas, G. B., Jr. (1961). *Probability with Statistical Applications*. Addison-Wesley, Reading, MA.

Nadarajah, S. (2002). A conversation with Samuel Kotz. *Statistical Science* 17, 220–233.

Neyman, J. (1934). On the two different aspects of the representative method: the method of stratified sampling and the method of purposive selection. *Journal of the Royal Statistical Society* 97, 558–625.

Neyman, J. (1937). Outline of a theory of statistical estimation based on the classical theory of probability. *Philosophical Transactions of the Royal Society (A)* 236, 333–380.

Neyman, J. (1938). L'estimation statistique traitée comme un problème classique de probabilité. *Actualités Scientifiques et Industrielles*. 739, 25–57.

Neyman, J. (1938, 1952). *Lectures and Conferences on Mathematical Statistics*. Graduate School of the U. S. Department of Agriculture, Washington, D.C.

Neyman, J. (1950). *First Course in Probability and Statistics*. Henry Holt, New York.

Neyman, J. (1957). "Inductive behavior" as a basic concept of philosophy of science. *International Statistical Review* 25, 7–22.

Neyman, J. (1961). Silver jubilee of my dispute with Fisher. *Journal of the Operations Research Society of Japan* 3, 145–154.

Neyman, J. (1967). *A Selection of Early Statistical Papers.* University of California Press, Berkeley.

Neyman, J. (1970). A glance at some of my personal experiences in the process of research. In Dalenius, Karlsson, and Malmquist, Eds.

Neyman, J. (1977). Frequentist probability and frequentist statistics. *Synthèse* 36, 97–131.

Neyman, J. (Ed.) (1949). *Proceeding of the Berkeley Symposium on Mathematical Statistics and Probability.* University of California Press, Berkeley.

Neyman, J. and Pearson, E. S. (1928). On the use and interpretation of certain test criteria for purpose of statistical inference. *Biometrika* 20A, 175–240, 263–295.

Neyman, J. and Pearson, E. S. (1933). On the problem of the most efficient tests of statistical hypotheses. *Philosophical Transactions of the Royal Society (A)* 231, 289–337.

Neyman, J. and Pearson, E. S. (1966). *Joint Statistical Papers.* University of California Press, Berkeley.

Neyman, J. and Scott, E. (1948). Consistent estimates based on partially consistent observations. *Econometrica* 16, 1–32.

Noskwith, R. (2001). Hut 8 from the inside. In Smith and Erskine, Eds.

O'Brien, R., Girshick, M. A. and Hunt, E. P. (1941). Body measurement of American boys and girls for garment and pattern construction. U. S. Dept. of Agriculture, Washington, D.C.

Olkin, I. (1987). A conversation with Albert H. Bowker. *Statistical Science* 2, 472–483.

Olkin, I. (1991). A conversation with W. Allen Wallis. *Statistical Science* 6, 121–140.

Olkin, I., Ghurye, S., Hoeffding, W. and Mann, H. (Eds.) (1960). *Contributions to Probability and Statistics: Essays in Honor of Harold Hotelling.* Stanford University Press.

Owen, D. B. (Ed.) (1976). *On the History of Statistics and Probability.* Marcel Dekker, New York.

Pearson, E. S. (1929). Review of Fisher, "Statistical Methods for Research Workers," 2nd Ed. *Nature* June 8.

Pearson, E. S. (1931). The analysis of variance in cases of non-normal variation. *Biometrika* 23, 114–133.

Pearson, E. S. (1938). *Karl Pearson: An Appreciation of Some Aspects of His Life and Work.* Cambridge University Press, Cambridge.

Pearson, E. S. (1939). William Sealy Gosset: "Student" as a statistician. *Biometrika* 30, 210–250.

Pearson, E. S. (1966). The Neyman-Pearson story. In David, Ed.

Pearson, E. S. (1966). *The Selected Papers of E. S. Pearson.* University of California Press, Berkeley.

Pearson, E. S. (1968). Some early correspondence between W. S. Gosset, R. A. Fisher and Karl Pearson with notes and comments. *Biometrika* 55, 445–457.

Pearson, E. S. (1990). *"Student": A Statistical Biography of William Sealy Gosset.* Clarendon Press, Oxford.

Pearson, E. S. and Kendall, M. (1970). *Studies in the History of Statistics and Probability, Vol. 1.* Charles Griffin, London.

Pearson, K. (1948). *Karl Pearson's Early Statistical Papers.* Cambridge University Press, Cambridge.

Pearson, K. (1978). *The History of Statistics in the 17th and 18th Centuries.* Charles Griffin, London.

Pitman, E. J. G. (1937). Significance tests which may be applied to samples from any population. *Journal of the Royal Statistical Society* Suppl. 4, 119–130, 225–232.

Pitman, E. J. G. (1939a). The estimation of the location and scale parameters of a continuous distribution of any given form. *Biometrika* 30, 391–421.

Pitman, E. J. G. (1939b). Tests of hypotheses concerning location and scale parameters. *Biometrika* 31, 200–215.

Pitman, E. J. G. (1979). *Some Basic Theory for Statistical Inference*. Chapman & Hall, London.

Pitman, E. J. G. (1982). Reminiscences of a mathematician who strayed into statistics. In Gani, Ed.

Pollard, D., Torgersen, E. and Yang, G. L. (Eds.) (1997). *Festschrift for Lucien Le Cam*. Springer-Verlag, New York.

Polya, G. (1945). *How to Solve It?* Princeton University Press, Princeton, NJ.

Polya, G. (1974, 1984). *Collected Papers* (4 volumes). MIT Press, Cambridge, MA.

Rao, C. R. (1945). Information and accuracy attainable in the estimation of statistical parameters. *Bulletin of the Calcutta Mathematics Society* 37, 81–91.

Rao, C. R. (1948). Large sample tests of statistical hypotheses concerning several parameters with applications to problems of estimation. *Proceedings of the Cambridge Philosophical Society* 44, 50–57.

Rao, C. R. (1962). Efficient estimates and optimum inference procedures in large samples (with discussion). *Journal of the Royal Statistical Society (B)* 24, 46–72.

Rao, C. R. (1965, 1973). *Linear Statistical Inference and Its Applications*. John Wiley, New York.

Rao, C. R. (1989). *Statistics and Truth*. Council of Scientific and Industrial Research, New Delhi.

Rao, C. R. and Kleffe, J. (1988). *Estimation of Variance Components and Applications*. North Holland, Amsterdam.

Rao, C. R. and Mitra, S. K. (1971). *Generalized Inverse of Matrices and its Applications*. John Wiley, New York.

Rao, C. R. and Shanbhag, D. N. (1994). *Choquet-Deny Type Functional Equations with Applications to Stochastic Models*. John Wiley, New York.

Rao, C. R. and Toutenburg, H. (1995). *Linear Models (Least Squares and Alternatives)*. Springer, New York.

Rao, P. and Sedransk, J. (Eds.) (1984). *W. G. Cochran's Impact on Statistics*. John Wiley, New York.

Rasmussen, J. L. (1991). SHAF HC: A FORTRAN implementation of Shaffer's multiple comparison procedure with HC enhancement. *Psychometrika*, 56, 153.

Rasmussen, J. L. (1993). Algorithm for Shaffer's multiple comparison tests. *Educational and Psychological Measurement* 56, 329–335.

Read, C. (2004). A conversation with Norman L. Johnson. *Statistical Science* 19, 544–560.

Reid, C. (1970). *Hilbert*. Springer-Verlag, New York.

Reid, C. (1976). *Courant—in Göttingen and New York*. Springer-Verlag, New York.

Reid, C. (1982). *Neyman—from Life*. Springer-Verlag, New York.

Reid, C. (1992). *From Zero to Infinity*, 4th ed. The Mathematical Association of America, Washington, D.C.

Reid, C. (1993). *The Search for E. T. Bell*. The Mathematical Association of America, Washington, D.C.

Reid, C. (1996). *Julia—A Life in Mathematics*. The Mathematical Association of America, Washington, D.C.

Reid, N. (1994). A conversation with Sir David Cox. *Statistical Science* 9, 439–455.

Rieder, H. (1994). *Robust Asymptotic Statistics*. Springer-Verlag, New York.

Rieder, H. (Ed. 1996). *Robust Statistics, Data Analysis, and Computer Intensive Methods (In Honor of Peter Huber's 60th Birthday)*. Springer, New York.

Rietz, H. L. (1927). *Mathematical Statistics*. Open House, La Salle.

Rizvi, M. H., Rustagi, J. and Siegmund, D. (Eds.) (1983). *Recent Advances in Statistics (Papers in Honor of Herman Chernoff)*. Academic Press, New York.

Robbins, H. (1944–45). On the measure of a random set. *Annals of Mathematical Statistics* 15, 321–323 and 16, 342–347.

Robbins, H. (1951). Asymptotically subminimax solutions of compound decision problems. *Proceedings of the Second Berkeley Symposium on Mathematical Statistics and Probability*, 131–148. University of California Press, Berkeley.

Robbins, H. (1952). Some aspects of the sequential design of experiments. *Bulletin of the American Mathematics Society* 58, 527–535.

Robbins, H. (1956). An empirical Bayes approach to statistics. *Proceedings of the Third Berkeley Symposium on Mathematical Statistics and Probability* 1, 157–163.

Robinson, D. (2005). Juliet Popper Shaffer. *Journal of Educational and Behavioral Statistics* 30, 93–103.

Rojo, J. (Ed.) (2006). Optimality (The Second Erich L. Lehmann Symposium). *IMS Lecture Notes,* Vol. 49, Institute of Mathematical Statistics, Beachwood, OH.

Rojo, J. and Perez-Abreu, V. (Eds.) (2004). The First Erich L. Lehmann Symposium. *IMS Lecture Notes, Vol.* 44. Institute of Mathematical Statistics, Beachwood, OH.

Rudra, A. (1996). *Prasanta Chandra Mahalanobis: A Biography*. Oxford University Press, New Delhi.

Savage, I. R. (1953). Bibliography of nonparametric statistics and related topics. *Journal of the American Statistical Association* 48, 844–906.

Savage, L. J. (1954). *The Foundations of Statistics*. John Wiley, New York.

Savage, L. J. (1976). On rereading R. A. Fisher (with discussion) (J. W. Pratt. Ed.). *Annals of Statistics* 4, 441–500.

Schappacher, N. and Scholtz, E. (1992). Oswald Teichmüller-Leben und Werk Jahresber. *der Deutschen Mathematiker-Vereinigung* 94, 1–39.

Schechter, B. (2000). *My Brain Is Open*. Touchstone, New York.

Scheffé, H. (1953). A method for judging all contrasts in the analysis of variance. *Biometrika* 40, 87–104.

Scheffé, H. (1959). *The Analysis of Variance*. John Wiley, New York.

Segal, S. L. (2003). *Mathematicians Under the Nazis*. Princeton University Press, Princeton, NJ.

Sen, P. K. and Singer, J. M. (1993). *Large Sample Methods in Statistics*. Chapman & Hall, New York.

Serfling, R. J. (1980). *Approximation Theorems of Mathematical Statistics*. John Wiley, New York.

Shaffer, J. P. (1980). Control of directional errors with stagewise multiple test procedures. *Annals of Statistics* 8, 1342–1348.

Shaffer, J. P. (1981). Complexity: an interpretability criterion for multiple comparisons. *Journal of the American Statistical Association* 76, 395–401.

Shaffer, J. P. (1986). Modified sequentially rejective multiple test procedures. *Journal of the American Statistical Association* 81, 826–831.

Shaffer, J. P. (2004). Optimality results in multiple hypothesis testing. In Rojo and Pérez-Abreu, Eds.

Smith, A. F. M. (1995). A conversation with Dennis Lindley. *Statistical Science* 10, 305–319.

Smith, M. and Erskine, R. (Eds.) (2001). *Action this Day*. Bantam Press, New York.

Snow, C. P. (1967). *Variety of Men*. Macmillan, London.

Speed, T. P. (1987). What is an analysis of variance? (with discussion). *Annals of Statistics* 15, 885–941.

Staudte, R. G. and Sheather, S. J. (1990). *Robust Estimation and Testing*. John Wiley, New York.

Stein, C. (1945). A two-sample test for a linear hypothesis whose power is independent of the variance. *Annals of Mathematical Statistics* 16, 243–258.

Stein, C. (1956). Inadmissibility of the usual estimator for the mean of a multivariate distribution. *Proceedings of the Third Berkeley Symposium on Mathematical Statistics and Probability* 1, 187–195. University of California Press, Berkeley.

Stein, C. (1972). A bound for the error in the normal approximation to the distribution of a sum of dependent random variables. *Proceedings of the Sixth Berkeley Symposium on Mathematical Statistics and Probability* 2, 583–602.

Stein, C. (1986). *Approximate Computation of Expectations*. Institute of Mathematical Statistics, Hayward, CA.

Stigler, S. (1973). Simon Newcomb, Percy Daniell, and the history of robust estimation. *Journal of the American Statistical Association* 68, 872–879.

Stigler, S. (1986). *The History of Statistics*. Harvard University Press, Cambridge, MA.

Stigler, S. (1999). *Statistics on the Table*. Harvard University Press, Cambridge, MA.

Stigler, S. (2005). Fisher in 1921. *Statistical Science* 20, 32–49.

Student. (1929). Statistics in biological research. *Nature* 124, 93.

Tanur, J. M., Mosteller, F., Kruskal, W. H., et al. (Eds.) (1972). *Statistics: Guide to the Unknown*. Holden-Day, San Francisco.

Taylor, H. and Taylor, L. (1993). *George Polya—Master of Discovery*. Dale Seymour Publications, Palo Alto, CA.

Tippett, L. H. C. (1927). *Random Sampling Numbers: Tracts for Computers No. 15*. Cambridge University Press, London.

Tukey, J. W. (1940). Convergence and Uniformity in Topology. *Annals of Mathematics Studies* 2. Princeton University Press, Princeton, NJ.

Tukey, J. W. (1960). A survey of sampling from contaminated distributions. In *Contributions to Probability and Statistics* (Olkin, Ghurye, et al., Eds.)

Tukey, J. W. (1961). Statistical and quantitative methodology. In *Trends in Social Science* (Ray, Ed.). Philosophical Library, New York. (Reprinted in Vol. III of Tukey's Collected Works.)

Tukey, J. W. (1962). The future of data analysis. *Annals of Mathematical Statistics* 33, 1–67, 812.

Tukey, J. W. (1977). *Exploratory Data Analysis*. Addison-Wesley, Reading, MA.

Tukey, J. W. (1980). Methodological comments focused on opportunities. In Monge and Cappella, Eds. (Reprinted in Vol. IV of Tukey's Collected Works.)

Tukey, J. W. (1984–1994). *Collected Works* (8 volumes). Wadsworth, Monterey (Vols. 1–6). Chapman & Hall, New York (Vols. 7–8).

Van Dantzig, D. (1957a). Statistical priesthood (Savage on personal probabilities). *Statistica Neerlandica* 11, 1–16.

Van Dantzig, D. (1957b). Statistical priesthood II (Sir Ronald on scientific inference). *Statistica Neerlandica* 11, 185–200.

Van der Vaart, A. (2002). The statistical work of Lucien Le Cam. *Annals of Statistics* 30, 631–682.

Van der Waerden, B. L. (1930–31). *Moderne Algebra* (2 volumes). Springer-Verlag, Berlin.

Van der Waerden, B. L. (1954). *Science Awakening*. Noordhoff, Groningen.

Van der Waerden, B. L. (1965). *Mathematische Statistik*, 2nd ed. Springer-Verlag, Berlin. (English translation, *Mathematical Statistics*, 1968, Springer-Verlag, New York.)

Van der Waerden, B. L. (1974). *Science Awakening, Vol. 2: The Birth of Astronomy*. Noordhoff, Leyden.

Van Zwet, W. R. (1964). *Convex Transformations of Random Variables*. Mathematisch Centrum, Amsterdam.

Von Mises, R. (1918). *Fluglehre*. Springer, Berlin.

Von Mises, R. (1919). Grundlagen der wahrscheinlichkeitsreehnung. *Mathematische Zeitschrift* 5, 52–99.

Von Mises, R. (1931). *Wahrscheinlichkeitsrechnung und ihre Anwendung in der Statistik und Theoretischen Physik*. Franz Deuticke, Leipzig.

Von Mises, R. (1947). On the asymptotic distribution of differentiable statistical functions. *Annals of Mathematical Statistics* 18, 309–348.

Von Mises, R. (1963–64). *Selected Papers of Richard von Mises* (2 volumes). American Mathematical Society, Providence.

Von Neumann, J. and Morgenstern, O. (1944). *Theory of Games and Economic Behavior*. Princeton University Press, Princeton, NJ.

Von Plato, J. (1994). *Creating Modern Probability*. Cambridge University Press, Cambridge.

Wald, A. (1939). Contributions to the theory of statistical estimation and testing. *Annals of Mathematical Statistics* 10, 299–326.

Wald, A. (1943). Tests of statistical hypotheses concerning several parameters when the number of observations is large. *Transactions of the American Mathematical Society* 54, 426–482.

Wald, A. (1945). Sequential tests of statistical hypotheses. *Annals of Mathematical Statistics* 16, 117–186.

Wald, A. (1947). *Sequential Analysis*. John Wiley, New York.

Wald, A. (1950). *Statistical Decision Functions*. John Wiley, New York.

Wald, A. (1955). *Selected Papers in Statistics and Probability*. McGraw-Hill, New York.

Wald, A. and Wolfowitz, J. (1948). Optimum character of the sequential probability ratio test. *Annals of Mathematical Statistics* 19, 326–339.

Walker, H. and Lev, J. (1953). *Statistical Inference*. Henry Holt, New York.

Wallis, W. A. (1980). The Statistical Research Group, 1942–1945. *Journal of the American Statistical Association* 75, 320–335.

Wallis, W. A. and Roberts, H. V. (1956). *Statistics—A New Approach*. The Free Press, Glencoe, IL.

Weaver, W. (1970). *Scene of Change*. Scribner's, New York.

Weintraub, E. R. (2002). *How Economics Became a Mathematical Science*. Duke University Press, Durham, NC.

Weiss, L. and Wolfowitz, J. (1974). *Maximum Probability Estimators and Related Topics*. Springer-Verlag, Berlin.

Westfall, P. H. (1997). Multiple testing of general contrasts using logical constraints and correlations. *Journal of the American Statistical Association* 92, 299–306.

Westfall, P. H. and Young, S. (1993). *Resampling-Based Multiple Testing*. John Wiley, New York.

Wilcoxon, F. (1945). Individual comparisons by ranking methods. *Biometrika* 1, 80–83.

Wilcoxon, F. (1946). Individual comparisons of grouped data by ranking methods. *Journal of Entomology* 39, 269–270.

Wilks, S. S. (1943). *Mathematical Statistics*. Princeton University Press, Princeton, NJ.

Wolff, Th. (1929). *Der Wettlauf mit der Schildkröte*. August Scherl, Berlin.

Wolfowitz, J. (1942). Additive partition functions and a class of statistical hypotheses. *Annals of Mathematical Statistics* 13, 247–279.

Wolfowitz, J. (1961, 1964, 1978). *Coding Theorems of Information Theory*. Springer-Verlag, Berlin.

Wolfowitz, J. (1970). Reflections on the future of mathematical statistics. In Bose, Ed.

Wolfowitz, J. (1980). *Selected Papers*. Springer-Verlag, New York.

Wolpert, R. (2004). A conversation with James O. Berger. *Statistical Science* 19, 205–218.

Working, H. and Hotelling, H. (1929). Application of the theory of error to the interpretation of trends. *Journal of the American Statistical Association* 24 (March supplement), 73–85.

Yahav, J. A. (1966). On optimal stopping. *Annals of Mathematical Statistics* 37, 30–35.

Yang, G. (1999). A conversation with Lucien Le Cam. *Statistical Science* 14, 223–241.

Yang, G. (2002). Lucien Le Cam 1924–2000. *Annals of Statistics* 30, 617–630.

Yule, G. U. (1899). An investigation into the causes of changes in pauperism in England, chiefly during the last two intercensal decades, I. *Journal of the Royal Statistical Society* 62, 249–295.

Zheng, Z. (1986a). Robust M-estimation of multivariate location and scatter in the presence of asymmetry. *Canadian Journal of Statistics* 14, 161–176.

Zheng, Z. (1986b). Selecting a minimax estimator doing well at a point. *Journal of Multivariate Analysis* 19, 14–23.

Name Index

Subject Index

CPSIA information can be obtained
at www.ICGtesting.com
Printed in the USA
BVOW06s1018131117
500225BV00036B/91/P